Nineteenth-Century Scientific Instruments

By the same author:

Descriptive Catalogue of Van Marum's Scientific Instruments in Teyler's Museum, Haarlem (1973)

Antique Scientific Instruments (1980)

Essays on the History of the Microscope (1980)

Collecting Microscopes (1981)

Nineteenth-Century Scientific Instruments

GERARD L'E. TURNER

Sotheby Publications

University of California Press

© Gerard L'E. Turner 1983
First published in 1983 for
Sotheby Publications by
Philip Wilson Publishers Ltd
Russell Chambers, Covent Garden
London WC2E 8AA

Published in the United States and Canada by
University of California Press
Berkeley and Los Angeles

ISBN 0 85667 170 3 (UK Edition)
ISBN 0-520-05160-2 (US Edition)
Library of Congress catalog card no 83-048656

Designed by A & S Burrell

Printed in Great Britain
by BAS Printers Limited
Over Wallop, Hampshire
and bound by
Robert Hartnoll Ltd
Bodmin, Cornwall

To the memory of Ernest Lefebvre

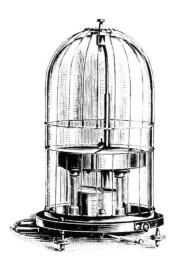

Foreword

In 1838 the chemist Thomas Graham wrote in his lecture notes for Wednesday 10th October:

> It is curious how much the progress of science depends upon the invention and improvement of instruments. How much the experimental Phil[er] is beholden to the perfection of tools with which he operates.

The nineteenth century was a crucial period for the invention and improvement of scientific instruments for research, for educational demonstration and for routine measurement. Their importance was acknowledged in 1876 by the South Kensington Museum (from which the Science Museum has grown) by a huge exhibition called The Special Loan Collection of Scientific Apparatus, the catalogue of which records 4570 entries. The committee organizing it represented the scientific establishment of the day including the President of the Royal Society, Sir Joseph Dalton Hooker, and eighty-one Fellows. The exhibition brought together renowned historical items from all parts of Europe, for example Galileo's telescopes, Antoni van Leeuwenhoek's microscope and Michael Faraday's coils. But the bulk of material exhibited consisted of contemporary instruments used for teaching and it was considered that the development of a new museum would 'tend to the advancement of science, and be of great service to the industrial progress of this country'.

I have known the author, Gerard Turner, and his work for many years and I am delighted that he has turned his attention to the rather neglected field of nineteenth-century instruments. It was, after all, the period when for the first time the ordinary man might have experienced their use at work and the first time a child might have been taught science in the changing school curriculum. Instrument-making itself underwent fundamental change: in 1800 Jesse Ramsden, who made the first circular dividing engine, was still alive; by the end of the century, the Cambridge Scientific Instrument Company was producing a full range of electrical measuring apparatus on a large scale. The rôle of instruments has not had its due share of recognition in recent studies in the history of science, and it is hoped that this book will help redress the balance.

Margaret Weston

Director of the Science Museum, London

January 1983

Acknowledgements

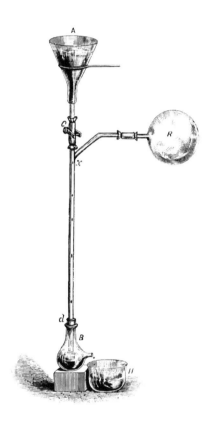

Without the help and hospitality of the individuals and institutions mentioned here, this book would have been hard to complete. I would like to express my thanks to them all; their support and encouragement has made the work a pleasure. The photographs acknowledged to the Science Museum, London, and to the Royal Scottish Museum, Edinburgh, are Crown copyright reserved.

I give particular thanks to my wife, Helen Turner, without whose organizational and verbal skills and constant interest the book might never have appeared. For opportunities to take photographs of their collections, I thank Mr F. R. Maddison, Museum of the History of Science, Oxford; Mr J. H. van Borssum Buisman, Teyler's Museum, Haarlem; Professor B. Zanobio and Dr F. Bevilacqua, Museo per la Storia dell'Università di Pavia, and Dr J. A. Bennett, Whipple Museum of the History of Science, Cambridge. For help in providing photographs and other information, I thank Drs A. J. F. Gogelein, Museum Boerhaave, Leiden; Professor P. Galluzzi, Istituto e Museo di Storia della Scienza, Florence; Mme M. Archinard, Musée d'Histoire des Sciences, Geneva; Mr A. Klut; Mr Bert Bolle, and the photographic department of the Science Museum, London. For printing from my own negatives, I have relied on the skills of Mr B. G. Archer, Oxford.

For discussions, information, and advice, I thank in particular Dr R. G. W. Anderson, Dr J. A. Bennett, Dr P. Brenni, Mr D. J. Bryden, Mr M. A. Crawforth, Dr S. Engelsman, Dr W. D. Hackmann, Dr G. M. M. Houben, and Mr A. V. Simcock. For agreeing to write the Foreword, I thank most warmly Dame Margaret Weston, D.B.E., Director of the Science Museum, London.

Contents

Colour plates

Abbreviations
used in the captions

MUSEUMS

Museum Boerhaave Museum Boerhaave, Steenstaat 1a, 2312 BS, Leiden, The Netherlands.

Musée d'Histoire des Sciences Musée d'Histoire des Sciences, 128 rue de Lausanne, 1202 Geneva, Switzerland.

Museo di Storia della Scienza Istituto e Museo di Storia della Scienza, Piazza dei Giudici, 1, 50122 Florence, Italy.

Museum of the History of Science* Museum of the History of Science, Broad Street, Oxford OX1 3AZ, UK.

Pavia University Museo per la Storia dell'Università di Pavia, Palazzo Universitario, Strada Nuova 65, 27100 Pavia, Italy.

Royal Scottish Museum The Royal Scottish Museum, Chambers Street, Edinburgh EH1 1JF, Scotland.

Science Museum The Science Museum, Exhibition Road, London SW7 2DD, UK.

Teyler's Museum Teyler's Museum, Spaarne 16, 2011 HA Haarlem, The Netherlands

Whipple Museum Whipple Museum of the History of Science, Free School Lane, Cambridge CB2 3RH, UK.

PUBLICATIONS

Deschanel Augustin Privat Deschanel, *Traité élémentaire de Physique* (Paris, 1868). Translated by J D Everett, *Elementary Treatise on Natural Philosophy* (London, 1872)

Ganot Adolphe Ganot, *Cours de Physique purement expérimentale* (Paris, 1859). Translated by E. Atkinson, *Natural Philosophy for General Readers and Young People* (London, 1872)

*Note: In Chapter 12 the numbers given for items in the Museum of the History of Science refer to *Catalogue I: Chemical Apparatus* (Oxford, 1971)

Griffin	*Scientific Handicraft . . . Catalogue of Scientific Apparatus manufactured and sold by John J. Griffin & Sons, Ltd,* 14th edn (London, nd [1910])
Guillemin	Amédée Guillemin, *The Applications of Physical Forces,* translated by Mrs Norman Lockyer (London, 1877)
Marion	Fulgence Marion, *L'Optique* (Paris, 1867). Translated by Charles W. Quin, *The Wonders of Optics* (London, 1868)
Negretti & Zambra	*Negretti & Zambra's Encyclopaedic Illustrated and Descriptive Reference Catalogue* (London, nd [1880])
Stanley	William Ford Stanley, *Surveying and Levelling Instruments* (London, 1890), 3rd edn (1901)
Tissandier	Gaston Tissandier, *Les Récréations scientifique ou l'Enseignement par les Jeux* (Paris, 1881). Translated as *Popular Scientific Recreations in Natural Philosophy* (London, 1882)

1 · Introduction

The Scientific Instrument Commission strongly urges the preservation of scientific instruments, especially those of the nineteenth and twentieth centuries.

Resolution carried *nem. con.*
at the XVI International Congress of the History of Science, Bucharest, 1 September 1981

One purpose of this book is to help in preserving scientific instruments of the recent past by providing an introductory guide to the range that may be found. The resolution at the head of this chapter was presented because it was realized that the nineteenth century was a period of dramatic change, invention, and development in scientific apparatus, which was produced in increasing quantity during the century. Many of these instruments are important in the history of science and technology, but may well be disregarded today, either because they are not recognized for what they are, or because all out-of-date scientific equipment is assumed to be expendable. In schools, colleges, and industrial laboratories where science was taught or practised around the turn of the present century, there are likely to be dusty cupboards where many of the instruments described here are hidden away. The many instruments available make this period particularly popular for the collector, who, it is hoped, will find that the task of identification has been made easier through the many illustrations of instruments and their detailed descriptions in the captions.

It must be stressed that this book offers only an introduction to a very big subject. It would be perfectly possible to write one, or more than one, book on the subject-matter dealt with in each chapter. The advantages of presenting a review of the entire range of instruments are that it should stimulate interest and inquiry, thus leading to further work, and that the cumulative effect of the book should convey the scientific flavour of the period in a way that more detailed and restricted studies cannot do. To put it another way, some of the chapters are highly scientific, others much less so. The pre-eminent discovery of the nineteenth century was that of current electricity, and another field largely developed in the same period was the science of sound; instruments for surveying and navigation, on the other hand, remained basically unchanged in type, but became more accurate and efficient. It is also interesting to see how the subject areas – distinguished for convenience into separate chapters (following the nineteenth-century terminology) – interact and overlap, sometimes with the scientists and inventors working in two or more fields. An entirely new factor that strongly affected the development and production of scientific instruments for the first time in the nineteenth century, was the demand for apparatus to test food for quality and purity, and to be used in the business of standardizing all kinds of products. Examples of this are such instruments as the saccharimeter and the hygrometer, and much of the weighing and measuring equipment described in Chapter 3.

CATEGORIES OF INSTRUMENTS

The instruments dealt with in this book can usefully be divided into four categories:

1. *Physical and analytical instruments*. These are the tools of the research scientist, such as electrostatic generators, galvanometers and air-pumps; and instruments used for analysis and measurement, such as precision balances and spectroscopes.

2. *Professional instruments*. These are the instruments used by land-surveyors, navigators, architects, meteorologists, and customs officers, among others, including the theodolite, the slide-rule, the anemometer and the hydrometer.

3. *Teaching instruments*. These again can be sub-divided, into apparatus to demonstrate a particular physical effect, such as the wave-machine designed to show the action of light waves, or a water pump with glass cylinders, to demonstrate the action of the pistons and valves; and into the apparatus used for a key experiment, such as Fresnel's bi-prism, which was produced over a long period for class teaching.

4. *Recreational instruments*. Here, too, there are categories. Some devices used purely for amusement, such as the kaleidoscope or the stereoscope, embody a scientific principle, and are therefore included; others had a dual rôle as scientific instruments, and for use by the amateur. The best example here is the microscope, which was markedly improved in the 1830s, so that it was used in many branches of science, but which continued to be popular for use in the home.

There are some categories of scientific instrument that have been deliberately excluded from this book. One group comprises instruments and apparatus too large or cumbersome for collection, except by specialist museums. Such are the majority of astronomical and observatory instruments, and some chemical and mechanical apparatus. Medical instruments are not included, because they are the subject of a recently published and thorough study, and because they are also very traditional in design, and were not, in general, made by scientific instrument makers. Not dealt with in detail are domestic clocks (though electric clocks are discussed), since they depend for their variety rather on their cases than their mechanism, and are, therefore, largely to be treated

[1] From the catalogue of Chadburn Brothers, Sheffield, 1851. *Science Museum*.

as *objets d'art*. Clocks are also the subject of an extensive specialist literature. The same is true of the domestic barometer, which has been studied in detail by two recent writers (see Bibliography). That most ubiquitous of instruments, the microscope, may not appear to have been given the attention it deserves in this book, but it has been dealt with elsewhere, and particularly in two books by the present author (see Bibliography).

TEXT AND ILLUSTRATIONS

The book presents its information in words and pictures. In the chapters, the objective has been to outline the contemporary knowledge of each subject through the course of the nineteenth century, and to describe briefly some of the chief discoveries and advances made. This should provide the setting into which the instruments illustrated fit,

[2] A mid-19th-century retailer's card.
Science Museum.

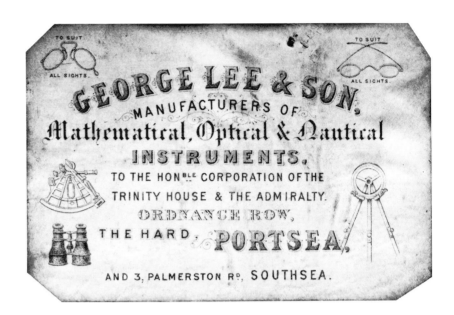

and is essential if they are to be understood and appreciated, both in relation to earlier instruments, and as the forerunners of modern apparatus. In providing the background, names are very important, not only those of leading scientists, whose discoveries are often embodied in teaching apparatus, but also the instrument makers and inventors, who went to work, once a discovery had been announced, to produce and perfect the practical applications. These are the men whose names often appear on the instruments themselves, and enable them to be dated.

Even though there are more than 400 illustrations in this book, the selection from the extensive range available is bound to appear arbitrary. The Negretti & Zambra catalogue of *c.* 1880 includes well over 3000 items. Griffin's catalogue, entitled *Scientific Handicraft*, and published *c.* 1900, contains at a rough count over 6000 pieces of apparatus, in the main for teaching. A more satisfactory basis for the selection of many of the instruments was to draw on the holdings of that unique teaching and research institution, the Teyler's Foundation, Haarlem, The Netherlands. This collection is not, as are most museums of science and technology, a Frankenstein monster, with the objects amassed haphazardly. Teyler's is an organic growth, for which the physical apparatus (there is virtually no chemical apparatus) was purchased within a few years of invention or first devising, and remains in almost mint condition. Several chapters, especially that on sound, have relied heavily on the collection in Teyler's Museum. For mechanics and hydrostatics, however, demonstration pieces bought in the late eighteenth century continued to be used in Teyler's, and therefore nineteenth-century versions are not to be found in the collection. Because it was a purely scientific institution, it is no use looking in Teyler's for a representative range of nineteenth-century microscopes, or surveying instruments. For such items, other collections have been used, for example, the Whipple Museum of the History of Science in Cam-

[3] A trade card of the late 19th century. The theodolite is of the Everest type. *Science Museum.*

bridge, England, which possesses a representative group of equipment for the surveyor, of which a catalogue has recently been published. Returning to Teyler's, another of its advantages is that instruments were purchased from makers in Germany, France, and England, as well as The Netherlands, something that would have been less likely to happen in the case of similar institutions in France or England. In these countries, the existence of a large indigenous trade would make it unlikely that there would be much buying from abroad. In America, until the end of the century, there was little choice but to import scientific instruments from Europe.

With each illustration, any signature present has been reproduced as accurately as possible typographically. The function of the instrument has been briefly stated, as has the material used in the construction, unless this is obvious. Dating has been given as accurately as possible, in the case of undated instruments, by referring to the date of original purchase in museum files, or to the dates of the maker, and his residence at any address given on the instrument. Sometimes, however, a spread of date has been unavoidable. Dimensions are given whenever possible, but some museums cannot readily supply measure-

[4] Trade card *c.* 1850. Colombi's patron, Le Prince de Joinville, lived from 1818 to 1900. *Science Museum.*

[5] Trade card of Jeremiah Watkins who traded on his own from 1799 to 1819, and then as Watkins & Hill. By 1857 the firm had been taken over by Elliott Brothers. *Science Museum*.

ments of instruments on display. Museum inventory numbers are given whenever they exist.

SOURCES

An important source, that has been used throughout, and from which readers could obtain further information, is the range of textbooks published during the nineteenth century in English, French, and German. It is worth remarking that in the second half of the century, some of the French textbook writers were so efficient, and used such excellent wood engravings for illustration, that their work was extensively translated into English, Spanish, and even Russian, using the same engravings. Another important source is provided by the catalogues issued by the manufacturers of scientific equipment. Those produced at the end of the century are not hard to come by, but earlier ones may only exist in specialist libraries. A word of warning must be added about using the publication dates of textbooks and catalogues to date engravings of instruments. The life of an engraving was often a long one, and it could appear in a range of different textbooks. Engravings in catalogues may have come from earlier catalogues of the same firm, or of other firms, or from textbook illustrators. A Griffin catalogue issued at the beginning of the twentieth century, for example, contains some wood-cuts identical to those that first appeared in 1850.

Modern studies have also proved useful. There are biographies of the scientists and inventors – though not, regrettably, of many of the instrument makers. One of the most important sources of biographical information has proved to be the *Dictionary of Scientific Biography*, edited by C. C. Gillispie (Charles Scribners Sons, New York, 1970–80), which is a highly competent and comprehensive work. Not

[6] Trade card of Henry Porter, successor to William Cary who died in 1825. This card is *c.* 1859. *Science Museum*.

[7] Hugh Powell (1799–1883) was at this address in the 1830s and traded as Powell & Lealand from 1841. *Museum of the History of Science*.

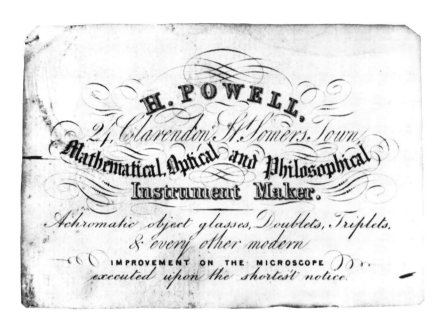

to be forgotten are the national biographical dictionaries. The bibliography at the end of this book lists a selection of works, and also guides to the specialist literature in the field of scientific instruments.

THE GREAT EXHIBITION

Exactly in the middle of the nineteenth century occurred The Great Exhibition of the Works of Industry of All Nations. This was held in London, at the Crystal Palace, in 1851, under the presidency of the Prince Consort. Class X of the exhibition was called 'Philosophical Instruments and Processes Depending upon their Use'. It is interesting

[8] William Harris & Co. were at 47 High Holborn from 1799 to 1812, and at No. 50 from 1813 to 1848. *Museum of the History of Science*.

[9] John Frederick Newman was at this address from 1816 to 1825, and at 122 Regent Street from 1827 to 1860. *Museum of the History of Science.*

to note that adjuncts to Class X were musical instruments (Xa), horological instruments (Xb), and surgical instruments (Xc). Class X had a wide range, and attracted makers and inventors from Europe and America. The names of the instrument makers have been extracted, and are printed as an appendix to this book.

SOME CONCLUSIONS

The nineteenth century may be considered in two distinct parts, dividing at the temporal mid-point – 1851 – which was also the year of the Great Exhibition. This international occasion was the peak of the Industrial Revolution, the triumph of steam-power technology and machine-tool engineering. In the second half of the century, a completely new phase of scientific and technical development began, the age of electricity. The changes brought about by the discovery of electromagnetic power constituted a revolution perhaps more truly scientific

[10] Three gentlemen with scientific instruments; 1850s. *Museum of the History of Science.*

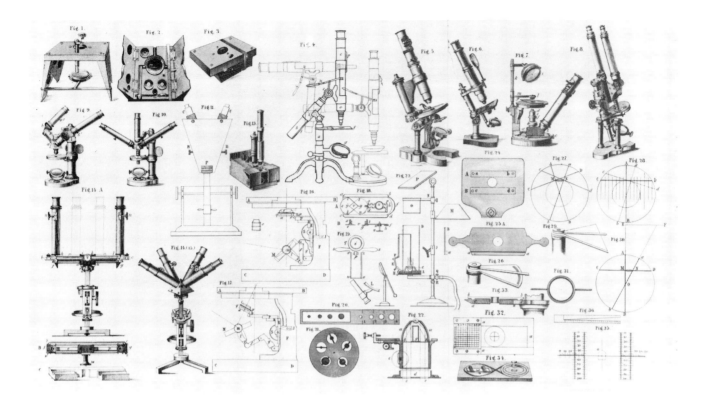

[11] Microscopes, mostly Nachet, and accessories; *c.* 1860. *Museum of the History of Science.*

than the events often so described of the seventeenth century. The earlier revolution, a period indeed of marked change, was philosophical and methodological. Francis Bacon, its leading proponent, taught that observation of natural phenomena, and the use of measurement, should be the basis of all theorizing about the world, a change of perspective from Aristotelianism that laid the foundations of modern experimental science. But the 'electrical revolution' of the latter part of the nineteenth century changed the whole way of life of western Europe and North America by universalizing a science-based technology.

Science became for the first time a profession during the nineteenth century. The word 'scientist' was actually coined by the Cambridge philosopher William Whewell in 1834 as the name for a new way of earning a living. Where science had been studied either by academics or by amateurs, it was now to be practised in laboratories employing numbers of people, engaged either in advanced research or in making and testing commercial and industrial products. The professional scientist of today, however, should not forget how great is the debt of science to men who received no formal scientific education. This fact emerges clearly from the broad review of the century carried out in this book. These men came from varied backgrounds, some being entirely self-taught, others having had a classical education but little or no training in science. Examples include Humphry Davy, Michael Faraday, and Léon Foucault among the well-known figures. Less famous, but of great importance, were such men as Zénobe Gramme, the Belgian who invented the first effective electric dynamo and thus launched the electric power industry; and James Glaisher, the founder of modern meteorology, an innovator in photography, and the man responsible for the official report on the Philosophical Instruments in Class X of the Great Exhibition. On the other hand, a rigorous mathematical training such as that provided by Cambridge University was necessary for the great theoretical synthesizers, William Thomson (later Lord Kelvin), and James Clerk Maxwell.

What provided the impetus towards much of the scientific discovery of the period was the popular interest in science, begun during the eighteenth century, and exemplified in the public lecture-demonstrations. Science was accessible to, and enjoyed by, ordinary people through lectures, through the meetings of scientific societies, and in the home, where science played an important part in recreation. It is for this reason that a chapter on recreational science finds a place in this book. In the course of the century, much scientific reading material was published. Extremely popular were the encyclopaedias that contained some excellent scientific articles, and were available through lending libraries and mechanics institutes. These included Abraham Rees's *Cyclopaedia* (1802–20), the *Penny Cyclopaedia* (1833–43), and the *Encyclopaedia Metropolitana* (1817–45) which was solely to do with science and technology. There were also many scientific magazines, appealing to a wide range of lay readership, including *The Mechanical Magazine*, published

[12] Frontispiece to C. R. Alder Wright, *The Threshold of Science* (London), 1892.

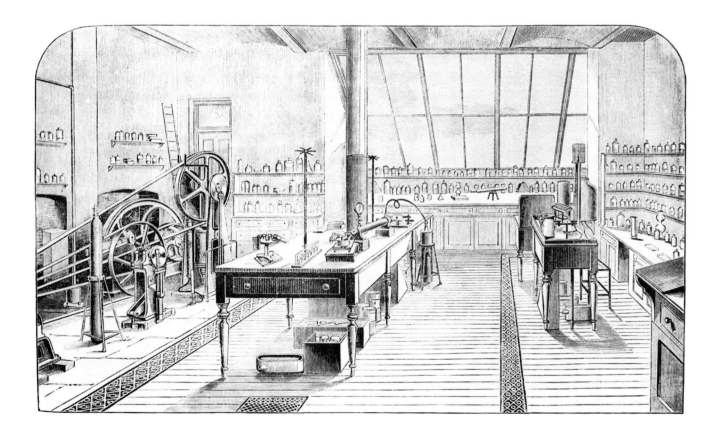

in London between 1825 and 1858, *The Engineer*, first published in 1856, and the journals published under the editorship of David Brewster from 1819: *The Edinburgh Philosophical Journal*, and *The Edinburgh Journal of Science*. In at least three European countries popular scientific journals with the same title appeared: in Britain, *Nature*; in The Netherlands, *De Natuur*; in France, *La Nature* edited by Gaston Tissandier.

That the enthusiasm for science was widespread is shown by an example from Manchester. Courses of *Science Lectures for the People* were held there in 1867, and again in 1871, and subsequently. The first course was attended by 4000 people, the second by 9000, while published texts of the lectures, at one penny each, sold editions of up to 10,000 copies. Such enthusiasm existed throughout the western world, and created a spirit of remarkable internationalism in science that was largely free of political influence. In 1813, when the Napoleonic wars were still in progress, Humphry Davy visited Paris to receive the medal awarded by the Institut de France for his electrical discoveries. Scientists could remain colleagues and respect each other's work, even when their countries were at war.

2 · Time

Our knowledge of time as of space owes more to the labours of mathematicians and physicists than to those of professed philosophers.

C. D. Broad (1921)

TIME-TELLING

Time presents formidable metaphysical and psychological problems, leading philosophers to attempt objective, subjective, and transcendental explanations. In science, time is one of the three fundamental dimensions, the others being mass and length. The astronomer's regulator, the domestic clock, and the sundial all measure different kinds of time, so some definitions are necessary at the outset in order that the function of the various devices can be understood.

Sidereal Time

This is astronomer's time, and it is the apparent rotation of the celestial sphere – the stars – brought about by the rotation of the Earth on its axis. The return passage of a fixed point (a chosen star) measures a sidereal day, which is divided into 24 equal hours. Astronomers reckon the sidereal day from the passage of the first point of Aries (the Vernal Equinoctial point) across the meridian. Because the Earth moves in orbit during the course of a rotation, the sidereal day is about four minutes shorter than the solar day.

Solar Time

This is the time used by ordinary people, and the solar day is defined by the passage of the Sun across the meridian. This is the time told by a sundial. The Sun's motion, being apparent only, is not regular. The Earth is tilted on its axis relative to the plane of its orbit round the Sun, and the Sun is at one focus of an elipse and not at the centre of a circle, so there are variations in the length of the day during the year. The going of a clock is regular, so when clocks became popular, from the seventeenth century onwards, a modified solar time was required.

Mean Solar Time

In classical times astronomers introduced the concept of a mean Sun for their special purposes, so it was an easy matter to introduce the concept into popular usage when clocks and watches were in more general use. The mean Sun is a useful fiction because it enables every day of the year to be the same length and each one to be divisible into 24 hours of the same length. (When only sundials existed, other hours were used, whose length varied throughout the year.)

Equation of Time

This is the difference between apparent, or true, solar time and mean solar time. Early in November the Sun is due South at 11.44 by mean solar time, and in the middle of February, the meridian passage of the Sun is at 12.15, mean time. There are four dates in the year when the mean and apparent times coincide: mid-April, mid-June, at the beginning of September and at Christmas. The greater accuracy of clocks and watches from the middle of the eighteenth century necessitated an equation of time to be engraved on sundials, since the sundial was the means by which clocks were checked.

Standard Time

In Britain, standardization came into being through the actions and requirements of three types of organization with national responsibilities: the Post Office, the railways and the electric telegraph companies. In 1840 the Great Western Railway kept London time at all its stations and in its timetables, and by 1848 virtually the whole of the British rail network ran to Greenwich time. With domestic clocks and watches now verifiable at the railway station clock or at the telegraph office, by mid-century the use of local time diminished, and with it the use of the sundial. The law courts, on the other hand, kept to local time until an Act of Parliament of 1880 required legally stated time to be Greenwich mean time.

The railway systems in Europe and in North America also brought about the change to standard time, but with large land masses, time zones had to be introduced, the United States having four, and Canada five zones. In 1883 'Railroad Time' was adopted by most people in North America, although the legalization of standard time had to wait until an Act of Congress in 1918.

Of international concern was the fixing of the prime meridian, the base line for all time measurement. Hitherto, countries had pleased themselves; Britain took Greenwich, the French, the Paris Observatory, the Dutch, Amsterdam. The International Meridian Conference was held in Washington, DC, during October 1884. Eventually, the delegates from 25 countries decided that the Observatory at Greenwich should provide the prime meridian for longitude. Reasons for this choice rested on the practicalities of commerce. The majority of charts used at sea were British, the *Nautical Almanac* (founded in 1767) sold 20,000 copies annually, as against 3000 copies of *Connaissance des Temps*, and 72 per cent of the world's shipping used Greenwich as the baseline for navigation.

THE DEVELOPMENT OF TIME-TELLING INSTRUMENTS

Astronomy and time-telling are closely related, for the measuring and recording of the passage of time have over the centuries depended on the rotation of the Earth on its axis (the day) and its motion in orbit round the Sun (the year). The measurement of time is traditionally based upon the translation of the passing of time into the traversing of space, by the recording of some form of regular motion. There are usually two factors involved here: the rate-governing process, and the method of recording. The simplest form of rate-governing device is the sandglass [1]. It incorporates no recording method; the flow of the sand through the orifice occurs at a steady rate, and is completed in a given period. The water-clock uses water flow in the same way as the flow of sand in a sandglass as the rate-governing process, but also incorporates a float as recorder. In the sundial, the movement of the Sun is directly recorded by means of a shadow cast by a pointer onto a surface which is marked out in hours. This instrument has been used in a wide variety of forms from antiquity, and is still with us today. The ringed candle and the oil clock use the chemical process of combustion for rate-governing, and the rings inscribed on the candle or oil reservoir for recording. Until this century, the recording method has always been spatial – that is, movement was recorded upon some form of dial. Today it is often digital, that is, by means of a sequence of numbers, visually displayed.

The history of time-telling instruments is all about the need to achieve ever greater accuracy. From the sixteenth to the nineteenth

[1] Two sandglasses. *Left*: oak frame, red sand, running for one hour. The central join is bound with wax and thread. Height 171 mm, diameter 123 mm. Late 18th century. *Museum of the History of Science (C. 384)*. *Right*: mahogany frame, white sand, running for 18 minutes. Here the two bulbs are blown as one piece. Height 195 mm, diameter 117 mm. Early 19th century. *Museum of the History of Science (C. 382)*.

centuries, this was done by perfecting the use of cyclic mechanical motion that repeats itself over and over again. The earliest mechanical clocks, those still in existence dating from the fourteenth century, operated by the fall of a weight on a rope, working against a restraining mechanism. Accurate time measurement, however, was first achieved by applying a swinging pendulum to control the rate of rotation of a wheel. Though others before him studied the working of the pendulum, Christiaan Huygens (1629–95) was the first to design an effective pendulum clock. There were many stages of refinement in the development of this type of clock, but the next major development in time-telling devices was the use of a spring drive and balance wheel, instead of a suspended weight, to apply the power to a clock mechanism. This made possible the construction of effective portable clocks and watches.

By the start of the nineteenth century, sundials were still in regular use to check the accuracy of clocks and watches. There was as yet no national standard time, and local time depended on longitude East or West of Greenwich. Every locality had its own time; local time at Oxford is five minutes slower than Greenwich, because Oxford is $1\frac{1}{4}$ degrees West of Greenwich in longitude. At Bristol, local time is ten minutes behind Greenwich. Clocks of reasonable accuracy were marketed for domestic use, made to run without winding for periods ranging from eight days to one year. They would, however, lose accuracy gradually, because the oil on which their smooth running depended became viscous. There was already a large and thriving watch industry in England, producing both ordinary movements in more or less elaborate cases for general sale, and time-pieces of high precision for specialist purposes. Two such uses were in the astronomical observatory and on board ship. Astronomical regulators were used in association with zenith telescopes to give sidereal time, which could be checked every 24 hours by the passing of a particular star at a certain point. The marine chronometer, invented after years of labour by John Harrison (1693–1776), was one of the great technological achievements of all time. By designing a chronometer which would continue to tell the time accurately on board ship, he made possible the exact computation of longitude at sea.

The Great Exhibition, held in London during 1851, collected all the most important innovations in science and technology, among many classes of exhibit gathered together under the roof of the Crystal Palace. An examination of the 'Reports of the Juries' shows what the international panel of judges thought of the innovativeness and quality of production of the goods displayed. Clearly, the section labelled 'Dialling' was not remarkable, including only a couple of spherical sundials for the garden, a cannon dial, and a portable dial; no prizes were awarded in this sub-group. Clocks, on the other hand, were dignified by a class on their own: Horological Instruments, Class Xb. There were five sections: the marine chronometer; astronomical clocks; turret clocks (for public buildings); 'house clocks' (the term used for domestic clocks; it was pointed out that the French call them 'civil clocks'); and watches.

A brief selection of comments from the Reports will serve to give an insight into the scientific status of the different types of time-telling instruments.

> The marine chronometer may be considered the most important of all machines for measuring time; and it is also the one in which an invariable rate of going is of the most consequence, inasmuch as longitude at sea is determined by means of chronometers, and they have frequently to go for a longer time without the means of being corrected by astronomical observations than astronomical clocks, which are generally accompanied by fixed transit instruments.

On one of the French domestic clocks there was an additional hand to show solar time as well as mean solar time ('equation work', so-called), thus making the clock slightly easier to regulate from a sundial. On the whole, the judges thought: 'there is not much room for difference, except in the merely ornamental parts, which we have nothing to do with.'

Carriage clocks were grouped with watches, as they were considered only large watches, set in cases like those of small clocks, and with the balance placed at right angles to the rest of the wheels.

Watches, like house clocks, are so much an article of general manufacture, and there is so little difference in the quality of several of the best makers, that it is difficult to establish any principle on which prizes can be given for them.

The Swiss exhibition of horology consists entirely of watches and watch-work; and, as is well known, a large proportion of the watches, especially the small and cheaper ones, are made in Switzerland.

The three places in England where watches are made are London, Liverpool, and Coventry.

The highest awards, the Council Medals, were given to E. J. Dent, United Kingdom, for a very large public clock, chronometers, and watches; to Japy Brothers, France, for cheap clock and watch movements, made by machinery; to C. Lutz, Switzerland, for hair springs; and to J. Wagner, France, for a collection of turret clocks. In addition, thirty Prize Medals were awarded.

By the end of the nineteenth century many changes had taken place. English pre-eminence in the watch trade, already challenged by the Swiss, was finally overtaken by American mass-production for the cheap market. Marine chronometers had a steady sale, the trade being in the hands of a few specialist firms who sold to a wide range of retailers all over the world. As we have seen, the establishment of national time ended the long useful life of the sundial, and this survived largely as a garden or architectural ornament. An important new invention in time-telling was the electric clock, which began life as a novelty, but became a very useful instrument, particularly because of its ability to control 'slave' clocks, for such purposes as 'clocking in' at a factory.

Sundials

Of all the mathematical instruments that may be collected, the sundial is the one most commonly met with. It is probably true to say that the great numbers of sundials made in the seventeenth and eighteenth centuries matched the equally large number of clocks in general use. Every church required a sundial to ensure that the turret clock kept time. Similarly, in the late seventeenth century and throughout the eighteenth, most country houses had a horizontal dial, usually mounted on a pedestal in the garden. Anyone who possessed a watch would very likely also own a pocket sundial, and the two instruments were sometimes combined in the same case.

[2] Horizontal dial made from slate, with a brass gnomon. Signed: *Francis Barker & Son, 12 Clerkenwell Road, London.* Made for latitude 51°30′, it carries the equation of time table, with the indications WATCH FASTER, and WATCH SLOWER. Diameter 305 mm. Mid-19th century. *Private collection.*

Most sundials function by casting a shadow on to a marked-out surface; the edge of a piece of metal, a rod, or a string, may be used to cast the shadow. Some sundials employ a small hole, so that the time is read by a spot of light. The edge that casts the shadow is called either the gnomon or the style. The gnomon is usually placed with its axis parallel to the axis of rotation of the Earth. The plate that receives the shadow has to be marked out with hour lines, and the common vertical and horizontal dials have the hour lines calculated for the latitude at which the dial will be used. Some types of sundial are universal, that is, they can be used at any latitude; the equinoctial ring dial, or armillary dial, are such types, where the hour lines are marked at 15-degree intervals round the ring – as the ring is parallel to the equator, it matches the Sun's apparent progress round the Earth. Although the principle of the sundial is so simple, many different types proliferated. During the early nineteenth century, the sundial was still

[3] Cannon dial on an octagonal, marble base. Signed: F. Amuel, Berlin. The brass bracket with a burning lens can be adjusted to the declination angle of the Sun, so that, with the base correctly oriented, the Sun's rays focused on the touch hole of the cannon will cause a discharge at noon. Base 240 × 240 mm; lens diameter 67 mm. Mid-19th century. *Museum of the History of Science (M. 23).*

required, but with greater accuracy, so that it was usually of some size, at least a foot (300 mm) in diameter. The pocket sundial was largely replaced by the pocket watch, but remained as a simple, inexpensive time-reckoner for the countryman.

The types of sundial commonly made during the nineteenth century are relatively few. The *horizontal*, or common garden dial can be round or square, made of bronze, brass, slate, or marble. The latitude for which the dial was marked can easily be found by measuring the angle between the gnomon and the plate. Dials made during the first half of the century will have been intended for serious use, and will probably

[4] Engraving of the cannon dial in the Palais Royal gardens in Paris. As the author remarks: 'Every fine day towards twelve o'clock, crowds of Parisians who have nothing to do may be seen bending their steps towards the Palais Royal to set their watches by the gun, which they believe to be superior as a time-keeper to the finest chronometer in the world.' 1868. *Marion, p. 122.*

[5] Brass, portable cannon dial, with compass, two bubble levels, and an equinoctial dial. Unsigned; the workmanship is French. Latitudes for eight European towns (Londres 51, St. Petersbourg 59), and two American (New York 41, Chicago 42). Plate 200 × 98 mm; height to top of plate 80 mm.
Late 19th century. *Whipple Museum* (369).

have an equation of time scale marked out thus: Watch Slow and Watch Fast (the variation can be as great as 18 minutes). Later dials were mainly intended for garden ornament, as they are today; nevertheless, a few accurate ones survive. Replicas were made in the twentieth century, and one must always distrust any dial bearing a Sun's face and a verse, such as: 'Set me right and treat me well/And I the time to you will tell'.

The *cannon* dial [3, 4 & 5] is a horizontal dial, usually in marble or stone, with the addition of a burning lens, so arranged that the Sun's

[6] Horizontal magnetic dial in silvered brass, signed: *Fraser, London*, and marked with the latitude: *55 29*. The bar-magnet under the pivoted dial plate can be adjusted for magnetic deviation. An equation of time table is provided. The maker was probably the son of William Fraser, at 3 New Bond Street. The son ran the business from 1799 to 1815. Diameter of case 84 mm, of dial 51 mm.
c. 1810. *Museum of the History of Science* (*156*).

rays are directed to the touch hole of a small cannon, which causes it to fire at noon precisely. The lens mounting has to be adjusted for the Sun's declination each week. Examples vary considerably in size, from about two feet in diameter (60 cm) to three inches (7·5 cm). The cannon dial was patented by Victor Chevalier (1770–1841), an instrument maker of Paris. In 1880 they were offered for sale in London for three guineas.

The *magnetic compass* dial [6] is a small, horizontal dial on an actual compass card. Below the pivoted card, and fixed to it, is the magnetic needle, This means that the dial is self-orienting; at least, it will orient to the magnetic North, and a correction will be necessary for declination. These small dials became quite popular in the first half of the nineteenth century, being produced by Fraser, and S. Porter, both in London. They are still being made today for adventurous small boys.

The *vertical* dial is frequently found on the wall of a church, probably incised into the stone of the structure. Some examples, in brass or slate, may be removable; those that were made to face due South may then be confused with horizontal dials. But a vertical dial cannot receive the Sun's light before 6 am or after 6 pm at any time of the year, so the missing lines reveal its type. The hours, too, appear to run anti-clockwise, the reverse of the horizontal dial.

A simple, portable version of the vertical dial is the *pillar* dial (also known as the *cylinder* or *shepherd's* dial) [11, facing p. 48]. The hour scale is marked on the outside of a cylinder which stands vertically. The hour lines are a series of curves that allow for the change in the elevation of the Sun during the year. The gnomon projects horizontally from the top, and is set to the date on which the dial is being used, a calendar scale being marked by lines running vertically round the cylinder. A pillar dial can be of very simple construction indeed, sometimes of plain wood with carved lines, a type used in the Pyrenees until

[7] Inclining dial, signed, in Russian: Morgan St Petersburg. The latitudes of Kiev, Kazan, St Petersburg, Archangel, Yaraslav, Moscow, Tula and Kaluga are engraved on the base. Two bubble levels help to level the instrument. The compass is marked N, W, S, E, in roman letters, which is normal for Russian-made compasses. Francis Morgan (d. 1803) worked in London before 1772, when he moved to St Petersburg. From 1772 to 1801 he was scientific instrument maker to the admiralty. Diameter 135 mm. *c.* 1800. *Museum of the History of Science* (*M.13*).

[8] Inclining dial, signed: *Benj͞ⁿ. Pike New York*. The dial is of silvered brass, set in a mahogany case. The latitude arc is engraved from 0° to 60°, and the angle of the gnomon is 60° to the plane of the chapter ring. The compass card is printed on paper. The instrument appears to be of English workmanship. Benjamin Pike was a considerable importer and retailer of all types of mathematical, optical, and philosophical instruments during the 1840s. His shop was at 294, Broadway, New York. Case 98 × 98 × 32 mm. *c.* 1845. *Museum of the History of Science* (*M. 14*).

the twentieth century. Others may have printed scales, and a few dials were made of ivory or porcelain.

A popular nineteenth century dial for the traveller was the *universal inclining dial* [7 & 8]. Based on the compass dial, some are small enough for the pocket, other suitable for a wide window ledge. There is a compass in the base, and large examples have three levelling screws and a pair of bubble levels. The hour plate is hinged, and can be set at any angle of latitude from the degrees marked on a curved arm fitted at one side of the base. The gnomon and the arm are hinged for packing flat, often into a black fish-skin case. The underside of the base usually has a list of principal towns with their latitudes. This dial works on the principle that any horizontal dial can be used at another latitude, provided the shadow-casting edge of the gnomon is parallel to the Earth's axis, hence the ability to tilt the plate is a provision in this type of dial. English examples from the nineteenth century are signed Dollond, Elliott & Sons, or Newton & Co.

In 1843 Edward John Dent, the noted chronometer-maker, put on to the market a newly patented device for noting the meridian passage of the Sun with great accuracy, which he named the *dipleidoscope* (double image viewer) [9]. The invention was by James Mackenzie Bloxam, patented as a 'meridian instrument' on 20 June 1843 (No. 9793). It consists of a hollow, right-angled prism, with two sides silvered and one of glass. The meridian transit was known by the coincidence of two images of the Sun by single and double reflexion, one from the top glass, and the other from both mirrors. Of course, the base of the instrument had to be accurately levelled and oriented, and with this done, the time could be read to seconds [10]. The instrument was made

[9] Two examples of the Dent dipleidoscope. *Left*, signed: E.I. DENT LONDON PATENTEE; inscribed below the base with the serial number: 1592. The prism housing is mounted on an axis that can be inclined from 0° to 90°. The hour arc runs from 9 to 3 o'clock, divided to 15 minutes. There are two bubble levels and two adjustable legs and a compass for correct orientation. This model can give an accurate time check to an explorer. Base 130 × 121 mm; overall height *c.* 215 mm. *c.* 1870. *Right*, signed: *E.J. DENT PATENTEE* 752. The prism is in a fixed mount, stamped on one side: INDIA. This is of the type for fixing to a window ledge. Base 72 × 50 mm; overall height 68 mm. *c.* 1845. *Museum of the History of Science* (*C. 984; nn*).

[10] Engraving showing how to check a watch with the dipleidoscope. The instrument was patented in 1843, and was marketed by Edward John Dent, the chronometer maker. The engraving is from his explanatory pamphlet of 1844.

[11] Signed: *Wheatstones Heliochronometer* ELLIOTT, 30 Strand LONDON. Quadrants adjust for latitude and for the Sun's declination. The time dial will then be on an axis parallel to the Earth's, and the sighting tube will match the passage of the Sun in the day. When the sighting tube is in line with the Sun, the clock dial will read the time. In the 1840s Charles Wheatstone also experimented with a polar clock to tell the time by the polarization of the sky, which is at a maximum opposite the Sun. Overall height 280 mm; diameter of clock face 50 mm.

c. 1850. *Whipple Museum (716).*

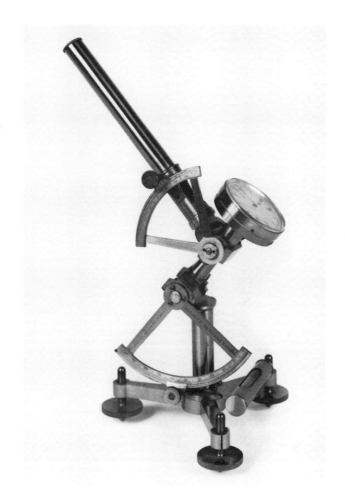

[12] Heliochronometer, signed: CHRONOMÈTRE SOLAIRE P.F. et Cie. Breveté S.G.D.G. Paris. The base is cast iron and the dial silvered brass. The equatorial hour plate is set for latitude, and the plate turned until the lens casts a spot of light on the line on the upright scale. This carries the graph of the equation of time to read mean time; the vertical line will give solar time. A vernier is provided to read to a minute. This instrument is illustrated in *Tissandier, p. 563*, where it is described as designed by Monsieur Fletchet. Diameter 150 mm.

c. 1880. *Museum of the History of Science (F. 84).*

in fixed and portable versions. The latter had levelling screws and bubble levels, latitude adjustment, and a magnetic compass needle. Dent cannot have profited as extensively as he may have hoped from this ingenious invention, because the new electric telegraph soon replaced the need for an accurate time check in the form of a sundial. It would, however, have remained in use in those countries slow to introduce the telegraph.

The early-nineteenth-century *heliochronometer* [11 & 12] derived from the mechanical equinoctial dials of the eighteenth century. An equinoctial disk is divided into hours and minutes, 15 degrees per hour, and this disk is supported so that it may be adjusted to lie in the plane of the equator. A spot of light from the Sun passes through a small hole in a circle of brass held above the disk on a stalk. The spot of light falls on to an oval plate mounted at the edge of the disk opposite the stalk. This oval carries a meridian line, an equinoctial line, and the equation of time diagram, rather like a figure-of-eight. The disk is turned until the light spot cuts the meridian line, when the solar time can be read from the edge of the disk, and to the nearest minute. For mean time, the light spot is set to the equation curve. There are some variations in construction, but the principle of orientation, and the presence of an equation of time diagram are common to all. Existing examples are usually of German or French construction.

The Marine Chronometer

Chronometer is the name for any exact timekeeper, but it has come to mean more specifically marine and some observatory timekeepers that have the appearance of overgrown watches [13]. The essential characteristic of the chronometer is the precision escapement, the one employed being the spring detent escapement invented in about 1765 by Pierre Le Roy (1717–85), and perfected by Thomas Earnshaw (1749–1829) and John Arnold (1736–99), by 1780. For use on board ship, a chronometer was generally mounted on gimbals, in a solidly constructed wooden box, though pocket chronometers were also made, especially towards the end of the century.

The marine chronometer industry came into existence in the 1780s, after sixty years of experiments by John Harrison in England, and Le Roy in France, to develop a timepiece sufficiently accurate to determine longitude at sea. Chronometers ceased to be made after World War I for two reasons: firstly, because the world stock of chronometers exceeded demand, instruments having been stock-piled by admiralties; secondly, because of the development of wireless telegraphy.

In the late eighteenth century, there was a high and sudden demand for chronometers, from ship's officers buying privately, from admiralties, and from the trading companies. At first, this was satisfied by family firms of watchmakers, such as the Mudge family in London, and the family of Berthoud in France. At this time, each instrument was individually made. The two Englishmen, Arnold and Earnshaw,

[13] Chronometer, signed on the face:
KNOBLICH, *ALTONA*, KRILLE
Nachfolger. No. 1700. The movement is not
signed. This model was intended to be an
observatory regulator, and so is not
provided with gimbals. Theodor Knoblich
(1827–92) succeeded Moritz Krille as a
chronometer maker, and continued the
serial number sequence. The Amsterdam
chronometer maker, A. Hohwü, has
provided a certificate on the going of this
instrument, dated 6 July, 1880. Altona is a
port on the Elbe, just west of Hamburg.
Outer wooden case, lined with green felt,
185 × 185 × 102 mm; inner case
140 × 140 × 60 mm.
c. 1870. *Teyler's Museum (10)*.

made the breakthrough to bulk production, and another important English maker (though with a French surname) was Paul Philip Barraud,
who produced about 1000 chronometers between 1796 and 1820. Bulk
production, however, was by no means factory production, even by
the end of the century. Neither the watch nor the chronometer industry
in nineteenth-century Britain ever broke free from the craft method
of production, using a large number of specialist part-makers, only a
few of whom were actually employed in the workshop where the finished instrument was assembled.

Initially expensive because of precision workmanship and high demand, the marine chronometer had, by about 1840, become a standard
article of commerce. The two main British producers of the latter half
of the century were Victor Kullberg and Arnold Mercer. Other makers
in a smaller way were Johannson, Usher and Cole, and E. J. Dent [14]
As with so many other technical products at that time, Britain supplied
the world. Foreign ships bought their chronometers in English ports,
because prices were lower. The records of the firm of Kullberg show
that he supplied many admiralties abroad, as well as foreign retailers.
Though the actual manufacturers were few in number, a wide variety
of names can appear on nineteenth-century chronometers. Kullberg
used his own name only on instruments supplied to the British Admiralty, and the firm of Mercer of St Albans also usually inscribed the

name of the retailer on chronometers supplied to the trade. For this reason, a foreign name on a chronometer should not be taken to imply foreign manufacture.

Around 1900 the chronometer firms were faced with static or declining demand, and spent much time in repair work. Chronometers neither wore out nor underwent fundamental redesign, so there was little room for market growth. A brief boom during World War I was followed by the death of the industry because of new technology.

The Regulator

An astronomical regulator, or more simply a regulator (clockmakers also required them), is a standard, precision clock used to regulate other timekeepers. In its usual form, it has a seconds pendulum, compensated for temperature, a dead-beat or gravity escapement, and is weight-driven; it is finely made, but as simple as possible, and therefore has no striking mechanism. There are three separate dials: hour, minute, and

[14] Marine chronometer, signed on the face: *ARNOLD & DENT, 84, Strand,* London. *No. 782.* The movement is not signed. The chronometer is hung in its case by gimbals. Edward John Dent (1790–1853) joined John Roger Arnold in order to manage the famous Arnold business in the Strand, London. From 1830 to 1840 the firm traded as Arnold & Dent. Case 142 × 141 × 145 mm. *c.* 1833. *Teyler's Museum (11).*

[15] *Left:* front view; *right:* back view. Electric clock signed on the face: C.
DETOUCHE, FOURNISSEUR DE L'EMPEREUR/RUE ST. MARTIN
NOS. 228 & 230 PARIS; and at the rear, in a cartouche: C. DETOUCHE 228
R. ST. MARTIN. 230 1764/3 BREVETÉ S.G.D.G. The ebony base
supports a chased, gilt-brass frame and case; the dial is enamelled. The
pendulum carries a semi-circular bar at the top. When the left-hand arm
touches a contact on the horizontal brass spring, the electro-magnet is
energized, attracting a soft-iron armature on the left. The motion is conveyed
by a lever to set the brass spring on the upper right, the spring being held
raised by a detent. As the pendulum swings to the right, the contacts open to
de-energize the electro-magnet. The cycle repeats from side to side. In this
mechanism the voltage of the battery need not be constant. C. Detouche, who
took out a patent in 1851 for an electro-magnetic pendulum, was associated
with Robert Houdin (1805–71) from 1850. Houdin, well-known as a conjuror,
devised the escapement used in this clock, and took out a patent in Great
Britain in 1856. Base 320 × 135 mm; overall height 410 mm.
c. 1855. *Museum of the History of Science.*

a second hand reading the full radius of the face. Of course, a chronometer could be used as a regulator, when it would not be mounted in
gimbals; it would also have a loud tick, so that the astronomer would
be able to count time while observing through his telescope.

The Electric Clock

Two inventions were necessary as prior requirements for the use of
electricity in clocks: the electric cell, discovered in 1800 by Alessandro

[16] Electric pendulum clock, signed on movement: M. HIPP. NEUCHATEL SUISSE. Marked on back of case in pencil: No. 6392. Walnut case with glass door. Matthaus Hipp (1813–93) patented a pendulum drive in 1842, and in 1860 produced a master clock with improved electric contacts. The pendulum not only regulates the going, but transmits motion to the wheelwork. The energy derives from an electro-magnet which pulls the pendulum at every oscillation. Height 570 mm; width 280 mm; depth 135 mm. *c. 1870. Teyler's Museum (673).*

[17] *Above:* Front view. *Below:* Back view. Electric clock, signed: FROMENT A PARIS. Glass dome removed. A pair of solenoids wired to a battery activate the mechanism by moving a lever which turns the wheelwork via a crank. A contact is then broken and the lever returns to the first position. Purchased in 1858 for Dfl. 116.20. Overall height 380 mm; outer diameter of dial 225 mm. *1858. Teyler's Museum (674).*

Volta (1745–1827), and the magnetic effect of an electric current, discovered in 1820 by Hans Christian Oersted (1777–1851).

The ideas in electric telegraphy and in electric horology are so interconnected that it is natural the same man should have contributed to both fields. Karl August Steinheil (1801–70), professor of mathematics and physics at Munich University from 1832, realized that the Earth itself could act as the return 'wire' in an electric circuit. In 1839 he applied his idea to transmitting a regular electric impulse from a central mechanical clock to outlying clock dials. This was applying electricity to time distribution, an extension of the telegraph. In Britain, the first man to apply electricity to time-telling was the Scot, Alexander Bain (1810–77), whose experiments began in 1838, and resulted in a working model sent for a patent application in 1840, the grant being made in 1841. As happens not infrequently in technical innovation, Steinheil and Bain made similar inventions quite independently.

Charles Wheatstone (1802–75), like Bain a man with no formal scientific training, was appointed in 1834 to the professorship of experimental physics at Kings College, London. Wheatstone, and his partner

[18] Fuller's Time Telegraph, signed: John E. Fuller; dated 1845 at Boston, Massachusetts. The central volvelle can be turned to suit the date for any year, so making a perpetual calendar. The reverse is a calculating instrument (see Chapter 15, plate 21) 1845. *Whipple Museum (1475)*.

[19] Non-clockwork metronome, signed: No. 2 Brevet d'invention METRONOME MAELZEL Paris. On the inside of the base is a paper label inscribed: WHEATSTONE No. 20, Conduit Str, Regent Str, London. Pivoted on knife edges, the arm of this early type of metronome oscillates under gravity. Johann Neponuk Maelzel (1772–1838), a German, was the inventor of the metronome. Charles Wheatstone (1802–75) was a musical instrument maker at 20 Conduit Street from 1829, and it remained the address of the firm for the rest of his life. c. 1830. *Museum of the History of Science* (47.9).

William F. Cooke, set up the Electric Telegraph Company in 1838, and also realized the potential of an electric impulse clock. Wheatstone exhibited his clock to the Royal Society some six weeks after Bain had applied for a patent on a similar device. The obvious conflict of interests led to litigation, and an eventual decision, in 1846, in Bain's favour.

Bain was the first to produce, in 1842, a clock powered by a voltaic electric battery (Daniell cells), which maintained a pendulum in motion electro-magnetically, using a solenoid and magnet. Also in 1842, but not before Bain, and quite independently, Matthaus Hipp (1813–93), a horologist of Neuchatel, Switzerland, invented a maintained pendulum, where the electro-magnetic impulse was given only when the extent of the swing fell below a certain angle [16]. With this arrangement, the varying power during the running down of the battery did not affect the rate of going of the clock. Paul Gustave Froment (1815–65), a graduate of the École Polytechnique, founded in 1844 a precision-instrument-making firm in Paris, which produced the first electric clocks in France, in 1854 [17]. These employed an electrically-controlled gravity escapement.

An electric current can supply the impulse to move the hands of a satellite clock; can rewind a mechanical clock at intervals, by means of a battery; can drive a small electric motor, or give periodic impulses to a pendulum or balance. What prevented the early adoption of the electric clock was the difficulty of making a fully reliable electric contact, the regular making and breaking being central to the accuracy of the clocks. Hipp, in 1860, tried to overcome some of the hazards of imperfect contacts, but the technical problems were not really solved until the last years of the century. Frank Hope-Jones (1868–1950) established the electric clock in 1895 with his synchronome remontoire. At first, this rewound the train of a pendulum clock; later it acted on the pendulum. It was used as a master clock, and became an observatory regulator in the twentieth century.

The synchronous electric clock depends on a widely distributed supply of alternating current to domestic consumers, for a small synchronous motor drives the hands, the accuracy depending on the main electrical generator. As there is no self-contained time-measuring mechanism, these are time indicators, not true clocks. The first patent for them was taken out in the United States in 1918.

The Metronome

The metronome is an instrument used by musicians for marking time, and was the invention of a German, Johann Neponuk Maelzel (1772–1838). In his original metronome, the arm oscillated under gravity, but in later models, clockwork was used to activate the inverted pendulum, with a sliding weight to adjust the speed.

3 · Weights & Measures

I often say that when you can measure what you are speaking about, and express it in numbers, you know something about it; but when you cannot measure it, when you cannot express it in numbers, your knowledge is of a meagre and unsatisfactory kind; it may be the beginning of knowledge, but you have scarcely, in your thoughts, advanced to the stage of science.

Lord Kelvin
Quoted in S. P. Thompson, *Lord Kelvin* (London, 1912)

Physics is the branch of science that includes the study of the movement of bodies, whether planets or atoms, which involves systematic measurement. Movement takes place in space over a period of time, and the energy involved is related to the mass of the body. Thus, length, time, and mass are fundamental in physics, and the large number of measured quantities that occur in physics are composed of these three fundamental dimensions, e.g.

$$\text{force} = \text{mass} \times \text{acceleration}$$
$$= \text{mass} \times \text{length} \times \text{time}^{-2}$$

Space is measured in lengths; motion in length and time; mass, or quantity of matter in a body, involves volume and density. Masses are compared by weighing them, which means comparing the forces of gravity acting on them. Time measurement has been considered in Chapter 2; here the measurement of length and weight will be discussed. The physicist distinguishes between mass (quantity of matter) and weight, which is the gravitational force acting on a body, and is equal to mass × acceleration due to gravity. Weight is therefore a force, and since it depends on the pull of gravity, the weight of the same mass will be less were it on the Moon rather than the Earth.

A balance that compares two weights compares their masses in any gravitational situation, but a spring scale does not, for it is calibrated at one particular gravitational point. This distinction is of no consequence in commerce, but it is vital in physics, because the gravitational pull of the Earth is not equal at every point because the Earth is not a perfect sphere.

The weights and measures we are familiar with today evolved through the establishment of agreed measures that are essentially arbitrary. These were applied by the use of subsidiary standards, regularly checked against the primary standard in the possession of the governing authority. Over the centuries, the degree of accuracy of measurement increased. Standards had to be remade to greater accuracy, and allowance made for corrosion, heat, even barometric pressure. There were fears for the safety of the primary standard, and so a natural standard was sought that could be returned to if the man-made one were destroyed. The English standard was based on dry barley grains, carefully selected from the middle ear; three grains end to end made one inch.

When the French, in the brave, reforming days after the Revolution, wanted a unified system of metrology, they chose the distance around the Earth through the Poles, and said that the basic unit, the metre, should be one ten-millionth part of the distance from the Pole to the Equator. The French scientists assumed that, should the metal bar one metre long that constituted the primary standard be lost, then it would be possible to re-measure the Earth. Unfortunately for such a bold scheme, errors were made in the computation, so the metre bar was simply a physical standard, just like the old Pied de Roi, or the Elizabethan yard. The twentieth century has also settled on a natural standard, that of the wavelength of a line in the emission spectrum of cadmium.

THE STANDARDIZATION OF WEIGHTS AND MEASURES

Strong, centralized governments, such as the Roman empire, have come closest to achieving standardization of weights and measures over large areas of the globe. On the Continent of Europe, with a multitude of small states and principalities, standardization was only fully achieved with the imposition of the metric system at the turn of the eighteenth century, under the Napoleonic empire. In Britain, where natural standards existed earlier than in most of the rest of Europe, it was again in periods of political stability under strong rulers that the important steps towards standardization occurred. At the end of the eleventh century, William the Conqueror gave the order for standards of weight and measure to be stamped and used throughout England, though he made no change in the Anglo-Saxon units. Magna Carta (1215) embodied the requirement that there should be one measure for wine, one for ale and one for corn throughout the realms of England. But it was the Assize of Weights and Measures of Henry III that established in England the 'troy' pound (probably derived from the French town of Troyes which had an important fair) for weighing gold, silver, corn, spices, and the 'merchant's' pound for other goods—later to be described as 'avoirdupois'; and the standard yard. The natural standards established by the Assize were to be kept in the Exchequer, and copies to be distributed throughout the country.

The next important developments in the story come with the Tudors. In 1497 Henry VII ordered new copies of all the standards to be made and distributed, on receipt of which, all old weights and measures were to be destroyed. In 1588, under Elizabeth I, new sets of avoirdupois weights were sent out to 57 towns and counties. The standards set

[I]. Four nineteenth-century book covers.

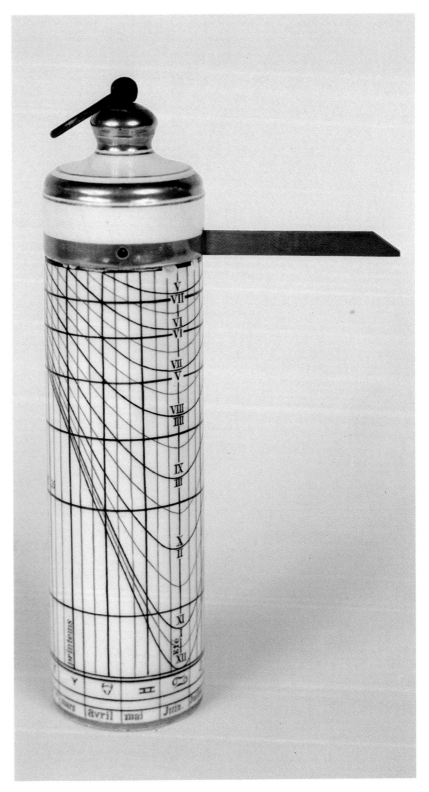

[II] Pillar dial, French, unsigned. This is unusually large and decorative for a pillar dial, made in white porcelain with gilded rims. The hour lines in black and the half-hour lines in red are drawn for the latitude 49°35′, which is marked on the pillar. Vertical lines in black delineate the Zodiac, and red vertical lines the months, which are divided into approximately ten-day periods. The four seasons are inscribed in French. The horizontal gnomon, which swivels into position over the date line, is pointed towards the Sun, when the vertical shadow will give the time. The line of latitude 49°35′ runs just below Cherbourg (49°38′) and Luxembourg (49°37′). Overall height 247 mm; base diameter 61 mm.
Mid-19th century. *Whipple Museum (739)*.

by the Tudors bear the name of Winchester, the ancient capital of England and for centuries a major centre of trade. *The Gouldesmythes Storehouse*, published in 1606 by H. G., Citizen and Goldsmith of London, states:

> There is onely two sortes of waightes used in England the which are allowed by Statute, the one called Troy waight, the other Haberdepois waight. The Troy waight cont[aineth] 12 oz. to the pound waight, and the Haberdepois 16 oz. to the pound waight. But the Troy waighte is the ground of the other, and of any other waighte used.

At that date, the number of grains in a troy pound was 5760, exactly the same as in the pound troy that became the Imperial standard weight by Act of Parliament in 1824. The number of grains in the avoirdupois pound in 1606 was 7680, considerably higher than the 7000 grains that became the Imperial standard in 1855.

The 1824 Act made the troy pound the primary standard of weight, and the yard of 36 inches the primary linear unit. At the date of the Act the national primary standard, a brass yardstick in the official possession of the Speaker of the House of Commons, was that made in 1760 by John Bird, copied from the Royal Society's copy of the Exchequer Standard yard. Bird made two yardsticks, one in 1758 and one in 1760, and it was the latter that was finally accepted in law. However, its official existence was short, for it was destroyed, together with other standards, in the fire at the Houses of Parliament in 1834. Fortunately, the Royal Astronomical Society had caused a standard yard to be constructed for its own use in 1832, that was closely comparable to Bird's official standard. This was therefore available to take the place of the Parliamentary standard destroyed in the fire. It was not until 1855, however, that a new Act of Parliament established this standard, and at the same time fixed the avoirdupois pound of 7000 grains as the primary standard of weight from which all other standards should derive. This reversed the 1824 Act's establishment of the troy pound as the primary standard, with the avoirdupois pound as subsidiary. From 1588 both types of pound had been concurrently in use for different purposes, and the fixing of one or the other as the primary standard did not affect this usage. The two types of weight system still exist today, though the troy pound is now abolished, and only the troy ounce remains.

Throughout the eighteenth century the scientific study of metrology was growing in importance in Europe. What was being investigated were the various possible means of relating a standard of linear measurement to a constant measurement in the natural world, so that, even if a material standard were destroyed, it would be a comparatively simple matter to repeat the basic measurement. In Britain, the leading figure in this research was Henry Kater (1777–1835) who served with the Royal Engineers in India, where he surveyed in the Madras region. This experience led him to improve geodetic instruments. He invented a reversible pendulum with interchangeable centres of oscillation and suspension. The distance between these conjugate points can be used in the equation for the simple pendulum, and so the length of a pendulum beating seconds can be found with considerable accuracy. This enabled Kater to obtain accurate values of g, the acceleration due to gravity. The Royal Society awarded him a medal for this work in 1817, and it led to his being asked to assist in the standardization of weights and measures in Britain. As a result of his work in the 1820s, the measure of weight was separated from length, and taken as the weight of a particular piece of durable metal.

In France, metrology was pioneered at the end of the seventeenth century by Jean Picard and Adrien Auzout, and, in the course of the following century, there were exchanges of information on the subject between the Royal Society in London and the Académie des Sciences in Paris. One of the first moves of the revolutionary National Assembly was to set up, in 1790, a committee of academicians to work on a national system of weights and measures, based on scientific measurement. The use of the pendulum was rejected in favour of a fraction of a physical standard which the committee was required to re-calculate. The length of the metre was thus established, and this was the fundamental unit from which the metric system was derived. A law of 10 December 1799 enacted the length of the metre, and the weight of the kilogramme, which was the weight of a litre of distilled water. The system was to become compulsory in 1801. In 1837 a new Act was passed to forbid, under severe penalties as from 1 January 1840, the use of any but metric weights and measures. The Bureau International des Poids et Mesures, at Sèvres, near Paris, makes and provides prototypes of the metre and kilogramme for subscribing countries. In 1897 the British Parliament allowed the use of the metric system in trade, and abolished the penalty for using or possessing a metric weight or measure. In England and in France the strong central governments had created a reasonably uniform system of weights and measures during the medieval period. The situation among the small states and free cities of Germany and Italy was completely different. Italy, with kingdoms, duchies, communes, and cities, never managed to achieve any standardization until the middle of the nineteenth century. It was the unification of the whole country in 1871 that allowed a national standard for the first time, and this was formed by the French metric system and not by choosing one of the indigenous systems.

The United States Constitution conferred on Congress the power to fix standards of weights and measures. But, for many years after 1789, Congress took practically no action towards the exercise of this authority. The problem was similar to the difficulties in the way of standardization in Europe: the opposition of people to change in their local traditions, and the difficulty of enforcing any new system. Each of the individual States had its own standards, and Congressmen would risk serious unpopularity by advocating new, countrywide standards. What brought matters to a head was the problem of how much gold

[1] Standard yard made of brass, in an oak case. The yard is defined by the inner sides of the blocks at each end. Signed: DE GRAVE, LONDON. Also inscribed: IMPERIAL YARD MANORIAL COURT LEET STOW ON THE WOLD GLOUCESTERSHIRE 1837. At one end is punched the Royal Cipher of William IV, and at the other the Exchequer mark. 1837. *Museum of the History of Science.*

should be put into coins, and of securing conformity in their weight. A brass troy standard pound was therefore acquired in London in 1827, and established as a standard in the National Mint at Philadelphia. This pound troy was the work of R. B. Bate, one of the leading London instrument makers of the period. It was to such craftsmen that the task of making the subsidiary standards of weight and measure was entrusted.

During the nineteenth century it became necessary to formalize the checking of primary standards, subsidiary standards and weighing instruments. In Britain, the Standards of Weights, Measures and Coinage Act 1866 created a special department of the Board of Trade called the Standard Weights and Measures Department, that was given custody of the primary standards and the job of verifying them, and also the subsidiary standards. By the Weights and Measures Act of 1878, local authority departments were established to deal with the stamping and verification of all weights and measures and connected apparatus for industrial and commercial use, as well as the detection and prevention of fraud in these areas. The Board of Trade also carried out verification for foreign countries that did not have their own standardizing departments. By 1900 there were such departments in all the chief European capitals. The United States Bureau of Standards was set up in 1901, under the charge of a Director. Like the British Department, it covers physics and chemistry, as well as commerce.

Linear Measures

The two standard linear measures in use at the beginning of the nineteenth century in Britain were the yard and the ell, the latter having been introduced in the reign of Elizabeth I as a measure of cloth, consisting of 45 inches; it continued as a legal measure until 1824. The actual length of the ell varied from one European country to another, and even the Scottish ell was shorter than the English, measuring only 37 inches. Ell rules, therefore, can be found in a variety of lengths, and there are also examples with different ell lengths marked; they are generally made of wood, with brass ends and scales. Yardsticks for domestic or commercial use are generally made of wood, but there are examples of standard yardsticks made of brass, usually with a case [1]. Those dating from the early part of the century may bear

[2] Standard metre made of glass, in its mahogany case. The metre is defined by the flat tips of the conical ends. Made by Olland of Utrecht in 1856.
1856. *Teyler's Museum (4).*

[3] Bushel volume measure, of oak and iron, branded: BUSHEL. Weights and Measures Department brand: N/G [Crown] R/567. Diameter 360 mm; height 385 mm.
c. 1912. *Private collection.*

[4] Bronze volume measure signed: *De Grave London.* Marked: *Quart Winchester,* and : HUNDRED OF RHYDDLAN COUNTY OF FLINT 1817. Diameter 110 mm; height 165 mm.
1817. *Museum of the History of Science.*

the name of a manorial court, and also a date and the royal cypher. After 1824 the ell was no longer in use officially, but yardsticks continued, and standard brass Imperial yards from the latter part of the century can be found, stamped with the crown and initials of the reigning monarch, and also probably a date. Later in the century, a selection of linear measures listed in retailers' catalogues could include: yard or metric rule of boxwood or steel; flexible steel rules; calipers of boxwood or steel; micrometer of German silver or steel.

[5] Standard gallon, of brass, inscribed: WEST RIDING COUNTY COUNCIL CENTRAL DISTRICT No. 479. Marked with the Royal Cipher of Victoria, and the department number 174. Base diameter 241 mm; overall height 262 mm. *c.* 1880. *Whipple Museum (2615).*

[6] Imperial pint and half-pint, brass, inscribed COUNTY OF HERTFORD 1879. *Science Museum (1945–28; 29).*

[7] Apothecary's reference standard measures, issued by the Board of Trade, 1878. A group of five brass measures from 1 fluid drachm to 3 fluid ounces, correct at a temperature of 62°F, with glass caps. 1878. *Science Museum (1931–1048).*

In France, prior to the adoption of the metric system, the linear standard was the Pied de Roi, which was equivalent to 12.7892 English inches.

Capacity Measures

The British Winchester standard capacity measures were those established by Henry VII in 1497, and were defined by the weight in troy ounces of their contents of wheat, by 'striked measure', that is, with the top levelled by a thin board. The measures, which were standard for wheat, wine and ale, were: the pint ($12\frac{1}{2}$ troy ounces of wheat); the quart; the pottle (4 pints); the gallon, and the bushel [3], which was a dry capacity measure, equivalent to 8 gallons, or 800 troy ounces of wheat. Standard Winchester metal measures, usually of bronze, can be found, dating from the early nineteenth century [4]. Prior to metrication, the French grain measure was the minot, which was equivalent to 1.108 English bushels.

There was confusion between the Winchester standard gallon, and the smaller, traditional wine gallon, which resulted in an Act of 1707 defining the English wine gallon as 231 cubic inches. By comparison the Winchester gallon had 268 cubic inches. So, from 1707, the wine and the ale gallons were officially different. The wine gallon passed into use in the United States, and became legally adopted there as a standard capacity measure in 1836. The Imperial gallon of 1824 consisted of 277 cubic inches, so that it is 20 per cent larger than the current United States gallon. The Imperial gallon is now defined as the space occupied by 10 pounds of distilled water at a given temperature.

Before metrication was adopted in France, the 'pinte' and the 'quarte' were used. The French pinte was equivalent to 0.984 of an English quart, and as there were 2 pintes to 1 quarte, the French quarte was roughly half an English gallon.

WEIGHTS

The basic English unit of weight has, since the thirteenth century, been the corn grain from the middle ear. The grain is the common unit between the troy and the avoirdupois tables of weight. The pound troy, made the Imperial standard in 1824, consisted of 5760 grains, and the pound avoirdupois, after considerable variations, was substituted as the primary standard of weight in 1855, at 7000 grains. British weights of the nineteenth century are likely to be from either of these two tables, or possibly from the apothecary's table of weights, which was still being used in the first half of the century for dispensing medicines. The British

[8] Set of six grain weights, in fitted, wooden case, 20 to 300 grains. The largest weight is inscribed: U.S. STANDARD 300 GRAIN H. TROEMNER PHILA[DELPHIA]. The US standard grain was introduced in 1828. Henry Troemner started making scales and weights in 1840, and the firm continues today. Case 120 × 70 mm.
Mid-19th century. *Museum of the History of Science* (80–17).

[9] Group of avoirdupois flat weights in iron, and a set of troy cup weights in brass. Flat weights signed: C.H. CRANE WOLVERHAMPTON (diameter of 2 lb, 90 mm); each stamped in a lead plug with the Royal Cipher of Victoria, and the Weights and Measures Department no. 65, which is that of Wolverhampton (after 1878). Charles Henry Crane was working a foundry from 1844, which continued into the 20th century. c. 1890. The cup weights, marked TROY, and the weight in ounces from 16 to $\frac{1}{4}$, are stamped with the Royal Cipher of Edward VII and the number 453 for Berkshire. Diameter of 16 oz., 68 mm. c. 1905. *Private collection*.

Pharmacopoeia of 1864 officially abolished the apothecary's table, by requiring Imperial weights to be used for weighing drugs.

Troy
1 penny weight = 24 grains
1 ounce = 20 penny weights = 480 grains (31.1 g)
1 pound = 12 ounces = 5760 grains (0.3732 kg)
14 ounces, 11 penny weights, 16 grains = 1 pound avoirdupois

Avoirdupois
1 dram = 27.4 grains
1 ounce = 16 drams = 437.5 grains (28.35 g)
1 pound = 16 ounces = 7000 grains (0.45359 kg)
13 ounces, 40 grains = 1 pound troy

Apothecary
1 scruple = 20 grains
1 drachm = 3 scruples
1 ounce = 24 scruples = 8 drachms = 480 grains
1 pound = 12 ounces (same as troy)

[10] White, earthenware weight, lead-filled, marked on the top: $\frac{1}{2}$ lb, and signed: J.T. SHENSTON MANUFACTURER 395, STRAND LONDON. James T. Shenston is in trade directories from 1836 to 1846.
c. 1840. *Museum of the History of Science* (7).

In the Netherlands and parts of Germany the weights in use at the beginning of the nineteenth century were similar, as would be expected since all derive from the old Saxon system. There were trade pounds divided into 16 ounces, troy pounds divided into 16 ounces except in England where it was 12 to a pound. And there were medicinal weights where the pound was divided into 12 ounces. What did differ considerably in some cases were the sizes of the weights, which is revealed by quoting the metric equivalent.

Commercial weights

	pound = 16 oz	divisions of an ounce
Amsterdam	494·1 g	16 wigtjes
Antwerp	470·2 g	16 handjes
Liège	467.1 g	—
Bruges	463.9 g	—
Gent	433.9 g	16 leeuwtjes
Paris	489.5 g	24 deniers
Cologne	467.5 g	32 pfennige
London	453.6 g	16 drams

Troy weights

	pound	divisions
Holland	492.17 g	16 ons of 20 engels of 32 azen
Brabant	470.2 g	16 ons of 20 esterling of 32 azen
France	489.51 g	16 once of 20 esterlin of 24 grain
England	373.24 g	12 ounce of 20 pennyweight of 24 grain

The French pound was the livre, consisting of 9216 French grains, or 7555 English grains; it was, as is shown by the table, considerably heavier than the English pound, though the heaviest of all was the Dutch pound.

In the Netherlands the metric system was brought into use in 1812. To make the transfer more acceptable the old names were retained for the new weight multiples. Thus 1 kilogramme was 1 Nederlands pond, and 100 grammes 1 Nederlands once; 10 g = 1 Ned. lood; 1 g = 1 Ned. wigtje. Abbreviations of these names can be found stamped on Netherlands metric weights. A similar situation applies to capacity measure, where, for example, 1 Netherlands maatje = 1 decilitre = 100 ml.

[11] Standard kilogramme weight, of brass, fire-gilded, in its wooden case. Made by Eduard Wenckebach of Amsterdam in 1856. Diameter of weight 50 mm.

[12] Dutch standard litre, also known as a *kop* or *kan*, made of brass. It bears two inspector's marks. Diameter 100 mm. *c.* 1820. *Museum Boerhaave (A 611).*

[13] Dutch pewter volume measure, inscribed on the handle: DUBB. NED. MAATJE. The 'Double Netherlands small measure' contains 200 ml. There are three series of inspectors' year-letters, 1858 to 1885, and 1891 to 1914/15. The first is preceded by the punch-mark of J. Everts, Arrondissements-Ijker (inspector) for 's-Hertogenbosch from 1820 until his death in 1865. Diameter of base 60 mm; height to lip 120 mm. 1858. *Museum of the History of Science.*

WEIGHING MACHINES

To determine the weight of bodies, and to compare mass, many different types of weighing instrument have been devised. These fall into four main categories: equal-arm balances; unequal-arm balances; spring scales; automatic weighing machines. The terms 'balance' and 'scales' are almost interchangeable in general use to signify a weighing instrument, though some balances do not incorporate any kind of scale, and a spring scale does not involve the principle of balance. It is worth noting, however, that makers of weighing instruments in the eighteenth and nineteenth centuries often described themselves as 'scale-makers'.

Equal-arm Balances

The term 'balance', which can be defined as meaning a state of equilibrium, has come to be applied to most forms of weighing instrument. It is even applied to the 'spring-balance', where, in fact, there is no question of two weights achieving equilibrium. Technically, however, there are two types of equal-arm balance: the beamscale, where two pans are suspended from a horizontal beam, which is either hand-held, or supported by a vertical pillar; and the balance, the more accurate construction. Here, the knife-edges and bearings supporting the beam and pans in the working position are relieved when the instrument is not in use by the operation of a lever and cam at the base of the pillar. This reduces wear on the knife-edges and the bearings, and is found particularly in balances for use in chemistry or in assaying; such balances are housed in a glass case to exclude dust and draughts.

The smaller beamscales that were intended to be hand-held, often by a silk tassle, were usually those used by apothecaries or for weighing coins. The *apothecary's balance* almost invariably has glass pans, though occasionally ivory may be used [14 & 15]; the balance should be contained in a box, and accompanied by weights marked in drachms, scruples, and grains, and frequently a small shovel and glass measuring container. The simple, hand-held beamscale was also used for weighing coins until the eighteenth century, when the folding gold balance was invented.

A larger version of the hanging beamscale came into use after 1836, when bakers were obliged to sell bread by weight, and therefore needed to have scales with them in their vans. These *bread balances*, designed either to be hand-held or hung from a hook, had slotted weights to hang on one side, and hooks to grip the loaf on the other.

Larger beamscales, for shops and other commercial uses, were made with a central pillar supporting the beam, or with a box base, sometimes containing drawers. There was no legal requirement to stamp weighing

[14] Apothecary's balance, signed: *I & W. Holt Scale Makers n 51 Hay Market St. James's*. Equal-arm steel beam (length 175 mm), with oval box ends, and ivory pans (diameter 80 mm). The mahogany case is fitted for cylindrical brass weights with knobs, with values from 1 grain to 1 oz, including drachms and scruples. The Holts were listed in directories for 1800 and 1807. Case 214 × 104 × 40 mm.
c. 1805. *Museum of the History of Science* *(1)*.

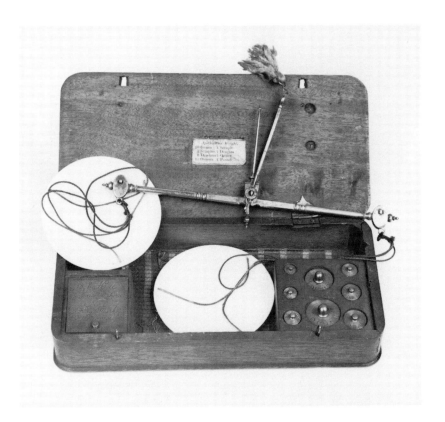

[15] Close-up of the signature on the brass locker cover in the balance case shown in plate 14.
c. 1805.

machines with their capacity until 1890, but after that date, an inspector's stamp can be found, impressed on a lead plug set in the beam.

Coming increasingly into commercial and domestic use during the Victorian period were equal-arm balances in which the pans are set above the beam. The principle on which these balances work was discovered in 1669 by the French mathematician, Gilles Personne de *Roberval*, and bear his name. The popular postal balances are frequently made to the Roberval design. A later design, invented in the mid-nineteenth century by another Frenchman, Joseph *Béranger*, and patented in 1847, improved on the sensitivity of the Roberval design by introducing subsidiary beams below the main double beam. The Béranger balance has a characteristic boxed-in base, enclosing the mechanism.

Unequal-arm Balance

The unequal-arm balance is of very ancient origin, and uses the principle of the lever. The *steelyard* [16], which is the type commonly found for a variety of uses in the nineteenth century, has an immovable axis or fulcrum, with a pan or hook attached to the shorter arm for holding the load, and a moveable counterpoise suspended from the longer arm. This arm is marked with a scale, and the weight of the object in the pan is discovered from the scale at the point where the counterpoise keeps the two arms, or beam, exactly horizontal. The steelyard principle was used particularly for weighing heavy loads, but steelyards in portable form are found for weighing bread, and also as letter scales (see below).

Spring Scales

Spring scales do not rely on achieving a balance, but are based on the deformation of one or more helical springs. As this is proportional to the weight that causes it, the graduation of the accompanying scale is simple. The spring is usually made of steel, and the accuracy can be affected by metal fatigue, and also by temperature. The instrument has to be calibrated by the maker, and should be checked at regular intervals.

Automatic Weighing Machines

The impulse towards the development of automatic machines was commercial. The object was to speed up the weighing of goods and working out the price, and to ensure a high degree of accuracy in both processes. The spring scale has the advantage that it immediately registers the actual weight of whatever is placed in the pan. Much work was done towards the end of the century to produce scales and mechanisms that displayed weight and price together.

Coin Balances

In the eighteenth century and the first half of the nineteenth, no professional or business man would have been without his own coin balance. Something more conveniently useable than the beamscale was

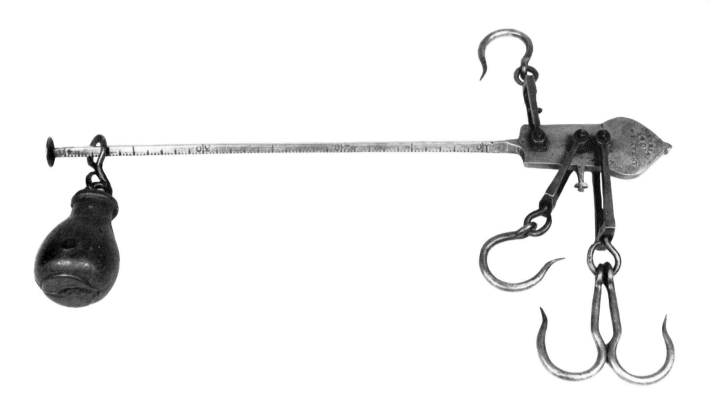

[16] Butcher's steelyard of the turn-over type, signed: W. & T. AVERY; also inscribed: IMPERIAL 40. The term Imperial was first used in 1826. Overall length 415 mm.
Mid-19th century. *Museum of the History of Science (8).*

clearly needed, and the folding coin balance filled this want, and was sold in large numbers. Credit for the invention was claimed by Anthony Wilkinson of Kirkby, Lancashire, between 1774 and 1782. The folding balance is contained in a slim rectangular box, and the balance lifts into position when the lid is opened. The weighing of gold and silver coins was necessary both because unfamiliar foreign coins were in general circulation, and because the actual weight of the precious metal in a coin of the realm could, either through use, or the dishonest activities of counterfeiters, be less than its nominal value. A coin, it must be remembered, was then not simply a token, but an object of intrinsic worth, because of the precious metal of which it was made. A factor in the weighing of coinage is the former use of both silver and gold for currency purposes. Both are legal tender, but the ratio in value (roughly 1 of gold to $15\frac{1}{2}$ of silver) between the two metals can vary according to economic factors, and the supply of the metals; an example was the Californian (1848) gold rush which made gold the principle currency metal in the United States.

The traditional English currency was based on the troy pound of silver, with 20 shillings each of 12 pennies, the silver penny being the coin in circulation; this was pre-Conquest. The first gold sovereign was minted in 1489, but it was subsidiary to the silver standard. The value of gold changed, therefore, like any other commodity, which is why there was a variable shilling and pence equivalent to the gold 'sovereign', e.g. 21*s*. 6*d*. in 1702. In 1696 there was a recoinage, and the guinea was eventually established in 1717 as 21 shillings by Isaac Newton during his period as Master of the Mint. England adopted gold in the eighteenth century and legalized the gold standard in 1816.

[17] Sovereign balances, *above* signed: DE GRAVE & SON, St. Martin le Grand LONDON; *below* signed: HARRISON. The upper is a self-erecting brass balance for checking the value of sovereigns or, employing the turn counterpoise, for half-sovereigns. The sliding weight determines discrepancies in pence or farthings. The sovereign was introduced in 1817, and the firm changed its name in 1844. Case closed 138 × 24 × 15 mm; height erected 75 mm. *c.* 1825. The cast brass device *below* is properly called a coin tester, as the actual weight cannot be found. The counterpoise just balances a true coin; the slots are to test thickness and diameter. The instrument is contained in a cardboard case. Samuel Harrison of Birmingham advertised such a device around 1830. Overall length 98 mm. *c.* 1830. *Museum of the History of Science* (*C. 389; 60–109*).

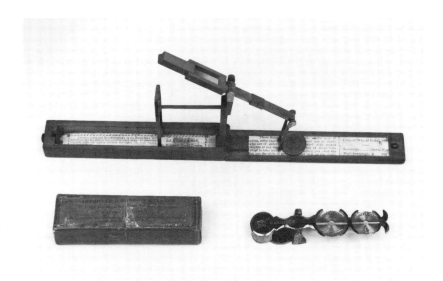

The theoretical economists in the middle of the century used the term bi-metallism in discussing the problems that arose.

Throughout the eighteenth century, guineas and half guineas were the gold coins in use in Britain. At the very end of the century, the seven shilling gold coin (one-third of a guinea) was introduced, and coin balances were made to accommodate this third coin. Over the period of the Napoleonic wars, few balances were made, because the circulation of gold coins was greatly reduced due to the cost of the conflict, and paper money was printed to take its place. The eighteenth-century guinea was replaced by the sovereign of 20 shillings in 1816. Folding coin balances of the early nineteenth century are designed to weigh five coins, the guinea, half-guinea, 7-shilling piece, sovereign and half-sovereign. By 1828 a sovereign balance [17] of a simple rocker design, made from cast brass, was in production. This fitted into a cap-ended case of leather-covered cardboard, and was designed to weigh and gauge the thickness and diameter of a sovereign and half-sovereign only. By the 1840s folding balances of the older type were being made to weigh the two new coins only. In the latter half of the century the rocker balance took over what was left of the market, but the general use by the public of such instruments declined steadily, until the minting of gold money for use in Britain ended in 1917. Rocker balances were also in use for weighing and gauging coins on the continent of Europe throughout the century. An adaptation of the rocker balance was made in 1851 to fit into the top of a counter or cash box, so that a variety of coins could be tested for dimensions and weight before dropping into a drawer, or the box below.

By the middle of the nineteenth century what was needed for coin weighing was not instruments for individual use, but a machine for use in banks, to replace the tedious, and inevitably inaccurate re-weighing of single gold coins, to check their weight. Such a machine was employed by the Bank of England, and by foreign banks, in the 1840s.

[18] Letter balance on the Roberval principle, which employs upper and lower cross beams. Brass mechanism on a mahogany base, with brass flat weights of 1, 2, 4 and 8 oz. The postal rates on the platform are those in force from 1871 to 1897. Base 240 × 130 mm; overall height 120 mm.
c. 1880. *Private collection.*

[19] Postal scales of the 'candlestick' pattern, signed: R.W. WINFIELD BIRMINGHAM. This brass, spring scale was introduced at the same time as the penny post. Robert Walter Winfield registered the design on 13 January 1840, and it lasted for some 25 years. The postage rate in the pence scale is that in operation between 1840 and 1865. Winfield was active from 1829 to 1860. Base diameter 85 mm; height 168 mm.
c. 1850. *Private collection.*

The solution came with an invention by W. Cotton, a former Governor of the Bank of England, who devised a machine with a hopper that could hold 500 sovereigns, and automatically separate light from full-weight coins. This invention was awarded a Prize Medal at the Great Exhibition of 1851, where a similar design devised by Baron Seguier for the Banc de France and made by Deleuil of Paris, was also exhibited.

Postal Balances

The Postal Act of 1840 introduced the modern postal system to Britain. Rowland's Hill's reform consisted in introducing postal charges based on weight, not on distance, and a system of pre-payment recorded by means of adhesive stamps. This had been adopted all over the world by 1860, and in 1876, the Universal Postal Union was established. The new system created the demand for instruments to weigh letters and parcels, in order to estimate the cost of postage. These were found in many homes, as well as in offices. The most popular designs were of the Roberval type [18], but there are also examples of the traditional beamscale pattern, others in the form of the steelyard, and also spring [19] and pendulum scales. The majority of Victorian postal balances carry details of the current postage rates, and this information can be used in dating the balances, as can the maker's name, and/or a patent date.

Chemical Balances

The assayers of gold and silver, and the apothecaries, used balances of some refinement and accuracy, but the use of the fine balance in chemical experiments is credited first to Joseph Black (1728–99), who taught chemistry at Glasgow and then Edinburgh University. His

[20] Chemical balance, with brass open-form beam (length 260 mm), and steel swan-neck ends; central steel knife edges riding on agate planes. The beam release slides on a central pillar and carries a horizontal bar with vertical projections that lift the beam near its ends. This advanced feature is offset by the crude, old-fashioned swan-neck ends. The mahogany and glass case has a sliding front (removed in the photograph). Case 395 × 197 × (height) 340 mm.
c. 1850. *Museum of the History of Science (chem. 160).*

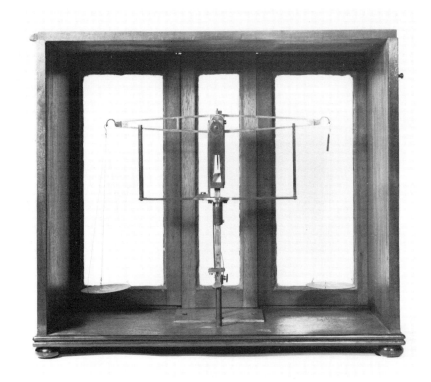

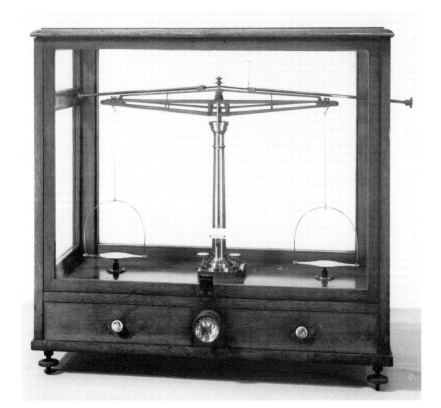

[21] Chemical balance, with a long beam (length 365 mm between knife edges), signed: *L. Oertling London.* The long beam balance was made from about 1847 to about 1920. The balance shown here was used by William Ramsay and Morris Travers in their work on neon and other rare gases in 1896.
c. 1890. *Science Museum (1957–11).*

[22] Chemical balance, with a short beam (length 140 mm), signed: PATENT. F. Sartorius, Göttingen. The beam is triangulated, of aluminium, with steel knife-edges and agate planes. This balance will discriminate to one part in a million. Florenz Sartorius founded his business in 1870.
1876. *Science Museum (1876–380)*.

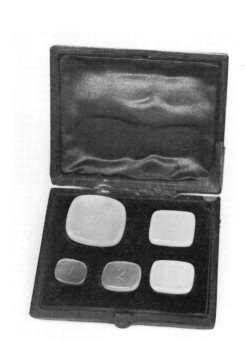

[23] Set of agate weights, 1, 2, 3, 5 and 10 grammes. Such weights can be used when corrosive substances might cause contamination. Base of case 85 × 68 mm. *c.* 1890. *Museum of the History of Science (68–414)*.

quantitative experiments in the 1750s on transforming limestone into quicklime by removing carbon dioxide ('fixed air' in those days) were the first of their kind, the weighings taken to one grain, or 0.065 g. But it was the father of modern chemistry, Antoine Laurent Lavoisier (1743–94), who believed in the principle of conservation of mass, and who consequently pressed for much more sensitive balances. The impetus he provided meant that the nineteenth century opened with some newly invented chemical balances from the workshops of precision instrument makers, not from common scale-makers. In London the most renowned mechanical engineer, Jesse Ramsden (1735–1800), put his inventive skills into balance design, to such effect that Lavoisier believed only Ramsden's instrument could match those made for him in Paris by Nicolas Fortin (1750–1831). Other advanced chemical balances known before 1800 are by Hurter & Haas of London, 1793, and W. & S. Jones of London, 1797.

In the early years of the nineteenth century, Edward Troughton was held in high esteem as a precision instrument maker and circle divider, and he made a number of chemical balances. From Kassel, F. W. Breithaupt & Sohn supplied a beautiful balance to Andrew Ure (1778–1857), the Scottish professor of chemistry who became, in 1830, a commercial

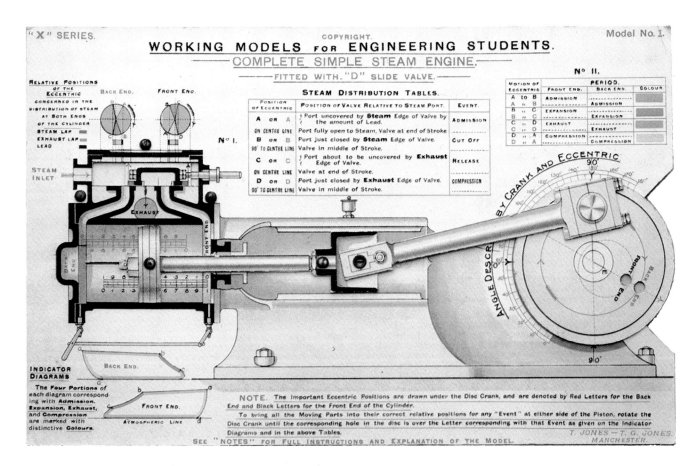

[iv] Cardboard, moving model of a steam-engine piston. Published by Thomas Jones and T. Gilbert Jones in Manchester, together with an explanatory booklet that is dated 1903. Area 241 × 152 mm.
c. 1900. *Museum of the History of Science (81–3).*

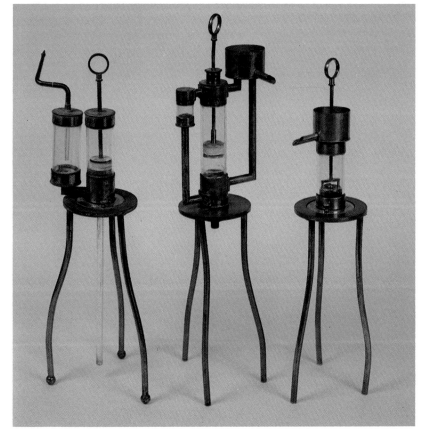

[v] Models of three water pumps showing the action of (from left) a force pump, a double-acting pump, and a simple lift pump. Heights 543 mm, 600 mm, 540 mm; cylinder diameter *c.* 43 mm.
Late 19th century. *Museum of the History of Science (AGU, AGV, AGT.).*

[VI] *Scientific Researches! – New Discoveries in PNEUMATICKS!* by James
Gillray, 1802. The lecturer is Thomas Garnett (1766–1802) and the assistant
is Humphry Davy. The air-pump on the bench has a frog under the bell-jar, and
in the store room is an electrical machine with electrical chimes. On the shelves
are demonstration pieces in electrics, mechanics, and chemistry. Standing at
the right is Count Rumford, one of the founders of the Royal Institution, which
opened in 1799.
1802. *Wellcome Institute Library.*

analytical chemist. A specialist maker of precision balances who caught the rapidly expanding market was Thomas Charles Robinson (1792–1841) of Portland Place, London. His instruments were used in connexion with the Imperial standard troy pound of 1824, and his were the first fine balances to be imported into the United States.

One of the great names associated with chemical balances is that of Ludwig Oertling (1818–93) [21], who was apprenticed in Berlin to his brother. By 1847 Ludwig had started a business in London, and it continues to the present day. He was given a Council Medal at the Great Exhibition of 1851, for a balance with a graduated beam and a form of rider. An Oertling vacuum balance was in use between 1872 and 1892 for comparing weights against the national standard.

Although Robinson had used short beams on his balances, the theory of the short beam was not worked out until 1866, by the German engineer Paul Bunge. It had been thought that the longer the beam, the greater the accuracy achieved, but this is not the case. Following Bunge's research, his ideas were actualized in the instruments of Florenz Sartorius (1846–1925), who founded his business in Göttingen in 1870, where it still continues to operate. The Sartorius balance [22] was made in the early 1870s with a $5\frac{1}{2}$-inch (140 mm) beam made of aluminium (then a new metal) and agate plates to support the steel knife edges that protrude from either side of the beam and about which it balances. This balance could (and still does) discriminate to one part in a million.

The Dutch firm of Becker exhibited at the Great Exhibition, and is responsible for supplying many chemical balances for use in schools, colleges and industrial laboratories. By the end of the century these balances were standard items in the catalogues of large retailers of scientific apparatus. The 1910 catalogue of J. J. Griffin and Sons Ltd., for example, lists chemical and analytical balances, cased and uncased, ten different models of balance for demonstrations in physics, two technical balances up to 10 kg, and eight for specific gravity work, as well as pharmacy and bullion balances. This represents the precision end of the market, and excludes the very extensive commercial and domestic trade.

The Chondrometer

The chondrometer [24 & 25] is a type of balance specifically intended for weighing samples of corn, barley, seeds, and the like, in order to test for quality. The English chondrometer, produced following an Act of Parliament which came into force on 1 January 1826, was of the steelyard type. It was fitted with a counterpoise sliding over a scale calibrated to read directly in pounds weight of grain per bushel.

The Makers

A particularly skilled and important maker was the specialist metrologist, Robert Brettell Bate of London (c. 1793–1843), who produced the standards of weight and measure when the new Imperial standards

[24] Chondrometer, or grain scale, signed: *WATKINS & HILL*. London. Made of brass and steel, packing into a mahogany case. A sample of grain is placed in the bucket and levelled by the wooden 'striker'. Along the arm of the balance slides a counterweight which acts as an indicator over the calibrated scale. This gives readings for the weight of grain in pounds per bushel. The printed instructions in the lid refer to an Act of Parliament of 1 January 1826. Case 230 × 90 × 70 mm; height of balance 70 mm; length of beam 210 mm. *c*. 1840. *Museum of the History of Science* (*4*).

[25] Austrian chondrometer, or grain scale. Steel, equal-arm beam (length 170 mm), supported in ornately decorated shears with a large, round sight-hole. The arc across the centre is graduated from 70 to 82, with 76 at the central balance point. The pan is very thick brass, deliberately pre-loaded (86.72 gm), and the truncated conical bucket (69.20 gm, 27.5 ml) is intended for grain. The value indicated will be that of the grain sample in Wiener Pfund per Metze (a volume measure). The style of beam and decoration is typically Austrian. Mid-19th century. *Museum of the History of Science* (*57-84/276*).

were introduced in the 1820s. The firm also made hydrometers and saccharometers for the Customs and Excise. Richard Vandome & Co. was another leading specialist maker, as was Whitworth & Co., to whom a Council Medal was awarded at the Great Exhibition of 1851, for a machine to compare a subsidiary standard with a national standard. Simms of London also exhibited standard yards made for Parliament, and two standard scales used in their own workshop for dividing linear scales. French firms which also won prizes for metrological work were Froment of Paris, and Perreaux, who exhibited a straight line divider.

Firms which specialized in the making of scientific precision balances in the nineteenth century include L. Oertling of London; Becker of the Netherlands; Marriott and Deleuil, both of Paris; A. Oertling and J. F. Luhme & Co., both of Berlin; Viberg of Sweden; and Bache of the United States. Founded in Paris in 1848 was the firm of E. and A. Collot, which specialized in precision balances and also provided metric standards of weight. Another Frenchman, Béranger, showed his sensitive shop balance at the Great Exhibition, and also a 'peso-compteur', which registered on a piece of paper the weight of the object in the pan.

A leading British manufacturer of all types of balance throughout the nineteenth century was W. & T. Avery. William and Thomas Avery took over the already established scalemaking business of Thomas Beach and Joseph Balden in 1817, operating at the Birmingham address. On the death of William Avery in 1843, the firm was taken over by his sons, who were also called William and Thomas. In 1870 the Atlas Foundry in West Bromwich was opened, and by 1885 the firm employed 770 people. W. & T. Avery became a public limited company in 1894 and a year later purchased the famous Soho foundry of James Watt & Co. that became the centre of what is now Britain's largest scale-making company.

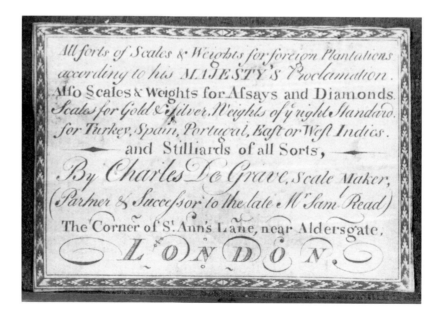

[26] Trade label of Charles de Grave, of 59 St. Martin-le-Grand, London, who succeeded Samuel Read in 1780. De Grave died c. 1799, and the firm continued under his widow, Mary, and a son.
c. 1790. *Museum of the History of Science.*

Charles De Grave, senior, was in business in London as a maker of weights and balances from 1767 to his death in 1799. His wife, Mary, took over the business, and continued to run it until 1844, using her name and the description 'widow of Charles De Grave' on her products. She was succeeded by her son, also Charles, and the firm eventually became De Grave, Short & Fanner, under which name it was taken over by W. & T. Avery in 1920, though the old name continued in use until 1962.

The folding gold balance was the invention of Anthony Wilkinson, *c.* 1775. Later makers of this type of balance were based in Lancashire or Birmingham; leading producers were: H. Bell & Co., R. Brown & Sons, Stephen Houghton & Son of Liverpool, Barnes & Aspinall, and James Bankes. The rocker sovereign balance was made in large quantities in Birmingham, and advertised by many retailers after 1828.

Leading spring balance makers were George Salter, John Sheldon and J. Cook, while the popular 'candlestick' spring letter scale was made by R. W. Winfield.

4 · Mechanics

Give me but a place to stand, and I can move the world.
Archimedes

The products of applied mechanics are bridges, roads, cranes, engines, the houses in which we live. The way in which all these things, and thousands more, are constructed depends on the theory of structures, and the theory of forces moving relative to each other. None of the products of these theories is a scientific instrument in the same sense as the theodolite and the galvanometer, that is, professional or experimental apparatus. But there have existed, from the beginning of the eighteenth century, pieces of apparatus which illustrate the fundamental principles governing mechanics, specifically intended for use in teaching.

These demonstration models have shown, over two-and-a-half centuries, the quality of inertia which is one of the fundamentals of mechanical theory. In the first decade of the eighteenth century it was discovered that natural philosophy could be effectively taught by demonstrating the various physical effects with three-dimensional models. Since the basic facts about the working of the material world have remained unchanged, the apparatus to demonstrate them has stayed virtually the same.

The substance of the lecture courses on natural philosophy was assembled and used at Oxford University by John Keill (1671–1721) in 1700, and then by Isaac Newton's successor as professor of mathematics at Cambridge University, William Whiston (1667–1752), in 1707. Three years later he was dismissed from the University for heresy, and moved to London, where he joined forces with Francis Hauksbee Snr (*c.* 1666–1713), who was a well-known instrument maker, and Operator to the Royal Society of London. Hauksbee's *Physico-Mechanical Experiments on Various Subjects*, published in 1709, combined the teaching of Whiston with his own practical demonstrations, and was responsible for launching the lecture demonstration. In 1715 a young Dutchman, Willem Jacob 's Gravesande visited England and met Newton, who, two years later, helped him to secure a professorship at Leyden University. In Leyden 's Gravesande found an instrument maker, Jan van Musschenbroek, who enabled him to illustrate his teaching with demonstrations, in the same manner as the Whiston-Hauksbee lectures. He, too, published his lecture course, and this was translated into English by John Theophilus Desaguliers (1683–1744), another leading lecturer, who succeeded Keill at Hart Hall in Oxford, and later moved to London. The succession of lecturers and publications, using the same basic material, continued throughout the eighteenth century, reaching across Europe, where many universities acquired collections of teaching apparatus, and extending to North America. Harvard University purchased a fine cabinet of demonstration pieces that still survives, and other institutions in the United States followed its example. Once established, the demonstration method continued to be used in formal teaching of science until after World War I, as is shown by the appearance in the catalogues of scientific equipment suppliers of the same demonstration items that were used by 's Gravesande and Desaguliers.

Mechanics formed an important part of these courses, subdivided into statics, that is, gravity, stability and equilibrium, and dynamics, or the laws of motion under the influence of forces. The mathematicians and engineers of antiquity, notably Archimedes of Syracuse (287–212 BC), and Hero of Alexandria (fl. AD 50–120) were the first to enunciate the principles of mechanics, but it was Newton who finally established them in a mathematical framework. In his *Principia* (1687) he expressed three fundamental laws of motion:

1. Every body continues in its state of rest, or of uniform motion in a straight line, unless acted upon by some external force. Perhaps the most familiar example of this is the force with which a car passanger is thrown forward on emergency braking, or impact in an accident.
2. The rate of change of momentum in a body is proportional to the applied force, and takes place in the direction in which the force acts. This law is particularly well illustrated by the behaviour of the balls in a game of billiards.
3. To every action there is an equal and opposite reaction. This is demonstrated by the recoil of a gun, or the operation of a jet engine.

The Lever

Archimedes was the first man to systematize and analyse the action of the lever. His book *On Plane Equilibrium* opens with the postulate: 'equal weights at equal distances are in equilibrium; equal weights at unequal distances are not in equilibrium, but incline towards the weight at the greater distance'. This, the principle of the Roman steelyard (see Chapter 3), led Archimedes to discover the centres of gravity of a variety of geometric shapes. There are three orders of lever, which depend on the positions of the fulcrum, the weight or load, and the power or effort exerted to balance or move the load. The ratio of the load over the effort is called the mechanical advantage of the device. Examples of levers are the chemical balance (see Chapter 3), the steelyard, and nutcrackers. The Roberval balance is composed of a jointed parallelogram, pivoting at the centres of the beams, the ends of the beams being linked together by vertical bars. The design of this balance seems to defy the law of the lever, and this provides a paradox that creates interest in it as a teaching device. Roberval's invention also found practical application in grocery and postal balances (see Chapter 3).

The Wheel and Axle

This apparatus demonstrates the action of a basic type of machine which for centuries has been used in well-head hoists and cranes, and in ships' capstans. It consists of two wheels of different diameters fixed to the same axis [1]. Effort applied to turning the larger-diameter wheel will haul up a load attached by a rope onto the smaller wheel, or axial shaft. The mechanical advantage is the ratio of the two wheels, the larger over the smaller.

Pulleys

A wheel with a groove in the rim that guides a rope is called a pulley. If one fixed pulley is used to raise a load to the top of a building, then the effort and the load are equal, and the mechanical advantage is therefore one. If the pulley is allowed to move, by fixing the rope to a beam,

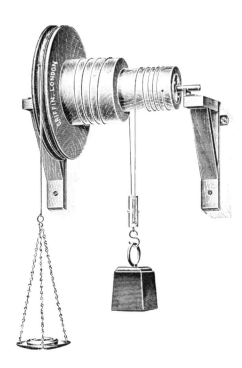

[1] Compound wheel-and-axle. *c.* 1900. *Griffin, p. 114.*

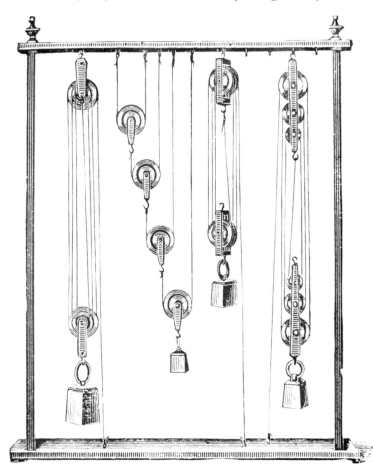

[2] Pulley frame, showing four different pulley-block systems. *c.* 1900. *Griffin, p. 120.*

[3] Inclined plane, with variable angle and load. *c.* 1900. *Griffin, p. 103.*

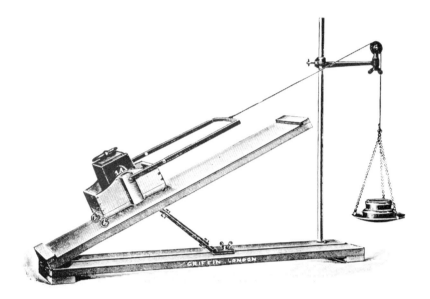

[4] Worm-drive to a wheel-and-axle. This example is probably Italian and is made of brass on a wooden base and pillar painted to give a marbled effect. Height 710 mm; base diameter 225 mm. *c.* 1800. *Museum of the History of Science (74–28).*

then the fixing point shares the effort, and the mechanical advantage is two. A series of pulleys, fixed and moving, can increase the advantage greatly. A system of pulleys that is known as a block and tackle consists of two or three pulleys attached to a beam, hauling a similar array of moving pulleys. Demonstration pulley frames can be found, usually showing five or six different arrangements to give varying mechanical advantage [2].

The Inclined Plane

A heavy load may be moved vertically with greater ease if it is hauled up an inclined plane. The mechanical advantage is the length of the slope divided by the height of the slope. Demonstration pieces of apparatus [3] are made so that the slope can be adjusted to various angles; in some of the more elaborate pieces, the load too can be varied. All have a pulley and scale pan, so that the effort may be varied by adding weights, of which more are needed, the steeper the slope.

Wedge

The action of the wedge may be demonstrated in its simplest form by being driven into a prepared hardwood block. A more elaborate demonstration shows the wedge being drawn between rollers that are held together by variable tension against the force of the wedge, which is varied by adding weights. The action of the wedge is both vertical and horizontal.

Screw and Worm

The screw is one of the most ubiquitous of mechanical devices, being used for holding wood and metal together. It is also an essential component in such machines as the vice and the jack, where the total effort required to hold or lift is very small compared with the weight of the load; an obvious example is a car jack. The screw also appears in the form of the worm drive; the worm is, in effect, a screw attached to an axle, so that it can mesh into the teeth of a large cog-wheel [4]. A small effort applied to the axle slowly turns the cog-wheel, which can raise a heavy load.

Parallelogram of Forces

Special demonstration pieces, in the form of vertical and horizontal boards, were constructed to demonstrate the interaction of forces. For example, a vertical drawing board, with paper pinned to it, and two pulleys clamped at the top edge, can be so arranged that a weighted string passes over each pulley, and is attached to a third string, also weighted and allowed to hang freely. It is then seen that the angles the three strings make with each other, and the ratios of the weights, can be represented by a parallelogram. This is used to explain the equilibrium of three forces acting at a point.

The Philosophical Table

A piece of composite apparatus, devised in the eighteenth century by Willem Jacob 's Gravesande of Leyden, and later by the London instrument maker, George Adams, was called the 'philosophical table'. The table was fitted with adjustable bars, brackets, etc. so that a number of different experiments in mechanics could be performed, using some interchangeable parts. The idea was developed in the mid-nineteenth century by Professor William Farish and Professor Robert Willis (1800–75), who was Jacksonian Professor of Natural and Experimental Philosophy at Cambridge from 1837. The two men devised what they called a 'protean mechanism' [5], a description of which Willis published in 1851, under the title: *A System of Apparatus for the Use of Lecturers and Experimenters in Mechanical Philosophy*. Its use was further developed by Sir Robert Stawell Ball (1840–1913), in his *Experimental Mechanics* (1882). Robert Ball was Professor of Applied Mathematics and Mechanics at the Royal College of Science, Dublin, from 1867 to 1874. The apparatus Ball described consisted of a kit of parts, rather like a Meccano set, and was capable of illustrating not only mechanical powers, but also the principles of bridge and roof construction, the fly wheel, jib crane and punching machine.

Centre of Gravity

The weight of a body is defined as the force with which the Earth attracts it. Although the attraction is to every part of the body, the result of the separate forces of attraction is equal to the weight of the body, and mathematicians regard it as acting through a point within the body, called the centre of gravity. The Leaning Tower of Pisa is the most famous example of the practical effect of the centre of gravity. Models, some elaborate, some simply shaped blocks of wood, were made of the Tower to show that its centre of gravity is still vertically above the

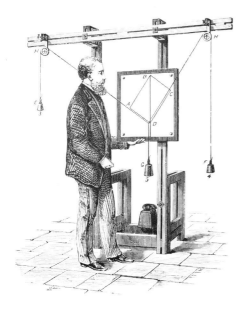

[5] Professor Ball's version of Professor Willis's 'protean mechanism' set to demonstrate the parallelogram of forces. The structure is made from standard units that can be re-arranged to make many of the demonstration set-pieces in mechanics. *c.* 1888. R.S. Ball, *Experimental Mechanics*.

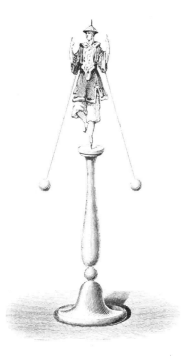

[6] The acrobat, or 'equilibrist', whose centre of gravity is below the point of balance. *c.* 1870. *Deschanel, p. 36*.

[7] Foucault pendulum, to prove that the Earth rotates daily. The effect was discovered in 1851 by J.B.L. Foucault. This model was made in 1856 by W.M. Logeman (1821–94) of Haarlem, and cost Dfl. 116.35. Overall height 740 mm; base diameter 290 mm; length of pendulum 420 mm.
1856. *Teyler's Museum (681)*.

base of the structure. If the Tower were ever to lean further than it already does, until the centre of gravity is at a point beyond the base, the building would then collapse. Another well-established and popular demonstration of this principle is the acrobat, or 'equilibrist' [6]. The puppet figure, shown balanced upon the pointed top of a pillar, is holding a bar with weights attached to bring the combined centre of gravity below the figure's point of contact with the pillar; this means that he does not fall off. The same principle is used by tightrope walkers. This device, and another using puppets to show a shifting centre of gravity, became playthings, and are also referred to in Chapter 16.

The Pendulum

The pendulum is a development of the plumb-line, a small, heavy body suspended on a light string, that is allowed to oscillate, and so control the escapement of a clock. The time taken for a complete oscillation is called the periodic time, which is proportional to the length of the pendulum, and to the acceleration due to gravity. The formula is:

$$T = 2\pi \sqrt{\frac{\ell}{g}}$$

Jean Bernard Léon Foucault (1819–68) was a self-taught experimental physicist, known for two of the most significant experiments of the nineteenth century: the determination of the velocity of light, and the mechanical demonstration of the Earth's rotation, using a pendulum [7]. He noted that the pendulum of a regulator he was using in another experiment kept to one plane of vibration. This led him to make a very long pendulum, by suspending a heavy weight on a steel thread, two metres long. The pendulum was then pulled to one side by a thread which was burnt through to release the pendulum. Foucault thus discovered that the plane of swing of the pendulum gradually turned in the direction of the diurnal movement of the celestial sphere. This experiment, first made on 8 January 1851, was repeated at the Paris Observatory, and elsewhere, with longer pendulums.

The Gyroscope

Further experiments in 1852 on the movement of the Earth led Foucault to invent the gyroscope [8], which also clearly demonstrates the Earth's rotation, and, like the magnetic needle, maintains its spin in a fixed direction. Both the Foucault pendulum and the gyroscope became demonstration pieces, particularly the latter, which also became a toy (see Chapter 16). Another version of the gyroscope was the invention of Georges Étienne Sire (1826–1906), who was director and professor of mechanics at L'École d'Horlogerie in Besançon, France. His device, which was called the polytrope [9], was designed to show the various movements of the globe, such as precession and nutation.

Centrifugal Force

Christiaan Huygens (1629–95) stated the formula that with a whirling body the outward-acting force varies according to the mass and angular

[8] Brass gyroscope, signed: *J. B. Dancer Manchester*. An early example of Foucault's gyroscope, invented in 1852. John Benjamin Dancer (1812–87), moved with Abraham from Liverpool to Manchester in 1841; from 1844 he traded alone.
c. 1860. *Museum of the History of Science (80–15)*.

[9] A development of the gyroscope, signed: Polytrope de M. SIRE E. HARDY à Paris. The brass ring represents a meridian on the Earth, and the vertical axis represents the polar axis. This demonstration piece was purchased in 1861 by the Teyler's Museum for Dfl. 234.
1861. *Teyler's Museum (59)*.

velocity. This was particularly relevant to the study of the planets, in whose movement the centrifugal force is balanced by gravitational attraction. In order to demonstrate this principle, the centrifugal machine [10] was devised, with which, by the use of a number of pulleys or gear wheels, it is possible to whirl different objects at speed. Among the objects were tubes containing particles suspended in a liquid, to show rapid precipitation; balls sliding on a rod; a model of Watt's steam governor; and elastic hoops, which flatten out when whirled at speed, illustrating the contour of the Earth, which is flatter at the poles, and wider at the equator.

A popular and graphic demonstration of a similar nature was the centrifugal railway [11]. Having descended from some height, the velocity of the carriage takes it round in a circular loop, so that there is a point where the carriage is bottom upwards, and remains in contact with the rails in opposition to the law of gravity. These and similar effects have given rise both to toys and to fairground rides.

Percussion Apparatus

Momentum and collision are illustrated using a ballistic pendulum, also called a percussion apparatus [12]. A series of metal or ivory balls is hung on strings, so that the centres of the balls are exactly in line. If one ball at the end of the row is swung so that it hits its neighbour the energy is transmitted to the other end of the line, where one ball will move away, the rest remaining stationary. If two balls are swung, only two will move at the other end, and so on.

Trajectory

A curved wooden chute and a vertical board can be arranged to show that the path of a body projected in a horizontal direction is a parabola [13]. A small ball is released from the top of the curve, and comes off the bottom of the curve horizontally. It then falls under gravity, and the resulting path of fall is a parabola. To demonstrate this, brass rings are fixed to the board, for the ball to pass through.

Another apparatus shows the effect of two balls falling under the guidance of tracks, which are curved in the form of a cycloid [14]. This is used to show that both balls will reach the bottom of the track simultaneously, though released from different points on the curve. This demonstrates the equal time of fall (tautochrone) property of the cycloid.

Fall in a Vacuum

An experiment that is as old as the air-pump (see Chapter 6), is known as the Guinea and Feather demonstration [15]. A tall glass tube is placed on the plate of an air pump, and at its top end is a brass cap with a release mechanism for dropping simultaneously a guinea and a feather. When the tube is evacuated, and the two objects released, it is demonstrated that the guinea and the feather hit the bottom at the same moment [16].

Atwood Fall Machine

A particularly large piece of apparatus was used to show the laws of motion uniformly accelerated or retarded, as well as those undergoing uniform motion. The apparatus was devised by the English mathematician, George Atwood (1746–1807), and published by him in 1784. The machine stands on a pillar over two metres in height, with at the top a pulley wheel on bearings that are nearly frictionless [17 & 18]. A cord loops over the pulley, and at either end are platforms on which disk weights may be placed. To one side is a pendulum clock for counting seconds. The disk weights pass through rings which allow additional bar weights to be added or taken off as the disk weights pass.

[10] Centrifugal force demonstration apparatus. *c. 1872. Deschanel, p. 64.*

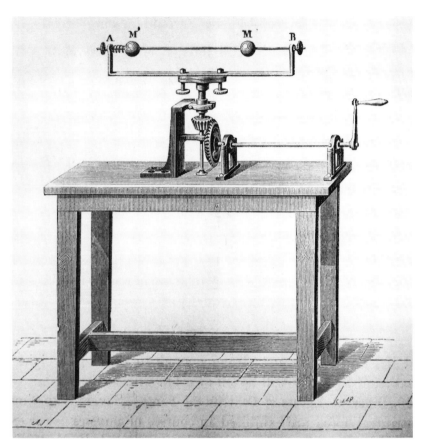

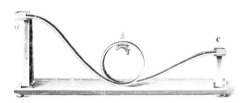

[11] Model of a centrifugal railway. This was offered for sale at £2.2s. *c. 1900. Griffin, p. 130.*

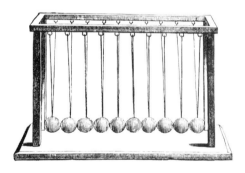

[12] Percussion apparatus for experiments on the collision of balls. *c. 1900. Griffin, p. 98.*

[13] Apparatus to show that the path of a ball projected horizontally is a parabola. Early 19th century. *Science Museum (1929–114)*

[14] Apparatus for showing the properties of the cycloid. The ball falling in the cycloidal curve will reach the bottom in the same time from whichever point in the curve it is released.
Early 19th century. *Science Museum* (*1927–1127*)

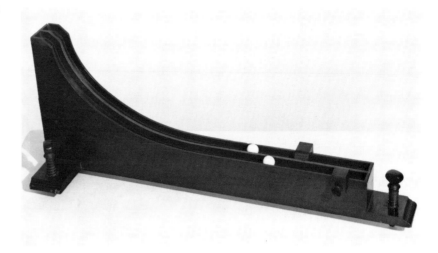

[15] Tall, glass cylinder which can be placed on an air-pump and evacuated. The brass cap at the top contains a release mechanism for a guinea and a feather, which will both fall through the vacuum in the same length of time.
Early 19th century. *Science Museum* (*1927–1308*).

[16] Engraving showing the 'guinea and feather' experiment in operation. 1860. J. H. Pepper, *The Boy's Playbook of Science*, p. 15.

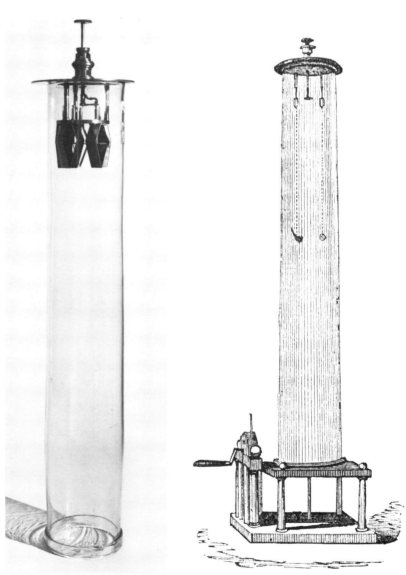

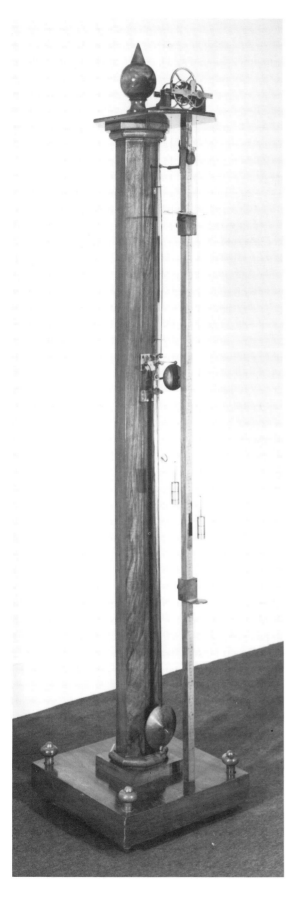

[17] Atwood fall machine, for experiments on the laws of motion. It is not signed, and is probably of French manufacture; the style is not English. The Parisian firm of Pixii is known to have made these machines. The Cambridge mathematician, George Atwood (1746–1807) invented the machine in about 1780, and published it in 1784. They were offered for sale throughout the century, but very few have survived. Base 493 × 502 mm; overall height 2300 mm.
Mid-19th century. *Whipple Museum (2501)*.

[18] Parts of an Atwood fall machine displayed. 1874. A. Ganot, *Traité élémentaire de Physique*, p. 43.

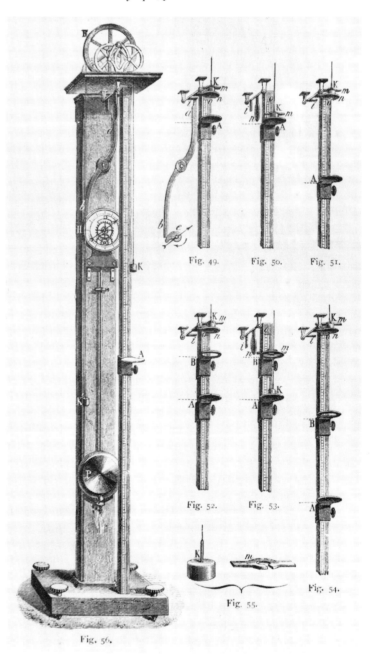

[19] Model to show the gearing in a mill. The crank turns a pin-wheel which meshes with a squirrel cage and so turns a circular platform. Height 260 mm; base 200 × 195 mm. Early 19th century. *Museum of the History of Science (R72).*

[20] Model jack, signed: BRETON FRÈRES Rue Dauphine, 23, Paris. The jack is moved by a crank handle and rack and pinion, the load being held in check by a pawl and ratchet wheel. Height of wooden case 295 mm. Mid-19th century. *Museum of the History of Science (74–27).*

Mechanical Models

So far, demonstration pieces have been described that show mechanical principles. There have also existed since the late seventeenth century, models of the actual machines made according to the principles of mechanics, to demonstrate the action of capstans, hoists, cranes, windmills, water wheels, dredgers, sawmills, and pile drivers. A pile driver, for example, was used in the construction of Westminster Bridge, over the River Thames, begun in 1738, and opened in 1750 [22]. In 1744 a model of the pile driver was described by Desaguliers, a well-known lecture-demonstrator, who stated that it was the invention of 'the late Mr Valoue, Watchmaker'. The same model continued to be used in lectures into the first half of the nineteenth century, and was advertised in simplified form as late as 1900. Exclusively nineteenth-century models are those of steam engines, such as the Watt beam engine, and locomotives. The action of gears and piston drives were also demonstrated by sectional models, having moving parts. By 1900 some of these models were being inexpensively made from cardboard [IV, facing p. 64], so that engineering students could buy their own sets.

[21] Model catapult, signed: WATKINS & HILL 5 CHARING CROSS LONDON. This model shows the effect of inertia. Length 310 mm. c. 1830. *Museum of the History of Science*.

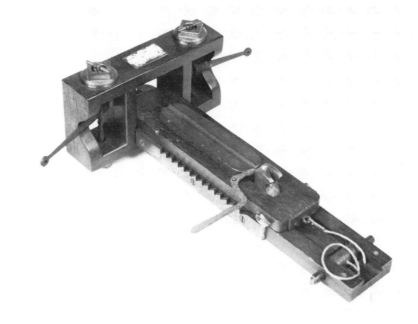

[22] Model of the pile driver used in the construction of Westminster Bridge over the Thames during 1738 to 1750. The action is automatic. The ram is released at the top of the structure, and the grab then falls after it, the capstan drive (by horses) remaining continuous in one direction. Overall height 430 mm; base 400 × 173 mm. Early 19th century. *Museum of the History of Science*.

5 · Hydrostatics

Hydrostaticks and Hydraulicks, that teach us to make engines and contrivances for the lifting up, and for the conveying of water.

Robert Boyle, 1671

The division of science into topics is an arbitrary one made for the purpose of study. Often boundaries melt away as a traditional subject of one era becomes absorbed by another subject in course of time. To a great extent this has occurred during the twentieth century, with chemistry which now looks more like a branch of physics than an autonomous field of study. The old positional astronomy has given way to astro-physics, and the biological scientists receive more and more help from the physicists.

Hydrostatics is an extension of mechanics from the investigation of solid bodies to that of matter in the fluid state. And here again it is possible to divide the fluid state into liquid and gaseous. So mechanics, hydrostatics, and pneumatics are three parts of one study, that of the equilibrium and motion of matter.

Water has been assumed to be typical of all other liquids, hence the use of the term hydrostatics, from the Greek, meaning the equilibrium of water. This is the general term customarily used to embrace the further division of hydrodynamics and hydraulics, which may be defined as follows: hydrodynamics, the study of the motion produced in liquids by applied forces; hydraulics, the forces exerted by moving water and the construction of machines.

The results of the study of hydrostatics are seen in the field of civil engineering; nevertheless, the engineers have to be taught, and instructional models have been used since the beginning of the eighteenth century. The range of these demonstration pieces matches the various points that have to be conveyed to illustrate the theory of the subject. There is remarkably little change in the appearance of the devices through the course of time.

In this branch of science the most famous name is undoubtedly that of Archimedes (287–212 BC) of Syracuse, Sicily, who is held to be the greatest mathematician of antiquity. The Archimedean screw for raising water is well known [1], and it has been in use continuously in

[1] Model of an Archimedian screw.
When the helix is turned, a ball placed at
the bottom will be raised to the top. This
example, made of brass and mahogany, was
used in teaching at the Clarendon
Laboratory, Oxford. Base 585 × 134 mm.
Mid-19th century.
Museum of the History of Science.

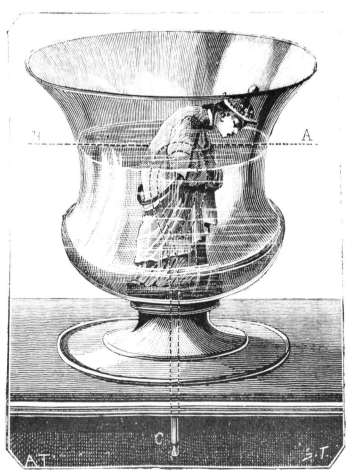

[2] Engraving of a Tantalus cup. The
syphon is hidden in the body of the figure
(see plate 7). *c.* 1880. *Tissandier, p. 67.*

[3] Communicating vessels. Whatever the shape, the water level is the same. *c*. 1900. *Griffin, p. 290.*

[4] Pascal vases, which show that the pressure on the bottom of a vessel depends only on the area of the base and the height of the column of water supported by it, and not on the shape of the vessel. *c*. 1900. *Griffin, p. 291.*

Egypt since his day. It was also used in Holland, driven by windmills, since it is more efficient and can raise water to a greater height than the water wheel. Archimedes is also universally known for his cry 'Eureka!' (I have found it!). What he had found was the principle of specific gravity, while deciding whether the king's crown was of pure gold or an alloy with silver. He set down the principles in his *On Floating Bodies.*

Another name from Hellenistic times is that of Hero of Alexandria (fl. AD 50–120). His *Pneumatics*, the text of which exists in Greek, whereas his *Mechanics* is known only through Arabic translations, is the fundamental work on hydraulics. This illustrates the problem of definition, because the *Pneumatics* describes 78 devices using water in syphons, fountains, the making of pumps and syringes, fire engines and so on. Many of the devices are 'conjuring tricks'; water poured into a vessel causes wine to flow out; water compresses air that sounds a toy trumpet. The eighteenth-century lecture-demonstrators took over a number of Hero's devices to instruct (and amuse) their audiences, and such pieces of apparatus continued to be made and used into the twentieth century [2].

By 1638 Galileo had noticed that a suction pump cannot raise water to a height of more than about 10 metres; this observation seemed to contradict the medieval Catholic doctrine that nature abhors a vacuum. Among those who repeated the experiment was Evangelista Torricelli (1608–47), who used a column of mercury. This reduced the maximum height to about 760 mm, because mercury is 13·5 times as heavy as water, and Torricelli was thus able, by 1664, to produce an effective barometer. The French mathematician, Blaise Pascal (1623–62), also experimented with liquids in very long glass tubes of different shapes, and in 1647 he published *Expériences nouvelles touchant le vide*, in which he claimed that a vacuum was possible, and could be created experimentally.

As a result of this work on the vacuum, Pascal was able to formulate a number of basic principles about the behaviour of liquids. One is usually expressed in the statement that water finds its own level. This was demonstrated by a series of differently shaped vessels, made to intercommunicate; if the apparatus is then filled with water, the vertical level it reaches in the different vessels, whether wide or narrow, will be the same [3].

Another apparatus that bears the French scientist's name is the Pascal vases [4]. The principle here is that the pressure exerted by a liquid on the sides of the vessel in which it is contained depends on the depth and the density of the liquid, but is independent of the shape of the vessel, and the quantity of the liquid. To demonstrate this, three or four glass containers are used, that are different in shape, but have bases of the same area. The base of each container is a closely fitted disk held in place by a lever balanced by weights. Water is then poured into each container in sequence, until the first drops begin to seep through the base; at that point, the height of the water in the container is noted. It can then be observed that seepage occurs at exactly the same height, whatever the shape of the container, thus establishing that pressure is dependent on the area of the base and the height of the column of liquid only.

Pascal also studied the nature of water pressure and discovered that pressure exerted anywhere upon a mass of liquid is transmitted undiminished in all directions, and acts with the same force on all equal surfaces, and in a direction at right angles to those surfaces [5]. The demonstration apparatus here consists of a hollow sphere of glass attached to a glass cylinder containing a piston. In the sides of the sphere are a number of small, open-ended tubes. When the sphere and cylinder are filled with water, and the piston depressed, water spouts from all the tubes equally, and not merely, or mainly, from those opposite the piston.

Attributed to Torricelli is an experiment on the dynamics of liquids. He discovered that the velocity of the eflux of water depends on what is generally called the head, that is the height of the water level above the point from which the water is discharged. Torricelli's theorum was: $v = 2gh$, where h = height and g = acceleration due to gravity. This can be shown by means of the spouting jar, a tall container with three or more holes at different heights in the side [6]. When water is poured into the jar, the jet that pours out with most velocity, and reaches furthest, is that from the bottom hole.

A very ancient hydraulic device is the syphon, and its purpose is to transfer liquid from one vessel to another. The syphon effect can even be employed for conveying water over long distances. The essential requirement is that the point at which the receiving end of the syphon

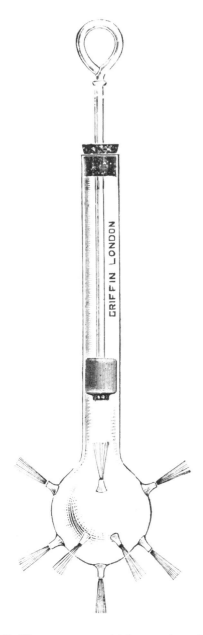

[5] Glass apparatus with jets, to show that pressure is transmitted equally in all directions. *c.* 1900. *Griffin, p. 290.*

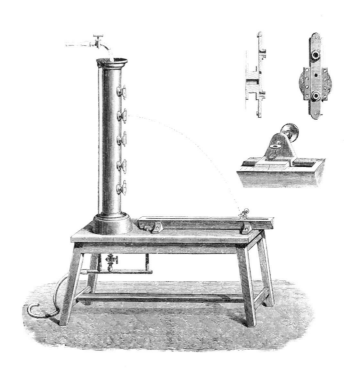

[6] Spouting can, showing that the velocity of the jet depends on the head of water. *c.* 1870. *Deschanel, p. 227.*

[7] Syphon glass, showing the working of a Tantalus cup (see plate 2). Height 136 mm, base diameter 70 mm. *c. 1890. Museum of the History of Science.*

[8] Glass model of Hero's fountain. The upper globe is nearly filled with water, the lower contains air. The fountain is activated by pouring water into the cup at the top. Height 590 mm; base diameter 120 mm. Late 19th century. *Museum of the History of Science.*

[9] Intermittent fountain. *c. 1870. Deschanel, p. 233.*

dips into the reservoir must be higher than the exit end. If this is arranged, and the process is started by ensuring that the syphon tube is full, it does not matter if, at some points, the tube is raised above the reservoir level. The flow of water will continue unchecked until the receiving end has access to no more water. The principle of the syphon was often graphically demonstrated by the so-called Tantalus beaker [7]. As the container is filled with water, it enters the short arm of the syphon tube; when the water level reaches the top of the tube, the syphon will be charged, and the process of discharge will begin, so that the water pours out through a hole in the bottom of the beaker. The beaker often contained a figure about to drink, generally representing the mythological character who was tortured by being constantly offered a drink that was always withdrawn before he could taste it.

The studies on liquids of Hero of Alexandria are recalled in the name of a long-established demonstration piece, Hero's fountain [8]. The apparatus consists of two linked containers, that can be made of brass, japanned tin, or glass. In order to make it function, the upper reservoir is nearly filled with water, while the lower contains air. Water is then poured into a funnel at the top, down a tube through which it falls into the lower reservoir. It condenses the air, which forces the liquid

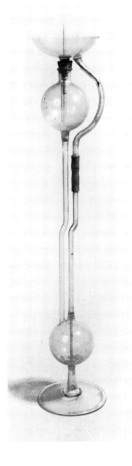

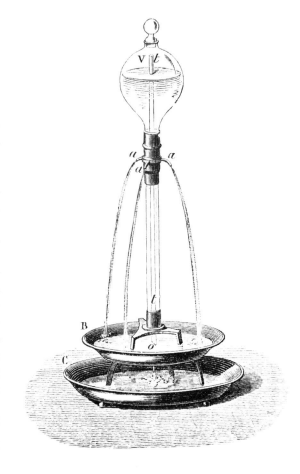

[10] Model of a fire engine of a type in use from the 17th century. Two force pumps give a continuous jet. *c.* 1900. *Griffin, p. 299.*

[11] Model showing the action of an undershot and an overshot water wheel. *c.* 1900. *Griffin, p. 301.*

in the upper reservoir out through a jet. Another fountain demonstration is really more a syphon effect, but is known as the intermittent fountain [9]. A globe placed above a dish is three-quarters filled with water, which pours out of spouts into the dish. The air return tube into the globe has its entrance near the bottom of the dish, so that when the water from the spouts fills the dish and covers the hole, the air is cut off, and flow from the spouts ceases. The dish has another small hole to the base tray, and when the water level falls again, the air can again enter the globe, and the water spouts afresh. Natural water springs often demonstrate this effect of intermittent flow.

Pumps have been used to draw water from wells for centuries, long before the principle on which the pumps operate was understood. The two main types of pump are the suction pump and the force pump; some can be double-acting[v, facing p. 64]. The suction pump has a valve at the top of the pipe which goes into the well (known as a clack valve), that is made of a hinged, circular leather flap, weighted by a brass disk to fall shut. Above is a cylinder with a piston, which has another valve in it. The pump has to be primed by pouring water into the top, to make an air-seal. On the downstroke of the piston, the valve opens, and water passes above the piston, the lower valve remaining shut. On the upstroke, the valve in the piston closes, and the water above is pushed out of the spout. At the same time, the lower valve opens to admit water from the well, which rises because the rising piston has reduced the air pressure to less than that of the atmosphere. Atmospheric pressure cannot support a column of water more than 34

[12] Barker's mill, or hydraulic tourniquet. The horizontal water jets turn the vessel. *c. 1870. Deschanel, p. 101.*

feet long, so, in order to raise water higher than this, a force pump is used. In this pump, the piston is solid, without a valve. Water is drawn up in the same way as before, but on the downstroke it is forced into a side chamber, on its way to the spout. The manual fire engine of the eighteenth and early nineteenth centuries consisted of a pair of force pumps, connected by a long handle, and worked by four men [10].

The natural flow of water in rivers and streams, and artificially flowing water, can be used as motive power by means of water wheels. A large-diameter wheel is provided with buckets, or float-boards, set round the circumference, on which the water acts either by pressure, or by impact. The principal types of water wheel are the undershot and the overshot, both mounted on horizontal axes. Overshot wheels receive the water at the top of the wheel, and are used when the quantity of water in the driving stream is small, but there is a high fall, for example, in mountain streams. Water is collected in specially shaped buckets which, as they fill, turn the wheel by unbalance of weight. The undershot wheel is used when there is a large quantity of water combined with a low fall. The stream hits the float-boards on the underside of the wheel and turn it by impact. Models of water wheels were usually made to show both types of wheel together [11].

Another form of motive power using water is the turbine, particularly the one known as Barker's Mill. The demonstration model can be made either of metal or of glass [12]. A water container is mounted above and below on a vertical axis, and at the bottom are a number of side jets, usually three or four. When the vessel is filled with water, it escapes through the jet holes, and this causes the whole vessel to rotate. This water turbine was also given the name 'hydraulic tourniquet', and was the invention of Dr Barker, shown in model form to the Royal Society in 1743 by John Desaguliers.

Pascal's principle of the transmission of pressure in fluids found an important application in the hydraulic press. When a fluid completely fills a vessel, and pressure is applied to any part of its surface, that pressure is transmitted equally throughout the whole of the enclosed fluid. The hydraulic press [13 & 14] was invented in 1795 by Joseph Bramah (1748–1814), an English engineer and cabinet maker, perhaps best known for his effective safety lock, patented in 1784. He also patented a fountain pen, and devised lavatories with tanks and syphons. In its simplest form, the hydraulic press consists of a cylinder and piston of large diameter, connected by a pipe to a force pump of much smaller diameter. The liquid used is oil, which is pumped from a supply tank into the cylinder, and the piston moves out like a ram, exerting considerable force. A valve is provided to release the pressure, and allow the oil to return to the tank after the press has done its work. The press can be used for the compression of soft materials, such as waste paper, and also for shaping motor-car bodies, and other kinds of plating.

Another popular model was that of the diving bell [15]. The glass dome, containing a model figure, is lowered into a tank of water; attached to the top of the dome is a flexible hose, through which air

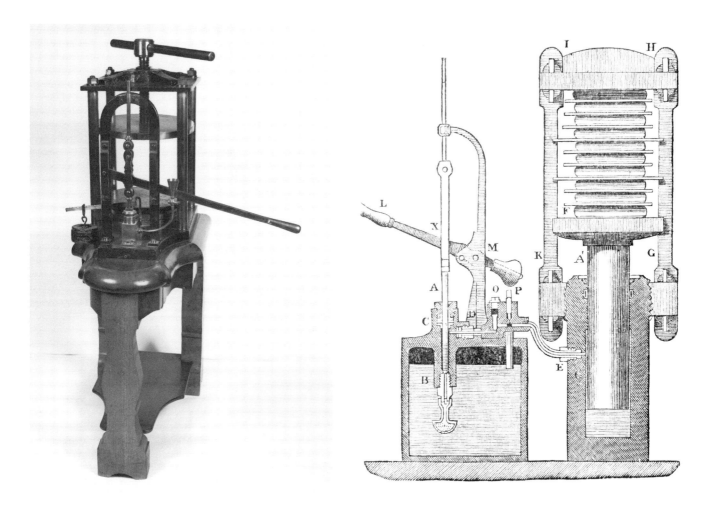

[13] Example of Bramah's hydraulic press: signed *LOGEMAN EN FUNCKLER Haarlem* 1858. This press was purchased in 1859 by the Museum for Dfl. 377.25. Overall height, including table, 1140 mm; pressure disk diameter 300 mm. 1858. *Teyler's Museum (99)*.

[14] Engraving to show the working of a Bramah press. 1831. D. Lardner, *A Treatise on Hydrostatics and Pneumatics*, p. 15.

is forced into the bell by a syringe, to ensure that the air pressure prevents water from entering the base of the bell. This type of diving bell was used to enable workmen to descend into water to dig the foundations of bridges.

The specific gravity of a substance is the weight of a given volume of the substance, divided by the weight of an equal volume of water; this is an application of Archimedes' principle. The traditional way of making the measurement was to use a balance, and to weight the substance in air, and then immersed in water [16 & 17]. The formula is:

$$\text{S.G.} = \frac{\text{weight in air}}{\text{apparent loss of weight in water}}$$

But a quick, simple test apparatus was needed for many purposes, and this need was supplied by the hydrometer.

The first account of the use of the hydrometer in England is that written by Robert Boyle (1627–91), and published in the *Philosophical Transactions of the Royal Society* (1675), under the title: 'A New Essay-instrument invented and described by the Honourable Robert Boyle

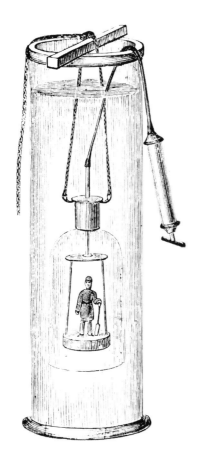

[15] Model of a diving bell, with a syringe to keep up a supply of air under the bell. *c.* 1900. *Griffin, p. 310.*

[16] Specific gravity balance, signed: TUTHER, *221, Holborn, LONDON.* The glass 'pear' is weighed in air and then in the liquid. John Tuther flourished during the 1820s. *c.* 1820. *Science Museum (1954–395).*

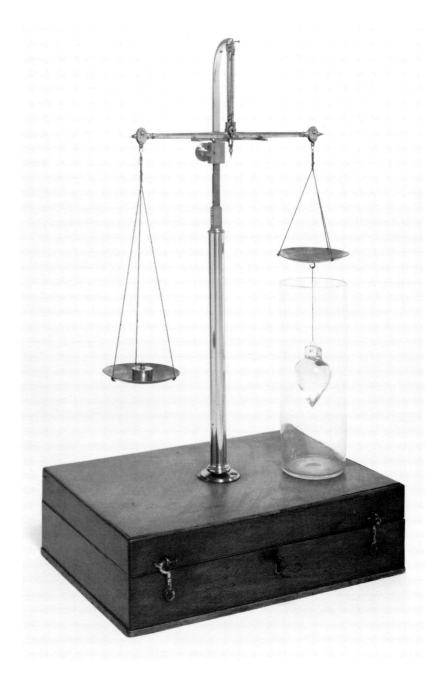

together with the uses thereof etc.' The practical purpose of the instrument was to detect counterfeit coins, especially false guineas. It was through Boyle that the word hydrometer came into the English language, from the Greek for water and measure. It is not difficult to see why the French word *hydromètre* signifies a rain gauge; in French, hydrometer translates as *aéromètre.*

Towards the end of the eighteenth century, methods for measuring the specific gravity of water/alcohol mixtures were developed for excise purposes, since a tax was levied according to the strength of alcohol.

[17] The specific gravity balance by Tuther (shown in plate 16) packed in its mahogany case. The counterweights are marked B for bucket, S for sinker (also called a 'pear'), W for water, and A for air.

The Royal Society was involved, and the *Philosophical Transactions* published, in 1790, a 'Report on the best method of proportioning the Excise upon Spirituous Liquors'. In 1794 the Society sponsored a detailed investigation, and Jesse Ramsden (1735–1800) made a precision balance with which to measure a wide range of specific gravities of water/alcohol mixtures.

The modern hydrometer differs little from Boyle's original. A graduated stem is attached to a hollow bulb, which is weighted so that the whole can float with the stem upright. The instrument adopted for used by the Excise was that form of the instrument proposed by Bartholomew Sikes, a collector of Excise for Hertfordshire at the end of the eighteenth century. As a result of the work of an advisory committee, Acts of Parliament were passed in Britain (the first coming into force on 5th January, 1817) that specifically refer to the Sikes' hydrometer, for taking the degree of strength of all spirits. Excise officers

[18] Sikes excise pattern hydrometer, in its case with thermometer and slide rule, signed on the float: *BUSS 33 Hatton G^{dn} SIKES 15735*. Signed on top of case: SIKES HYDROMETER BUSS 33 HATTON GARDEN LONDON. All counter weights are stamped: BUSS 15735. The mercury thermometer on a bone base is a replacement by a firm that also made similar sets; it is signed: W.R. LOFTUS LTD 821 OXFORD ST LONDON. A book of tables with the set by Thomas O'Dempsey Buss (successor to the late R.B. Bate), is dated 1883. Case 245 × 106 × 52 mm; length of float 171 mm. c. 1883. *Museum of the History of Science (69–46)*.

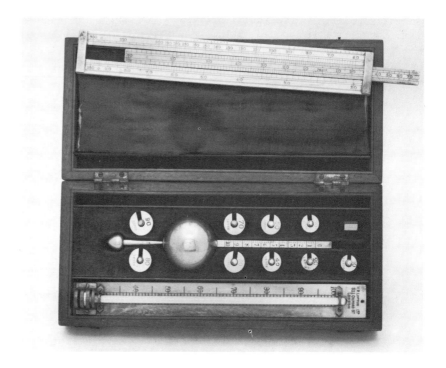

adjusted the readings to a standard temperature of 62°F, which was the temperature at which the Imperial gallon was defined: the volume containing 10 pounds of distilled water. Thus the specific gravity of a sample of spirits, multiplied by ten, gives the weight in pounds of an Imperial gallon of the bulk liquid.

The Sikes hydrometer is made of gilded brass, and employs weights to keep the stem floating at a definite mark. It is usually supplied in a box, with a thermometer, and a slide rule to adjust for temperature

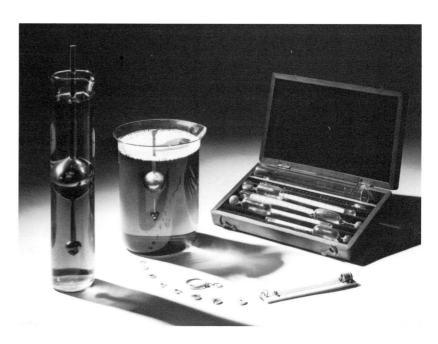

[19] Two brass Sikes hydrometers in use, and a case of glass hydrometers calibrated for different ranges of specific gravity. Late 19th century. *Science Museum (photograph 801/64)*.

[20] Westphal apparatus for determining the specific gravity of liquids to four places of decimals. The sinker weighs 15 grammes and displaces 5 grammes of distilled water at 15°C. The four sizes of rider vary by a factor of 10, so allowing measurement to four decimal places from the graduated arm. Height 210 mm; beam length 195 mm. *c.* 1900. *Private collection.*

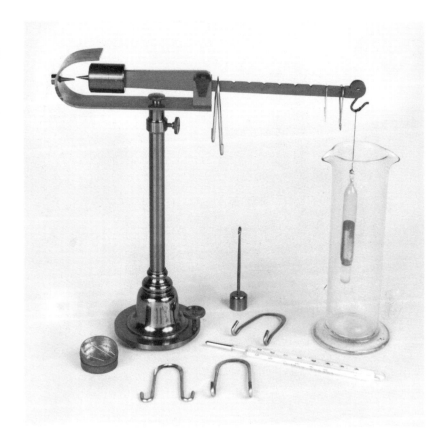

(and sometimes a book of tables for the same purpose) [18 & 19]. Hydrometers made in glass have graduated stems, and no weights to be added, the liquid level giving the specific gravity from the reading on the stem [19]. There are a great many hydrometers made for special purposes, since the technique is a simple one for checking solution strengths. Special purpose include: brines (the salinometer); acids (the acidimeter); milk (the lactometer); brewing (the saccharometer, not to be confused with saccharimeter, see Chapter 12); alkaline leys in bleaching; ammonia, which is lighter than water [20 & 22].

An important variation on the hydrometer is that of William Nicholson (1753–1815), an inventor, and one of the first scientific journalists. In 1785 he published a paper on his new instrument for measuring the specific gravity of solid bodies. This type of instrument is made of brass or tin-plate, and usually has a cylindrical body with conical ends, below which hangs a cup, and above is a thin rod supporting a flat pan [21]. The instrument is floated and weights placed in the pan so that a mark on the stem matches the level of liquid. If a solid is to be measured, then distilled water is used, and the solid put in the pan together with appropriate weights to float the whole to the mark. Then the solid is put into the cup at the bottom, and weights added to the pan to float to the mark again. It is then possible to calculate the specific gravity of the specimen. The Nicholson hydrometer was also adapted for special purposes, an example being Bate's gravimeter.

[21]. The Nicholson hydrometer in use: *left*, crystal in air, *right*, crystal in the liquid. *c.* 1870. *Deschanel, p. 115.*

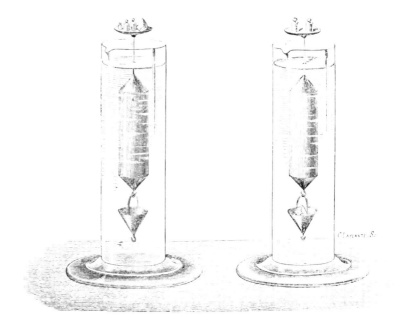

[22] Group of floats for measuring specific gravities of liquids. *Left to right*: for S.G. below 1 (length 312 mm); signed: *Townson & Mercer, London* (length 290 mm); Nicholson's hydrometer in brass (length 180 mm); signed: *C. Baker, 244 High Holborn* (length 243 mm); for heavy liquids (length 202 mm). Late 19th century. *Museum of the History of Science.*

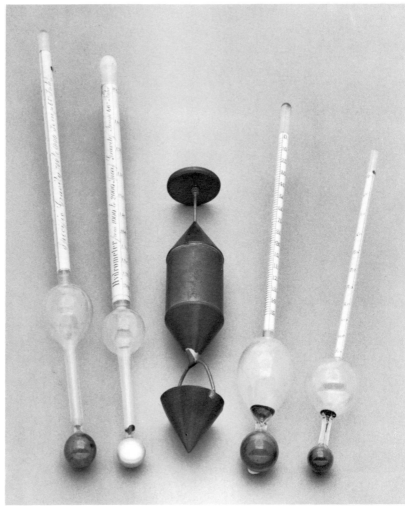

Spirit Beads
Carefully Adjusted
At Temperature 80° to
correspond with the following
Scale of per Cents. of Over and
Under Proof Spirits, according to the British
Excise Hydrometer:—

Bead.	Over Proof.	Bead.	Under Proof.
No. 12 adjusted to 65		No. 26 adjusted to 5	
13	60	27	10
14	55	28	15
15	50	29	20
16	45	30	25
17	40	31	30
18	35	32	35
19	30	33	40
20	25	34	45
21	20	35	50
22	15	36	55
23	10	37	60
24	5	38	65
25	Proof.	39	70
		40	75

MADE BY
JOHN GALLETTI,
Optician & Mathematical Instrument Maker.
24 Argyll Arcade, Glasgow.
f the Spirits be Proof, the Bead will
slowly to the Bottom.

[23] Set of 'spirit beads' or 'philosophical bubbles', signed: MADE BY JOHN GALLETTI, . . . 24 Argyll Arcade, Glasgow. The fifteen glass beads, each with a short stalk, are so weighted that they neither rise nor sink when in the liquid that exactly matches their particular calibration, thus indicating the degree of proof spirit. John Galletti was at the Glasgow address from 1851 to 1896. Case diameter 87 mm. Late 19th century. *Museum of the History of Science (chem. 319).*

Another variation on the measurement of specific gravity is the 'Philosophical Beads', which operate in the same way as for testing eggs, which sink in water when new, and will float when old, because made lighter by enclosed gas. The use of glass beads was invented in about 1757 by Alexander Wilson (1714–86), and a method for their calibration was patented in 1805 by Isabell Lovi: 'Apparatus for determining the specific gravity of fluid bodies'. The beads were supplied in sets, to cover a range of specific gravities for a particular temperature [23]. The bead that did not sink or float matched the liquid, and so indicated the degree of proof spirit (a measure of the alcohol content). Curiously enough, beads of exactly the same shape, and working on the same principle, were used to measure temperature by the Accademia del Cimento in Florence *c.*1660.

[24] Trade label of J.D. Potter, 31 Poultry, London, who also claimed he was a successor of R.B. Bate, who died in 1843. Mid-19th century *Science Museum (photograph 696/68).*

6 · Pneumatics

PNEUMATICKS: *the doctrine and experiments of the gravitation and pressure of elastick and compressible fluids, especially the air.*
PNEUMATIC ENGINE: *an instrument commonly called an air-pump, used to shew the several properties of the air.*

A New General English Dictionary (1760)

In the modern dictionary Pneumatics is described as: 'that branch of physics which deals with the mechanical properties of air, or other elastic fluids or gases' (Oxford English Dictionary). Both these very similar definitions bear out the blurred nature of any divisions made between mechanics, hydrostatics and pneumatics. This is particularly the case with hydrostatics and pneumatics since matter in the fluid state comprises both liquids and gases. As has already been noted in the chapter on hydrostatics, the *Pneumatics* of Hero of Alexandria is concerned almost exclusively with liquids. The important book published in 1657 by Kaspar Schott under the title *Mechanica Hydraulico-Pneumatica* emphasizes that studies of the behaviour of both liquids and gases, as well as of solid bodies, are branches of mechanics.

The controversy over whether there can be such a thing as a vacuum dates from Greek times. Aristotle believed that a vacuum was a contradiction in logic, and this was transformed by the medieval schoolmen into the religious belief that a vacuum was unnatural. During the Renaissance, there was debate between those who supported and those who opposed Aristotle's argument, Galileo being among the latter. The phenomenon that in a suction pump the water does not rise above a certain point (calculated to be about nine metres) was observed by Florentine well-diggers, and to explain this, Galileo advanced the hypothesis of a force capable of balancing a column of water of a given height; this he described as 'the force of vacuum' (See also Chapter 5).

These were the preliminaries to the invention, in 1644, of the first instrument to give the exact measure of the pressure of the atmosphere; this, at the same time, established the existence of a vacuum. The man responsible for the invention of the barometer was Evangelista Torricelli (1608–47), whose letters on his experiments with a column of mercury were circulated first among Italian scientists, and then

[1] Magdeburg hemispheres being put to the test. *c.* 1896. A. Ganot, *Natural Philosophy*, p. 124.

throughout the rest of Europe, giving rise to much experimental and theoretical activity.

About ten years later, another key experiment was performed by the Bürgermeister of Magdeburg in Germany, Otto von Guericke (1602–86). He constructed two large iron hemispheres which were butted together, after which the air between them was pumped out. Teams of horses were then used to pull the two halves apart against the force of air pressure. This experiment was described in 1657 by Kaspar Schott in his book, *Mechanica Hydraulico-Pneumatica*, already referred to above, and became a standard demonstration, using small, brass hemispheres [1]. This was the basic pneumatical experiment, to show the existence of a vacuum through the operation of air pressure.

Schott's book, and the Magdeburg hemisphere experiment, influenced Robert Boyle (1627–91) to begin 'the making of Pneumatical tryals', as he put it. At Oxford, Boyle, with Robert Hooke as his assistant, made the first successful air-pump, which Boyle described in his *New Experiments Physico-Mechanicall, Touching the Spring of the Air and its Effects* (1660), and which Hooke illustrated in his *Micrographia* (1665). By the beginning of the eighteenth century, Hauksbee's double-barrel air-pump was the established model in England, though in Holland, the larger, single-barrel pattern of Jan van Musschenbroek, first made in 1695, was preferred.

Boyle's work on the physics of gases, their volume, pressure and conductivity, gave rise to the famous, and currently taught Boyle's law: $PV = $ a constant. It has since been discovered that there are variants unless a constant temperature is maintained, but the Law still holds good. Pneumatic chemistry produced two important instruments, the eudiometer (see Chapter 12), and the hydrometer (see Chapter 5).

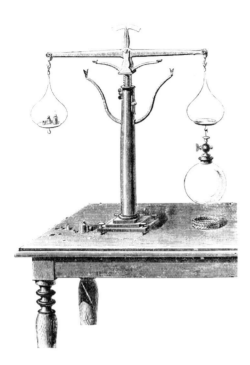

[2] Engraving to show the method of weighing air. A glass globe with a stop-cock is evacuated by an air-pump and then weighed on a balance. The stop-cock is opened and the air fills the globe, bringing the balance down on that side. Until the middle of the seventeenth century it was thought that air had no weight.
c. 1880. *Tissandier, p. 50.*

At the very beginning of the nineteenth century, the medical applications of gases were investigated, notably by Thomas Beddoes (1760–1808), who lectured on chemistry at Oxford in the 1790s. In 1798 he established a Pneumatic Institution at Clifton, near Bristol, for treating various diseases by the administration of gases. This type of treatment enjoyed a brief vogue, but the Institution's chief claim to lasting fame is that in 1801, it provided employment for a young man of 19, named Humphry Davy. It has been said of Beddoes that the discovery of Davy was his most important contribution to science.

The development of the air-pump during the eighteenth century was largely in mechanical improvements, such as better piston seals of leather and wax, and more efficient valves. The original overall design changed little over two centuries for use in teaching, though different techniques were being developed for use in research laboratories towards the end of the nineteenth century; these included diffusion and rotary pumps, electrically driven.

The Air-Pump

At the beginning of the nineteenth century, the commonly used air-pump was the double-barrelled table model, which has brass clamps to fix it to a table top. In other respects it was similar to the Hauksbee design, though modified in mechanical details by Davenport, Smeaton, Cavallo and Haas in the previous century. The pump by Benjamin Messer of London [3], dating from about 1815, is typical, and it may be compared with other, later instruments [4] and with the version advertised by J. J. Griffin & Co. in about 1900 [5]. Here there is the additional horizontal, single barrel of the Tate pump, which is capable of reaching a lower pressure than the double-barrelled pump.

It must be explained how pressure in a vacuum is designated. It is compared with the air pressure, which is taken to be standard at 760 millimetres of mercury – the height of the barometer. Consequently, a reading of 10 mm signifies the height of the mercury column that is supported by the pressure of the air under the bell-jar, or in the vessel that has been exhausted.

It was customary to measure using a mercury manometer, which is tapped into the pipe leading from the bell-jar to the pump. The manometer is like a small barometer tube, and is in the form of a U, closed at one end and open at the other. At the beginning of an experiment, the air pressure forces the mercury to the closed end of the tube. Under reducing pressure, the mercury falls, because the perfect vacuum in the closed end is being matched by the vacuum that is created in the open end. The difference in level between the two mercury columns gives the measure of the degree of vacuum.

There is always a limit to the vacuum, conditioned by the design of the apparatus; leakage from the valves, the pistons, the seating of the bell-jar; dead space at the bottom of the piston; and, in particular, the lubricating oil, which has a density of its own, and can contain

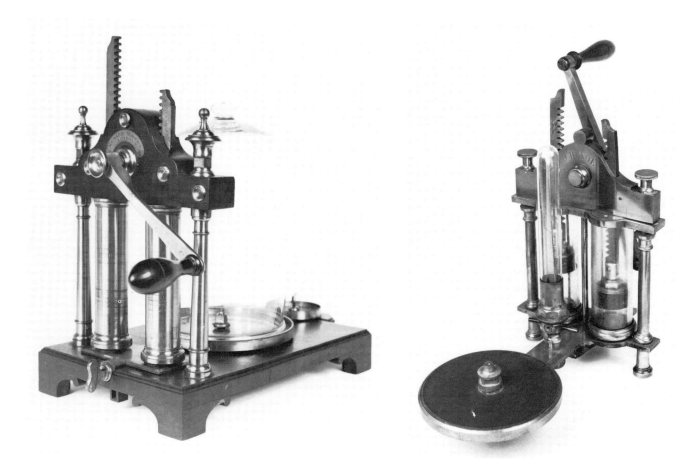

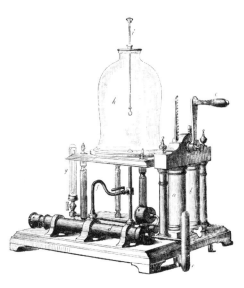

[5] Two-pump model advertised by J.J. Griffin & Co. at the end of the nineteenth century. At the back is a conventional double-barrel pump, and lying horizontally is a Tate pump, which will achieve a higher vacuum. The bell-jar has a manipulator rod passing through a stuffing-box in the brass disk. *c.* 1900. *Griffin, p. 315.*

[3] Double-barrelled air-pump, signed: MESSER Minories LONDON. There are two plates, one for a bell-jar (shown) and one for a glass cylinder. Benjamin Messer was at Wapping in the 1790s, and at 155 Minories from 1810 to 1825. Base 375 × 252 mm; height 340 mm; diameter of plates, 190 mm, 78 mm.
c. 1815. *Whipple Museum (1209).*

[4] Double-barrelled air-pump, signed: CH. NOÉ *Constructeur Rue Berthollet, 8, Paris.* Mercury pressure gauge, and glazed receiver plate. The pistons are in glass cylinders, a practice frequently employed in French air-pumps. Charles Noé founded his firm in 1862, and it continued into the next century. Plate diameter 170 mm; overall height 325 mm.
c. 1870. *Museum of the History of Science (79–9).*

absorbed air and water vapour. A good double-barrelled pump of about 1900 could give a vacuum of 10 mm. Since 1958, the British Standards Institution has adopted the unit named the 'torr', which was used in Germany for many years before this date. The word derives from Torricelli, and commemorates his discovery of the barometer. In fact, the word, torr, merely replaced the longer expression, millimetres of mercury. Thus, a standard atmosphere, by definition, has a pressure of 760 torr.

In the Great Exhibition at the Crystal Palace of 1851 there were nine British exhibitors of air-pumps, two French, and one Danish. This was a small group taking up only one page in the Reports of the Juries, a fact that was 'regretted'. The best pump was thought to be that shown

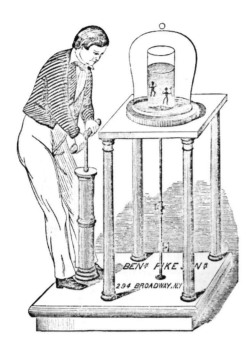

[6] Engraving from the 1848 catalogue of Benjamin Pike, Jr., of 294 Broadway, New York. It is described as 'Pike's Improved Single Barrel Air Pump with raised plate'. 1848.

[7] Single-barrel air-pump, signed: H. OLLAND UTRECHT. A floor-mounted model, with a long lever, rack and quarter pinion to move the piston and linkage to the valve. The receiver plate has a glass surface. H. Olland (1825–1901) started a factory in 1862 at Utrecht. Table top 522 × 310 mm; overall height 970 mm; plate diameter 303 mm. *c.* 1875. *Teyler's Museum (124).*

by John Newman, 122 Regent Street, London, which combined a normal double-barrelled pump, capable of exhausting to 10 mm, and a single barrel with an oil cistern as the upper part. When this pump took over, it was considered that the pressure could be brought as low as 0.5 mm. The plate on this pump was of ground glass to avoid damage from sulphuric acid. Newman received a Council Medal for the instrument.

A Prize Medal went to Watkins & Hill, 5 Charing Cross, London, for their double-barrelled air-pump, which had oiled-silk valves, and conical pistons. Honourable Mention was awarded to George Yeates, 2 Grafton Street, Dublin, and to Julius Nissen of Copenhagen, who exhibited a double-acting single-barrel air-pump 'of an ingenious construction'. Deleuil of Paris showed a double-barrelled pump with glass cylinders following the principles of Jacques Babinet (1794–1872), the valves being opened by wires passing through the pistons. This meant that the valves would open even when the pressure in the vessel was very low. The machine was thought capable of reaching 1 mm in pressure.

Thomas Turner Tate (1807–88), a teacher of engineering and mensuration, invented in 1856 his pattern of double piston air-pump which could achieve higher degrees of vacuum [8]. The design was first constructed by the firm of Griffin under the supervision of Tate. The earlier pumps work easily at the beginning of the exhaustion process, but they become progressively harder to crank against the air pressure on the outside of the piston, which is felt the more as the vacuum increases. With Tate's double piston pump, the contrary effect is produced. At first the resistance is great, but after a few strokes, the action becomes easy, because the atmosphere is cut off from the pistons by the valves at the ends of the barrel. A Tate pump in good condition is capable of creating a vacuum of 3 mm pressure.

The double-barrel was so designed to maintain suction when one piston was on the return stroke, but this can be done in another way with just one barrel, as had been the case with water pumps (see Chapter 5). With a hollow piston rod and a valve in the piston, and interconnecting valves at each end of the cylinder that leads to the bell-jar, a continuous evacuation is possible with one cylinder. This is the mode of action in the Bianchi air-pump, which is made in cast iron.

[8] Tate double-action air-pump, which contains two pistons in one barrel. Air is taken in from the receiver in the middle and is expelled at the extremities of the barrel. It was first described by Thomas Tate in 1856.

c. 1900. *Griffin, p. 316.*

[9] Bianchi air-pump, with a single barrel but double-acting. The cylinder is pivoted at its base, and oscillates as the crank is turned. *c.* 1870. *Deschanel, p. 190.*

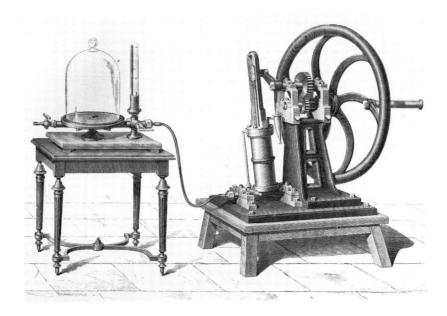

The cylinder is pivoted at the bottom, and it oscillates, following the motion of the crank [9].

An ingenious variant of the Bianchi pump depends on precise engineering, and on knowing the physics of gases. A gas forms a very thin molecular layer round any solid, and it is difficult to move the gas in this layer. This principle was used in his modification of the Bianchi pump by L. J. Deleuil, who published his free-piston pump in 1865 [10]. Deleuil, son of the founder of a Parisian instrument-making firm, had premises at 8 Rue du Pont-le-Lodi, Paris, and also at 7 Althorpe Street, Gray's Inn Lane, London. In his pump, a long metal piston had grooves cut in the side, and moved in its cylinder without touching,

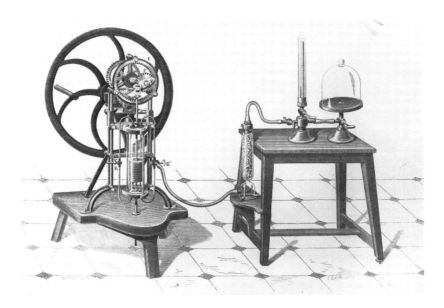

[10] Deleuil-type, single-barrel, free piston air-pump, invented in 1865. A very thin air film separates the piston from the glass cylinder. *c.* 1870. *Deschanel, p. 201.*

[11] Fleuss pattern hydraulic air-pump, using a special oil of low vapour pressure. In addition to the receiver plate, is a side tube with a Magdeburg hemisphere experiment attached. Base 600 × 350 mm. *c*. 1900. *Private collection*.

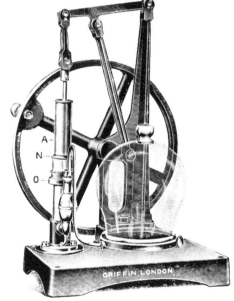

[12] Fleuss pattern air-pump, as advertised by J.J. Griffin & Co. *c*. 1900. *Griffin, p. 321*.

the gap between the walls and the piston being only 0.025 mm. This avoided using lubricating oil, which itself limits the vacuum obtainable, through moisture and its own vapour pressure.

A completely new way of constructing an air-pump came at the end of the century, with the development of a special oil which was pure, dry, and had a lower vapour pressure. In this patent vacuum pump, devised by H. A. Fleuss, the piston worked in oil, with all joints oil-sealed, and the valves moved mechanically, so that the air received no resistance [11 & 12]. The oil obviates the clearance space between the bottom of the piston and the base of the cylinder, a dead space that had always been a limiting factor in the degree of vacuum obtainable. Such a pump could achieve a vacuum of 0.3 mm of mercury.

A non-mechanical vacuum pump was invented by the glassblower and mechanic to the University of Bonn, Johann Heinrich Wilhelm

[13] Non-mechanical air-pump using mercury, invented by J.H.W. Geissler (1815–79) in 1855. It gave a high vacuum in small glass vessels. *c. 1870. Deschanel, p. 196.*

[14] Mercury air-pump, invented in 1865 by H. J. P. Sprengel (1834–1906). It gave an extremely high vacuum to a small volume. *c. 1870. Deschanel, p. 197.*

Geissler (1815–79) for experiments on electric discharges in gases. He wanted a high degree of vacuum in a small glass tube, so speed of action was not as important as the low pressure. The Geissler pump uses mercury, and produces a vacuum in the manner of the original Torricellian experiment. The apparatus is of glass and rubber tubing [13]. By manipulating the stop-cocks, and by raising and lowering a long column of mercury in the rubber tube, it is possible to create a good vacuum in a small glass vessel, perhaps 0.1 mm of mercury. The work was begun in 1855, and the pump was shown to the public in 1858.

An improvement on the Geissler pump was made in 1865 by Hermann Johann Philipp Sprengel (1834–1906). Originally from Heidelberg, Sprengel became a naturalized British subject, and worked in the Royal College of Chemistry from 1862; he became a Fellow of the Royal Society in 1878. In this design, a column of mercury is constantly falling in a narrow tube from a funnel to a flask, from which it is tapped into a bowl so that it may be poured into the funnel again [14]. At the side of the down tube is attached the vessel in which the vacuum is to be created. As the mercury falls in the tube it traps some of the air from the side tube and carries it down. As the process continues, the portions of trapped air get smaller and smaller until the mercury column is continuous, when the process is stopped, leaving a very good vacuum in the vessel, perhaps 0.0006 mm of mercury. Commercial versions were soon made for use in research laboratories [15]. A model that proved rapid and effective in the laboratory was the rotary mercury pump invented in 1905 by Wolfgang Gaede (1878–1945).

Exhausting and Condensing Syringes

From Hauksbee's time there have been the single-barrelled hand pumps that look somewhat like bicycle pumps [16]. They are called syringes, are usually made in brass, and can be made to extract air from a vessel, or to pump it up; the latter type are called pressure syringes. Such a one is used with an air-gun [17], a demonstration piece that is illustrated in Desagulier's textbook of 1744, and was still advertised by Ducretet in 1893. When one of these syringes is mounted on a small baseboard, and connected to a plate with a bell-jar, it is called a single-barrel air-pump. These were used for simple experiments, such as the bladder and weight (see below).

Air-Pump Accessories

An air-pump can be made to condense air inside a vessel, a condition achieved by the valve system. Naturally, the vessel has to be held firmly on to the base plate, so special clamps are required to grip the vessel to the base plate, or a stout piece of wood is screwed down on to the vessel by turnbuttons on side pillars [18].

During the seventeenth and eighteenth centuries a number of standard demonstrations were devised to explain the properties of air. One was to put an animal under the bell-jar to show that it needs air to

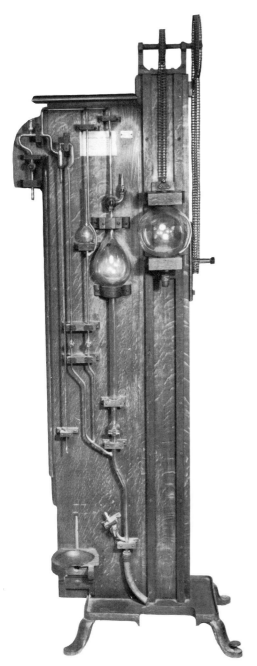

[15] Sprengel mercury air-pump, signed: ALVERGNIAT frères PARIS 10, RUE DE LA SORBONNE. Serial number stamped in wood: 59. After use in the laboratory of the Duke of Marlborough at Blenheim Palace, Oxfordshire, it was given in 1892 to the Clarendon Laboratory, Oxford. The Alvergniat brothers founded their firm in 1858; in 1890 it passed to Victor Chabaud. Height 1,915 mm; width 560 mm. *c.* 1885. *Museum of the History of Science* (25–13).

[16] Small air-pump with a suction syringe to one side. Plate diameter 106 mm; height to top of handle 230 mm. *c.* 1890. *Museum of the History of Science.*

[17] Air-gun, where the iron stock forms the pressure chamber. The barrel is unscrewed from the stock and a pressure syringe substituted to 'charge' the gun. With the barrel replaced, a pellet is fired by a mechanism simulating a flint-lock. 1874. *Guillemin, p. 70.*

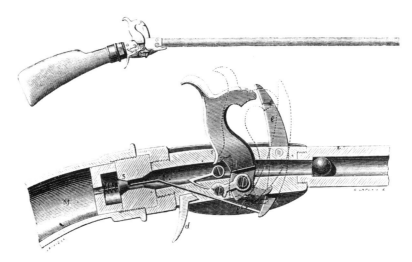

stay alive (the animals were usually revived after becoming unconscious). The nineteenth century did not continue with this experiment, but many others became established, and continued into the twentieth century. Some of these classical experiments were as follows:

Magdeburg Hemispheres The oldest of all, this experiment has already been described above. A variation is to put the pair under a jar and then to compress the air around it. It is possible to pull the spheres by rods passing through seals, to show that it is the difference in pressure inside and outside the spheres that holds them together.

[18] Pressure vessel, with condensing syringe to one side. The wooden bar and screws keep the lid on the glass vessel. The base has lost its name plate, but the apparatus was made by Nairne in London. Base 460 × 300 mm; height 500 mm. *c.* 1800. *Musée d'Histoire des Sciences (948).*

[19] Group of accessories for demonstrations with an air-pump. *Back row, left to right:* burst bladder, bladder and weight, glass cylindrical receiver (height 443 mm) with brass manipulator, single transfer plate (diameter 125 mm), three glass globes (height 360 mm), single Magdeburg hemisphere, candlestick, cup. *Front row, left to right:* jet nozzle for fountain, bell, porous cup for mercury shower, fire-piston, Magdeburg hemispheres (length 222 mm, diameter 82 mm).
This last is *c.* 1850; all the rest belong to a kit *c.* 1900. *Museum of the History of Science (82–8).*

Burst Bladder   A cylinder of glass is placed on the plate of an air-pump, and a bladder, or rubber sheet, is stretched and firmly attached to the top. As the air is removed the membrane dips inwards, and then bursts with a bang.

Fountain in Vacuo   A small glass jar is fixed to a brass base which has a stop-cock so that the jar can be evacuated. Inside is a jet tube, so that when the entry tube is put under water, and the cock turned, water is sucked in and a fountain is displayed.

Guinea and Feather   This experiment is described and illustrated in Chapter 4. It shows the law of fall, but needs a vacuum for the purpose.

Bladder and Weight   A brass frame supports the weights that sit on a deflated bladder. Under the vacuum the residual air in the bladder expands and lifts up the weights.

Mercury Shower   At the top of a glass cylinder is attached a disk with a rod of boxwood inserted through it. Above is a wooden cup which is filled with mercury. The vacuum below pulls the mercury through the pores in the wood, so making a fine shower of the liquid metal.

Bell   A manipulator sealed into a disk at the top of a glass cylinder can be used to agitate a small bell. As the vacuum increases, the sound of the bell decreases, till it cannot be heard, showing that sound needs air for transmission.

Three Glass Globes   These are connected vertically by copper tubes so that the pressure of the atmosphere is made to force water up from the bottom globe into the top one. In preparation, the bottom globe is half-filled with water, and the apparatus is placed under a bell-jar which is evacuated. Air is sucked out of the middle and top globes,

[20] Apparatus for freezing carafes of water. Water boils under greatly reduced pressure at normal temperatures. In changing state from liquid to gaseous *without* an external heat source, the water cools and freezes. Sulphuric acid is needed to absorb the water vapour, which is drawn into the reservoir that contains the acid. *c.* 1880. *Tissandier, p. 85.*

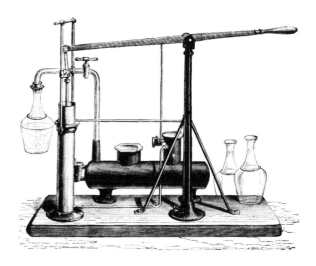

and the water enters the middle one. When air is let into the bell-jar the water rises into the top globe.

Freezing Water   A dish of water is placed under a bell-jar, and as the pressure is reduced, there comes a point when the water will boil. The boiling point is reached at a given temperature, when the saturated vapour pressure equals the atmospheric pressure. This change of state from liquid to gaseous requires heat, which is taken from the latent heat in the water, to such a point that the remaining water will freeze.

Industrial and Commercial Applications

Besides the use of the air-pump in the laboratory and for teaching, there are several industrial applications that developed during the nineteenth century. Compression pumps force carbon dioxide into water to make soda water and other fizzy drinks. The air-pump is used by sugar refiners to lower the boiling point of the syrup. Compression or suction can be used to operate despatch tubes, in large shops with centralized accounts offices. The atmospheric railway, on the same principle, was attempted in England and France, but the practical difficulties of keeping a vacuum seal precluded success. Vacuum and compression brakes were introduced for greater safety on railway trains. Compressed air is used in caissons under water, so that foundations of bridges can be dug (see Chapter 5), and is also used in iron works to supply air to furnaces. In the late 1880s, the carbon filament electric lamps of Edison and Swan required the use of air-pumps. Such industries provided the economic impetus for the development of new, faster pumps, the rotary oil pump being one.

7 · Heat

One of the most important events in the history of nineteenth-century physical science was the emergence, in the late 1850s, of a well-founded and generally acceptable kinetic theory of gases.

Robert Fox (1971)

HEAT AND GASES

The study of theories of heat is intimately involved with the study of gases. A key experiment is that of Joseph Black (1728–99), who showed, in his thesis of 1754, how 'fixed air' (i.e. carbon dioxide) was released when magnesia alba (basic magnesium carbonate) was heated. Black's experiment was given added importance by his use of the balance to make his results quantitative. Soon after this identification many other common gases were isolated and identified, by Henry Cavendish (1731–1810), Joseph Priestley (1733–1804), and Carl Wilhelm Scheele (1742–86) of Sweden. Oxygen was discovered in 1773 by Scheele, and in 1774, independently, by Priestley. There thus arose a branch of science known as pneumatic chemistry. In order to collect the gases given off, Priestley invented the 'pneumatic trough' through which the glass tubing could pass the gas into a glass collector sealed by the mercury or other liquid in the trough. Priestley also devised a long, graduated measuring tube to collect and test the quality of the gases, for example, exhaled air, or gas over combusted material. The tube was named a eudiometer (Greek: measure of goodness), and the branch of science involving its use is known as eudiometry (see also Chapter 12).

The discovery of oxygen led Antoine Laurent Lavoisier (1743–94) to propose a new theory of combustion, which was to drive out the phlogiston theory that postulated heat as a kind of substance or 'principle' contained in bodies (see also Chapter 12). To Lavoisier we owe the first useful interpretation of combustion, and of oxidation, his arguments being based on quantitative experiments of novelty and elegance. He completely disproved the phlogiston theory, which died away during the early years of the nineteenth century along with its now aged advocates.

Obviously, the newly discovered gases had thermal properties that had to be measured: the way they expanded with heat, temperature changes when they were allowed to contract or expand. Once again we must go back to Joseph Black of Glasgow University, who proposed, in about 1760, the concept of specific heat, which he called heat capacity. Specific heat is defined as the heat required to raise the temperature of a unit mass of a substance through one degree of temperature. There are two measures of the specific heat of gases, one with the pressure constant (C_p), and one with the volume constant (C_v).

Soon after this Black proposed the concept of latent heat. This is the heat taken in, or given out, when a body changes state, that is changes from gaseous to liquid, or liquid to solid (or the reverse). The heat is transferred to change the state, but the temperature does not change. For example, ice turns to water at 0°C (at normal pressure), with a take-up of latent heat. This encouraged the idea that heat was a material substance that could enter into a sort of chemical combination with matter, not detectable by the thermometer, and so termed 'latent'.

Before 1800 little work was done on the thermal properties of gases, but in 1802 John Dalton (1766–1844) published his results on nine gases, which showed that for a particular temperature rise, all gases expand the same amount, the external pressure remaining the same. Curiously, the identical conclusion was reached and published at the same time in France by Joseph Louis Gay-Lussac (1778–1850), another example of independent discovery. To these experiments on the expansion of gases by heat may be added the complementary ones on the sudden expansion or sudden compression of a gas, the process being known as adiabatic heating (adiabatic, from Greek: impassable). The point is that the process is so rapid that the change in volume and pressure occurs without the time necessary to exchange heat with the surroundings.

It was noticed on a number of occasions that the jet on a cylinder containing compressed air becomes cold when the air is released. So by 1800, with new theories and new instruments, the phenomenon was being investigated to more purpose, and in 1802 Dalton published in Manchester his paper 'Experiments and observations on the heat and cold produced by the mechanical condensation and rarefaction of air'.

A curious application of the sudden compression of air is the fire syringe, or fire piston [1]. The effect on which it is based was discovered accidentally by a workman in the armoury in St Étienne in 1802.

[1] Two fire syringes, or fire pistons. *Above*, with glass barrel, the Dumotiez pattern, first made in 1805; *below*, all brass, the Dubois pattern, patented in 1806. The latter is unusual in having a turncock to reveal the glowing tinder, which is ignited by ramming the piston home hard. Early 19th century. *Teyler's Museum (208, 209)*.

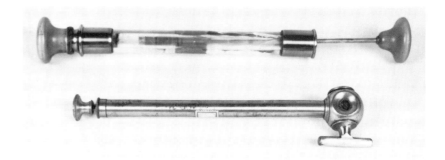

He noticed that a piece of linen stuck in the exit tube of an air gun caught fire. The effect was communicated to the Académie at Lyons on 29 December 1802, by Joseph Mollet, professor of physics at the École Centrale in Lyons. The device is a tube of brass, or of thick glass for demonstration purposes, with a closely fitting piston some 8 to 12 mm in diameter. When the piston is rammed down its tube the air is compressed so fast that it heats up to the point of igniting tinder. Commercial production of the fire syringe (briquet pneumatique) was started by the Parisian firm of Dumotiez in 1805, and it is thought that these instruments were similar to the one patented in London by Richard Lorenz on 5 February 1807, 'to produce instantaneous light and instantaneous fire'. A brass fire syringe with a turncock at the end was patented in 1806 by Dubois of Lyons. The tinder was ignited and the end turned to reveal the fire, a process for getting the fire quickly, superior to earlier models. In glass or brass, large or small, such syringes were established as demonstration pieces well into the twentieth century; one in an air-pump kit is shown in Chapter 6, plate 19. It is interesting to note that the diesel engine achieves ignition by compression of the fuel in the cylinder, and that its inventor, Rudolph Christian Karl Diesel (1858–1930), who made his first engine in 1897, was inspired by a lecture-demonstration of the fire-piston.

THE CALORIC THEORY

The theory of heat that dominated the first half of the nineteenth century was named the 'caloric' theory. In gases, the particles were said to be stationary, and repulsive forces were thought to keep them in place. The repulsive forces were brought about by a material which was considered as a weightless, highly elastic heat fluid, known as caloric. During the early years, this material theory of heat was widely accepted, though there were notable critics, such as Humphry Davy. Indeed, the third edition of the *Encyclopaedia Britannica* published in Edinburgh in 1797 said that heat 'is almost universally believed to be the effect of a fluid'. In this analogy one probably sees the influence of the 'fluid' theories of electric charge that had grown around the Leyden jar.

It is impossible to go into detail here on the development and overthrow of the caloric theory, but one at least of its leading supporters must be mentioned. Taking his inspiration from engineering rather than physics, and in particular from steam engines, Nicolas Léonard Sadi Carnot (1796–1832) was the first to show, in a work published in 1824, the relationship between heat and mechanical energy. For this he proposed a cycle of operations in an ideal heat engine, with its compression and expansion strokes. He was led to the concept of what became called the Carnot cycle, where the energy in a closed cycle of operations could be calculated. Although his premises based on caloric were faulty, he was correct in his conclusions, and so became the founder of modern thermodynamics. His principles developed into the second

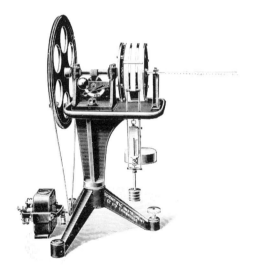

[2] Callendar's apparatus for measuring the mechanical equivalent of heat. The cylindrical calorimeter, on a horizontal axis, contains a known quantity of water which is heated by friction. The frictional heating occurs when the cylinder is rotated against the weighted silk belt. Advertised by the Cambridge Scientific Instrument Co. Ltd. Hugh Longbourne Callendar (1863–1930) established the platinum resistance thermometer as a new standard of accuracy, and the thermodynamic properties of steam. *c.* 1902.

law of thermodynamics, that heat can never pass from a colder to a hotter body.

Gradually, the concept of energy, or work, began to emerge, and Thomas Young (1773–1829) first used the term energy to refer to the capacity for doing work of a moving body. Eventually, during the decade 1840–50, there were performed a series of experiments that established the nature of heat. The experimenter was James Prescott Joule (1818–89), who had been a pupil of Dalton. One of his most famous pieces of apparatus is the calorimeter of copper, with rotating and fixed vanes inside, intended to be filled with water. The energy to drive the vanes was provided by falling weights, and so was calculated. The temperature of the water rose because work was done in resisting the vanes. The temperature rise was so small that the thermometers, made by Dancer of Manchester, could read to 1/100th of a degree. The outcome, given in a lecture in 1847, was the statement of the mechanical equivalent of heat as the number of units of work required to produce one unit of heat. In later years it was realized that Joule's experiments had given the first reliable evidence of the principle of the conservation of energy, a most profound law of modern physics.

James Clerk Maxwell (1831–79), in his paper 'Illustrations of the Dynamical Theory of Gases' (1860) gave a statistical formula for the distribution of velocities in a gas. Statistics had been used before for analysing results, but never before Maxwell had they been used to describe actual physical processes. With this paper, and another published in 1866, Maxwell established the modern kinetic theory of gases, both by brilliant and novel theorizing, and by outstanding experimental work. Heat was now quite simply the energy of moving molecules.

EXPANSION

A central topic in the practical application of heat is the expansion it causes in materials. The mercury thermometer depends for its operation on the expansion of the liquid metal. Another everyday example when wooden wheels were extensively used was the application of the iron tyre that was heated before fitting, so that when it cooled it would tighten the wooden wheel and the spokes. The classic demonstration to show that heat expands solid bodies is associated with Willem Jacob's Gravesande (1688–1742) and is called the ring and ball [3]. A brass ball will just pass through a brass ring when cold, but when the ball is heated in boiling water it expands so that it no longer passes through the ring. The ball and ring demonstration has been in use from the early eighteenth century to the present day. An associated phenomenon is that different metals expand to a different extent over the same temperature range. This fact was put to practical use in the compensated pendulum, known as 'the gridiron' because it was composed of alternate rods of iron and brass. A piece of apparatus to measure expansion of materials when heated was invented in about 1730 by Petrus van Musschenbroek (1692–1761). The dilatometer was a device that heated

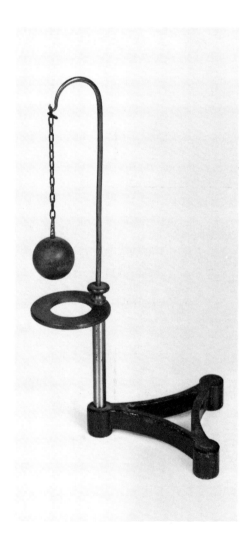

[3] The ring and ball of 's Gravesande. When hot, the ball will not pass through the ring. Height 260 mm; ball diameter 29 mm.
c. 1900. *Private collection.*

[4] *Left:* Dilatometer, with the rod specimen positions marked K, M, E, St, Z. The sixth rod is of glass. The rods are heated in the revolving vessel and the expansion is shown by the arm, via a short lever. Height to top of pillar 214 mm; drum diameter 77 mm. *Right:* Conductivity of heat demonstration, Stoehrer's pattern. The rod positions are labelled: *Kupfer, Messing, Eisen, Zink, Glas.* At the ends of the rods ball-bearings are attached by wax. The rod conducting heat the best will release its ball first. Base 110 × 51 mm; height 112 mm.
Late 19th century. *Teyler's Museum (822, 739).*

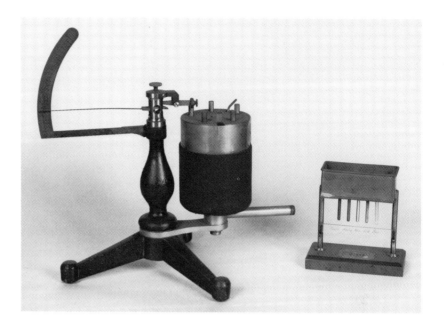

metal specimen rods, and incorporated a dial to indicate the amount by which they expanded. This, like the ball and ring, continued to be demonstrated until the early twentieth century. A nineteenth-century version of the dilatometer had a revolving vessel in which the rods were heated, so that each could be measured in turn [4].

Different materials also conduct heat more, or less, readily. A simple demonstration of this is provided by an apparatus named after Jan Ingenhousz (1730–99). Five or six rods of various metals, and glass, are fitted into a water bath. The rods are initially coated with wax which melts as the rods get hot, thus demonstrating the different rates of conductivity in the different metals.

THERMOMETRY

Thermometry is the measurement of temperature, or the degree of hotness, and it is the first step in the development of the science of heat. Before truly scientific principles could be evolved in the study of heat, it was necessary to invent the thermometer, a device to indicate the temperature, and measure its changes. Galileo made a crude thermometer with an air bulb that moved a column of water, the air responding quickly to small changes of temperature. This device was called a thermoscope [5], and became a common demonstration piece when part-filled with coloured alcohol which responds to the warmth of the hand by bubbling – giving the name 'pulse-glass'. The differential air thermometer, based on the thermoscope, was invented simultaneously by John Leslie (see below) and Benjamin Thompson, Count Rumford (1753–1814). Both men intended the instrument to be able to detect very small changes in temperature, in particular, in experiments on radiated heat. Rumford's model had a horizontal scale [6], Leslie's a

[5] Thermoscope: a narrow-bore glass tube connects the bulbs, which are evacuated and part-filled with dyed alcohol. When one bulb is held in the hand the liquid boils vigorously.
1864. J. Salleron, *Notice sur les Instruments de Précision*, p. 225.

vertical scale [7]. Leslie used his instrument to measure light, as well as heat or infra-red, and it was essential to detect the heat emitted from a Leslie cube, with which it was originally associated. Fahrenheit was the first to use mercury in a thermometer in 1717; his work, and the various scales used on thermometers, are described in Chapter 13. At the end of the eighteenth century and the beginning of the nineteenth, it was found necessary to extend the scale of heat measurement to well below the freezing point, and above the boiling point of water. Dollond made a mercury thermometer that was calibrated from $-290°$F up to $610°$F, though this was ridiculous, since mercury freezes at about

[6] Rumford differential air thermometer, signed: Thermoscope de Rumford. J. Salleron à Paris. With one bulb in line with a radiant heat source, and the other well clear, the expansion of air is indicated by a thread of mercury in the horizontal tube. Maison J. Salleron was founded in 1855 and was continued by A. Démichel from the end of the century. Overall height 440 mm; width 385 mm.
c. 1870. *Teyler's Museum (174).*

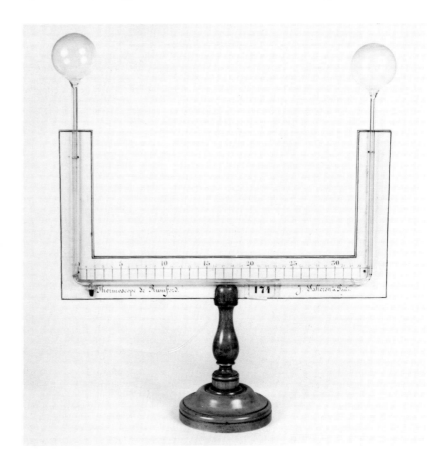

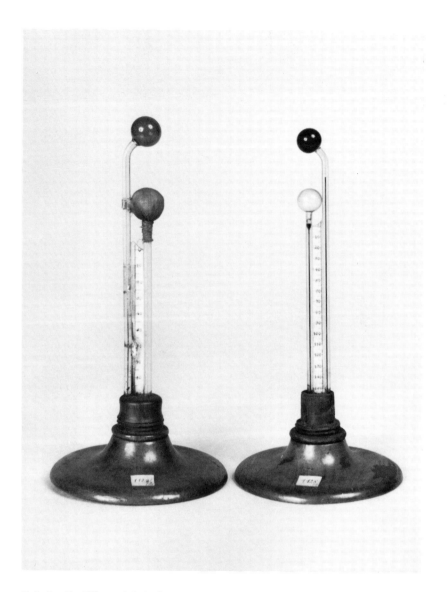

[7] Leslie differential air thermometers, probably by Miller & Adie, Edinburgh. *Left*: adapted as a hygrometer, with a dark-blue bulb and one covered in grey silk. When the silk is wetted with pure water, the depression of the column represents the lowering of the temperature by evaporation, and thus the relative humidity. Compare with the Daniel hygrometer, Chapter 13, plate 22. *Right*: adapted as a photometer. When put in a beam of radiant heat or light, the black bulb will absorb heat and expand the air inside, moving the liquid across the scale. Both instruments were purchased in 1802. Height 176 and 171 mm; base diameter, 87 and 84 mm.
1802. *Teyler's Museum (1128/2,1).*

[8] Mercury thermometer, signed: *Dud⁹. Adams Charing Cross.* The silvered brass register plate is calibrated from 5° to 212° Fahrenheit, and −13° to 80° Réaumur. Some standard points are marked. Dudley Adams (1762–1826) continued the family business after the death, in 1795, of his brother, George Adams Jr. Length of glass thermometer tube 510 mm.
c. 1800. *Museum of the History of Science (30–8).*

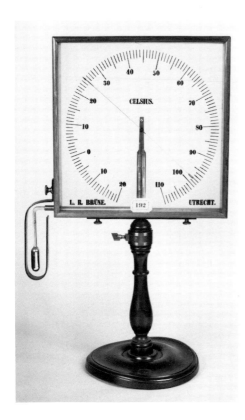

[10] A Wedgwood pyrometer, signed: *J. Newman 122 Regent S.ᵗ London.* The brass tapered channels are graduated 0–120 and 120–240, arbitrary divisions which can be calibrated: 0 = red heat, 27 = melting copper, 32 = melting gold, 130 = melting cast-iron. The gauge pieces are prepared blocks of Cornish porcelain clay, which shrink according to the temperature they experience. Originally in Lisle Street, the firm of J. Newman was in Regent Street from 1827.
Mid-19th century. *Science Museum (1927–1812).*

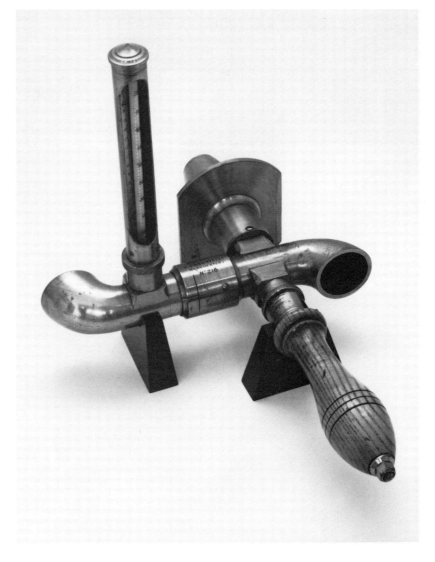

[9] Mercury thermometer with dial, signed: L. R. BRÜNE UTRECHT. The large dial is painted on glass, with opal glass behind to give good contrast when viewed by students. The mercury column moves a float, as in the wheel barometer. Height 630 mm; frame 335 × 335 mm.
Late 19th century. *Teyler's Museum (192).*

[11] A hot-blast pyrometer, signed: Hobson's Patent Hot Blast Pyrometer J. CASARTELLI *MANCHESTER* No. 216. The design was patented by H. Hobson in 1873.
c. 1890. *Science Museum (1897–134).*

[12] Optical pyrometer, signed: Lunette pyrométrique DE MM. MESURÉ & NOUEL Ste. des Établissements DUCRETET a PARIS DEPOSÉ. This pyrometer operates by observing the colour changes in a quartz crystal between crossed nicol prisms, when a beam of light from an incandescent source passes through the optical tube. Overall length 242 mm; diameter of register plate 70 mm. c. 1892. *Museum of the History of Science* (*81–12*).

—37°F while the column breaks up at over 570°F. The need to measure very high temperatures arose in order to control industrial processes, and it was also necessary to measure extremely small changes in temperature, and with a fast response time.

For the first purpose, Josiah Wedgwood introduced in 1782 his 'pyrometer' [10], which depends on the fact that a sample of clay shows a measurably different amount of shrinkage on heating, depending upon the temperature to which it has been heated. After it had been taken from the furnace, the sample was allowed to cool, and then measured by placing it in a tapered groove in a brass plate. The clay would reach further towards the narrow end of the groove, the higher the temperature to which it had been heated. Although rather crude, this was the first step towards measuring very high temperatures. These pyrometers were used well into the nineteenth century, and examples can be found, signed by Newman of London, and Kipp en Zoon of Delft. Another attempt to provide a means of measuring high temperatures in furnaces was the hot-blast pyrometer patented in 1873 by H. Hobson [11]. This was intended to determine the temperature of air supplied to a blast furnace through a hot-blast stove. This air is frequently at a temperature in excess of 700°C, so that a mercury-in-glass thermometer would be destroyed. The pyrometer embodied the means to

[13] Engraving of the 'Lunette pyrométrique', mounted for use in foundries or glassworks, from the 1893 catalogue of E. Ducretet & L. Lejeune, 75 rue Claude Bernard, Paris. The firm claimed a sale of 600 to industrial users by 31 July 1893. The crucible at the right has a tube into which the instrument is to be sighted. 1893.

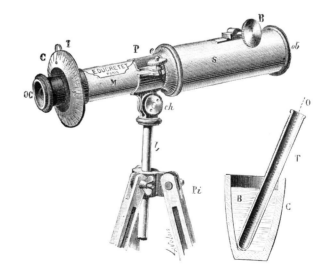

mix the hot air samples with a large quantity of cold air, so that the temperature of the resulting mixture was within a range of an ordinary thermometer. The scale of the glass thermometer extends to 500°C, with another scale engraved alongside, running from 400° to 1700°, to give the actual temperature of the hot air, the amount of cooling having been allowed for. In the absence of a suitable instrument, the heat of a furnace has to be assessed simply by the eye, which judges the colour of the interior: at 800°C, the inside will look red, at 1200°C, it will look white. Sometimes the eye was aided by a colour scale. An early attempt at providing an optical pyrometer was the instrument invented in about 1890 by two Frenchmen, Mesuré and Nouel [12], and advertised by Ducretet, of 75 Rue Claude-Bernard, Paris, in his catalogue of 1893 [13]. This device operated by observing the colour changes in a quartz crystal between crossed nicol prisms, when a pencil of light from an incandescent source (the furnace) passed through the

[14] Metallic thermometer, signed: THERMOMÈTRE DE BRÉGUET (glass dome removed). It operates by the differential expansion in a bi-metallic helix, which has an index at the lower end. Invented c. 1820 by Abraham-Louis Bréguet (1747–1823), the Parisian watchmaker, it became established as a demonstration piece into the twentieth century. Base diameter 95 mm; overall height 110 mm.
c. 1825. *Museum of the History of Science.*

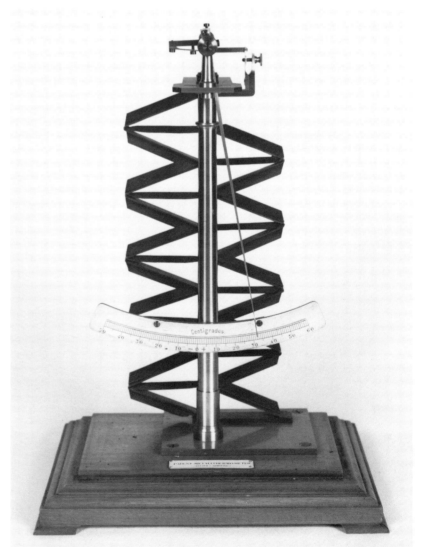

[15] Metallic thermometer, signed: PATENT METALLTHERMOMETER (SYSTEM C. ADMIRAAL). A structure composed of bi-metallic strips moves a long index over a scale divided 50°–0–60°C, to show changes in temperature. Made by C. Admiraal at De Rijp, North Holland, in 1895. Base 210 × 155 mm; overall height 295 mm.
1895. *Teyler's Museum (834).*

optical tube. It may be regarded as a quartz polarimeter. The angle rotated is calibrated to a temperature scale. This instrument was, however, soon superseded by the disappearing filament pyrometer, which used an electric wire, with the current running through it so adjusted that it would become invisible against the background of the furnace interior in the temperature range between 700° and 2500°C. This type of optical pyrometer was first produced in 1901.

Delicate measurement and quick response were provided for by an invention of Abraham-Louis Bréguet (1747–1823), the well-known Parisian watch-maker. His thermometer [14] operated by the differential expansion in a bi-metallic helix, which has an index arm at the lower end. The coil gives extra sensitivity, and the temperature changes inside a vacuum could be detected. This invention became an established laboratory demonstration piece, and was still being offered for sale in 1910 by J. J. Griffin & Co, for £2. 12s. 6d. A good account of Bréguet's invention was given by Fanny Edgeworth to Harriet Beaufort, writing from Paris on 10 July, 1820: 'Bréguet has made a new thermometer for delicate experiments . . . The extreme sensibility of the coil of metal shows every slight variation in the temperature of the surrounding air *immediately*. I saw the common mercury thermometer and this compared under the receiver of an airpump. It shews the rapid change in the temperature in vacuo – before unknown or at least not known to its full extent.' [*Maria Edgeworth*, edited by Christina Colvin (Oxford, 1979)].

RADIANT ENERGY

The heat received from a radiating body, such as the sun, or a fire, presents certain special theoretical problems. This type of heat, usually described as radiant heat, is more accurately described as radiant energy. It was discovered that its behaviour closely resembles that of light, which also produces a heating effect. William Herschel (1738–1822) showed the similarity between radiant heat and light, and so linked theories concerning them even more closely. In 1801 he proved, using thermometers, that there existed invisible heat rays beyond the red of the light spectrum. These heat rays – infra-red – were shown to obey the laws of reflexion and refraction in a way similar to light. Thomas Young, who has already been mentioned, lectured at the Royal Institution from 1801 to 1803, teaching that all the principal thermal phenomena could be explained by means of a vibrational theory. Young also strongly supported the wave theory of light, against the corpuscular theory, and the comparison of heat with light as a vibration in the ether readily explained radiant heat.

The corpuscular, that is, Newton's theory of light, and so of heat, was favoured by John Leslie (1766–1832), who became professor of natural philosophy at Edinburgh. In 1804 he published *An Experimental Inquiry into the Nature and Propagation of Heat*, in which several fundamental laws of radiation were put forward. These were that the

[16] Leslie's cubes. This pair of cubes, named after John Leslie (1766–1832), is made with turned brass bases and pillars surmounted by open-topped cubes of sheet brass. Different reflecting surfaces can be hung on the sides of the cubes, and there are plates in brass, coated in lampblack, polished, and painted white. The cubes are filled with hot water and the emissivity of the surfaces compared using a differential thermometer. Height 200 mm; cube edge 80 mm.

c. 1810. *Teyler's Museum (1127).*

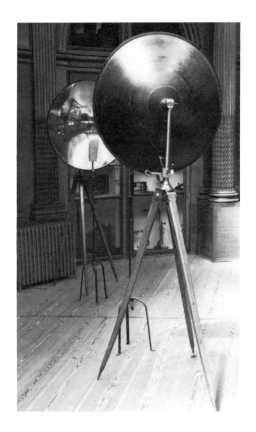

[17] Parabolic mirrors of brass, unsigned but by Hendrik Hen (1770–1819) of Amsterdam. Such a pair of mirrors, polished on the inside and painted black on the back, can be used for focusing heat from one mirror to the other, or for transmitting sound. The wire basket on a standard at one focus holds incandescent material, while the other standard at the focus of the second mirror has a spike to which combustible material is fixed. This will ignite when the mirrors are accurately positioned, and over a considerable distance. Height of stand to centre of mirrors, *c.* 1620 mm; diameter of mirrors 820 mm.
c. 1810. *Teyler's Museum (180).*

[18] Three Crookes radiometers. The vanes are coated black and white, and when placed in light they rotate, because molecules are ejected more vigorously from the black side, which absorbs heat more readily. *Right*, the vanes are fixed and a mica disk revolves. Height 215, 247 and 160 mm.
c. 1895. *Museum of the History of Science.*

emissivity and absorptivity of a surface are equal; the emissivity of a surface increases as the reflectivity decreases; the intensity of heat radiated from a surface is proportional to the sine of the angle of the rays to the surface. Leslie's apparatus for showing the different radiating power of black and white, dull and bright surfaces is famous as 'Leslie's Cubes' [16], and is still used today. His sensitive heat detectors, based on the thermoscope, are less well known.

Radiant heat is a form of energy that is part of the same electromagnetic spectrum as X-rays, light, and radio waves. Heat is transferred from a source to a receiver without heating the air between, and passes even in a vaccum. Most of this is twentieth-century knowledge, but in earlier days there was an apparent anomaly between heat transmitted by conduction or convection, and that passed by radiation. There were two popular demonstrations of the effect of radiant heat. A pair of mirrors [17] can be used for focusing heat from one to the other, an experiment devised by Marc Pictet (1752–1825) and H-B de Saussure (1740–99). A red-hot iron ball was placed in a basket at the focus of one mirror, and this ignited gun-cotton or phosphorus, on a spike, set at the conjugate focus of the mirror system. Another device that was used for demonstration and became a toy was the radiometer of Sir William Crookes (1832–1919), devised in 1871 [18]. Four vanes, each blackened on one side and left white on the other, were set in a glass bulb which was roughly evacuated. When placed near a light source, the vanes rotated, because radiant energy is absorbed by the vanes, but more on the black side than the white. This

[19] Thermoelectroscope, signed: *W.M. Logeman, fecit, Haarlem.* Known as Seebeck's rectangle, with a bismuth arch on a copper plate, and a magnetic needle between the two metals. A light pointer above the disk indicates the position of the needle. Mounted in wood on a turned brass pillar and base. The Museum purchased thermoelectroscopes in 1840 and 1843 for Dfl. 14. Overall height 295 mm; base diameter 123 mm.
c. 1843. Teyler's Museum (652).

occurs because molecules of gas remaining in the bulb collide with, and are ejected by the black surfaces more vigorously than the white, causing the vanes to move by recoil.

A completely new, sensitive, heat-detecting device was the thermocouple [19], which works by the thermo-electric effect first observed by Thomas Johann Seebeck (1770–1831) in 1821. The point is that a junction between two different metals, such as iron and platinum or bismuth and antimony, will create a small electric current when the junction is heated. A whole series of junctions can be put together with

[20] *Left*: a Leslie cube above a spirit lamp on a brass, adjustable mounting (height 460 mm), signed: E. DUCRETET & Cie A PARIS. *Right*: a thermopile of 32 elements on a telescoping stand, unsigned. The thermopile was invented by Leopoldo Nobili (1784–1835) and improved by Macedonio Melloni (1798–1854). It consists of a chain of alternate elements of bismuth and antimony, and is much more sensitive than a differential thermometer. The firm of E. Ducretet was founded in 1864. Base diameter, *left*, 134 mm; *right*, 85 mm.
Late 19th century. *Teyler's Museum (182, 1017)*.

one set of joins towards a heat source, and the other set of joins protected from the source. The device is called a thermopile, and the temperature is read from a galvanometer; it can cover a wide temperature range, up to some 1200°C. The thermopile was invented by Leopoldo Nobili (1784–1835), and was improved by Melloni [20].

Macedonio Melloni (1798–1854) was originally professor of physics at the University of Parma, but lived in Paris from 1831 to 1839. There he studied radiation, using a thermopile, and tried to find out how light and heat (calorific radiation, as it was then called) differed from each other. According to Thomas Young, and to Augustin Jean Fresnel (1788–1827), light was a transverse wave in the ubiquitous medium called 'luminiferous ether', and heat was thought to be rather similar, although there were anomalies. Melloni's experiments were on transmission through various substances, reflexion and polarization. He found that heat rays could be polarized, but not in the same way as light is polarized. He concluded that heat and light are distinct modes

[21] Melloni's thermo-multiplier, the
combination of a thermopile and
galvanometer. *c.* 1870. *Deschanel, p. 441.*

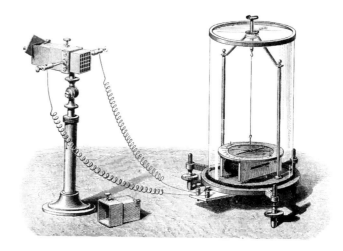

[22] An 'optical' bench for the study of the
properties of radiant energy, signed:
Ruhmkorff, rue des Orfèvres 6, Paris. The
accessories are: heat source, bright brass
screen, two prismatic cells, mica disk, black
glass, aperture and mica sheet tiltable,
aperture disk, thermopile, mahogany table,
reflector on divided plate. The metre bar is
divided to half-centimetres. Purchased by
the Museum in 1845 for Dfl. 292.12.
Heinrich Daniel Ruhmkorff (1803–77) was
famous for his induction coil. Base
680 × 182 × 88 mm; bar 1012 mm.
1845. *Teyler's Museum (183).*

of the same process. For his work he employed a bench with a series
of accessories in the same manner as an 'optical bench' [22] is used.

This brief and necessarily generalized summary provides some background to the accepted knowledge that heat and work were equivalent
forms of energy, a principle that was extended to electrical and chemical
energy. The new techniques of thermodynamics allowed secure calculations to be made in pure science, and in applied science, especially in
the design of steam engines, and in other methods of power generation.

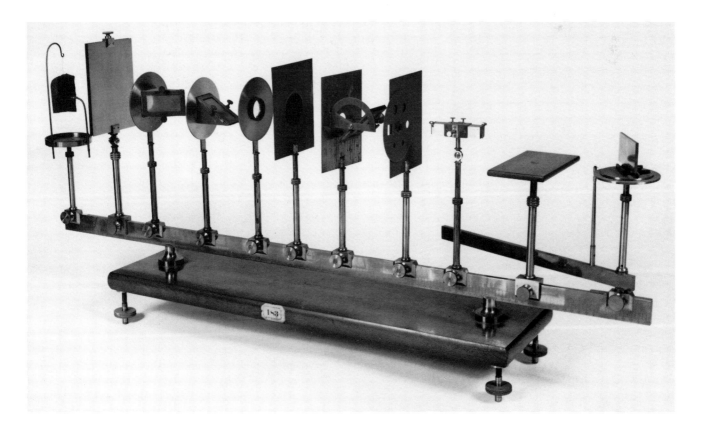

STEAM POWER

The fact that boiling water produces steam that in turn creates pressure, which can provide propulsive force, was known to the Greeks, and Hero of Alexandria is credited with the invention of the aeolipile, or jet cart [VII, facing p. 144]. This device consisted of a metal sphere mounted on a wooden carriage; the water half-filling the sphere was heated and allowed to boil, and the steam to build up in the sealed container, being eventually allowed to escape in a jet which caused the carriage to move. This apparatus continued to be used as a demonstration piece into the nineteenth century.

The first steam engine actually employed to do practical work was invented by Thomas Savery in 1697, and was used for draining mines.

[23] Self-acting spirit blowpipe; unsigned. The mahogany base is leaded to give weight, and supports a copper sphere in a ring. A spirit lamp is fixed to the base. Alcohol is poured into the sphere and heated, so that its vapour escapes through the curved tube below and ignites on passing through the flame from the lamp. The flame is long and hot, suitable for glass blowing. On general sale early in the nineteenth century, it can be seen on the bill-head of F. Accum (Chapter 12, plate 9). Overall height 205 mm; diameter of base 145 mm, of sphere 88 mm. *c.* 1810. *Teyler's Museum (201).*

[24] Advertisement of 1842 for a working model of a locomotive, offered at £25 by Edward Palmer, 103 Newgate Street, London. 1842.

Steam from a separate boiler was admitted to press upon the surface of water in a container, and thus force it up through an ascending pipe. On the condensation of the steam, water from a lower level was raised into the vessel by atmospheric pressure. The condensation was produced by applying cold water to the outside of the container. Savery's engine was in fact a steam-pump, and was succeeded by the atmospheric engine, devised by Thomas Newcomen (1663–1729), so called because the descent of the piston was produced by atmospheric pressure, on the condensation of the steam beneath it. It was while repairing a model of Newcomen's engine that James Watt (1736–1819) first turned his attention to steam power, and devised two improvements that revolutionized its operation. The first was to introduce a separate vessel for the condensation of the steam, so that the cylinder could be kept permanently hot, thus saving greatly on fuel. His second improvement was to substitute the pressure of steam for the atmospheric pressure which, in Newcomen's engine, caused the downward stroke of the piston. The upward stroke was driven by a counterpoise, the steam being admitted to press equally both above and below the piston. This was Watt's single-acting engine, because only the down-stroke of the piston is produced by steam pressure. He then went on to devise a double-acting engine, using steam to produce both the up-stroke and the down-stroke of the piston. Watt's work on the steam engine was so significant that a textbook of the 1880s could state: 'We may add that the improvements introduced in the steam-engine since Watt's time have been a matter of detail rather than of principle'.

The development and use of the steam engine were of the greatest scientific and industrial importance throughout the nineteenth century. Working demonstration models [VIII, facing p. 145] of the various types of engine were produced for use in teaching, alongside other mechanical models. Given the popular appeal of the railway locomotive, an obvious step was the production of toy train sets, actually powered by steam (see Chapter 16).

LIGHTING AND HEAT

The close association of heat and light has already been discussed. Three specialist lamps, invented between 1780 and 1825, deserve to be mentioned here, because they are related to heat in different ways. The Argand oil lamp [25] was patented in 1784 in Britain by the Swiss chemist, Aimé Argand (1750–1803), and was initially used as a convenient heat source in the chemical laboratory. The novel feature of the lamp was the free circulation of air round, and through the middle of, the circular wick, set in a perforated tube. This produced a bright, hot, smoke-free flame, and was also very economical on oil. The famous Davy lamp [26] was invented by Humphry Davy to solve the problem of safe illumination in coal mines, and first demonstrated in 1816. What had to be avoided was the risk of explosion, caused by the ignition of gas through the heat of any type of light source. The Davy lamp

[25] Argand lamp, signed: ARGAND'S PATENT. The oil reservoir is in the shape of an urn, and the lamp has a glass chimney and a paper shade. The inventor was Aimé Argand (1750–1803) of Geneva. His British patent was granted on 15 March 1784, for a 'lamp producing neither smoke nor smell, and giving more light than any before known'. The circular wick allowed free circulation of air, giving a bright, hot flame, economical of oil. Overall height 385 mm; base 130 × 130 mm. *c.* 1790. *Teyler's Museum (213).*

[26] Davy lamp, similar to those supplied by J. Newman of London. The brass base, painted black, contains the oil, and the flame burns behind a wire-gauze cylinder held by iron rods. Sir Humphry Davy (1778–1829) studied the problem of safe illumination in coal mines in 1815, and his safety lamp was demonstrated at Hebburn Colliery, Co. Durham, in January 1816. Overall height 270 mm; base diameter 60 mm. *c.* 1820. *Teyler's Museum (211).*

[27] Miner's lamp, signed: THE PROTECTOR LAMP & LIGHTING CO. LD. MAKERS ECCLES, MANCHESTER. Overall height 265 mm; base diameter 85 mm. Early 20th century. *Private collection.*

[28] Döbereiner lamps, the invention, in 1823, of Johann Wolfgang Döbereiner (1780–1849). Hydrogen produced by acid and zinc is ignited when the jet passes over fine platinum. Second from right is signed: FOSTER & WEST BROAD ST CITY PATENT. Dimensions, *left to right*: height 150, 150, 195, 220 mm; diameter of glass section, 95, 95, 70, 80 mm. Mid-19th century. *Museum of the History of Science* (*chem. 380, 381, 378, 384*).

provides light from a wick dipped in an oil reservoir, but the flame burns behind a wire-gauze cylinder held by iron rods, the cooling effect of the gauze preventing sufficient heat escaping to cause an explosion. The secret of the Döbereiner lamp [28 & 29] was the discovery by its inventor, Johann Wolfgang Döbereiner (1780–1849), of the catalytic effect of platinum. Catalysis means the acceleration (or retardation) of a chemical reaction by a substance that does not suffer permanent change. Döbereiner was Professor of Chemistry at Jena when he made the discovery in 1823, and his 'instantaneous light' lamp consisted of a jet of hydrogen, produced by acid on zinc, coming into contact with spongy platinum, and thereupon creating, by catalytic reaction, sufficient heat to ignite the gas. The novelty was that no spark was needed from a tinder box to light the lamp.

[29] Part of an instruction sheet for a Döbereiner lamp.

THE

HYDROGEN INSTANTANEOUS
LIGHT LAMP.

a is the stopcock, through which the gas passes to,

b, which is the jet.

c is a handle which, on being pressed down, allows of the escape of the gas through *b*. A spring on the handle makes it to close the stopcock, on removing the hand.

d is a brass cap enclosing the spongy platina.

e e is the inner glass tube, containing,

f, which is a wire supporting,

g, the piece of zinc.

h h is the outer glass vessel, and

i is a brass cover fitting loosely at the top of *h h*.

k is the acid and water.

The cut represents the appearance of the Lamp when *e e* is filled with gas, and after the acid water has been driven out, by the pressure of the hydrogen. The Lamp, in this state, is ready for use.

8 · Sound

The experiments of Moll and Van Beek. In 1823 these observers made a determination of the velocity over a distance of 17,000 metres between Zevenboompjes and Kooltjesberg, near Utrecht, reducing the interval between firing at the two ends to one second. They found $U_0 = 332.4$ m./sec.

J. H. Poynting & J. J. Thomson. *Sound* (1899)

[1] Glass globe with brass collar and stopcock, for attachment to an air-pump for evacuation. A bell stands inside the globe, to show that sound needs air for its transmission. Overall height 410 mm; base diameter 268 mm.
Mid-19th century. *Teyler's Museum (789)*.

Acoustics is a word often used to denote the science of sound. On the other hand, when we speak of 'acoustics', we usually mean the quality of hearing in a room or theatre, so it is probably better to restrict the use of the word to imply sound with hearing. As there is much more to the study of sound than that part concerned merely with the human ear, the word sound will be used here, because it is more comprehensive. In this chapter the physics of sound will be considered, because that is the scientific study that grew rapidly during the nineteenth century. Although the use of the ear is important, the physicist always tries to make his science as objective as possible, and the use of the ear, however well-trained, remains subjective.

The association of the art of music with science began in the school of the Greek philosopher, Pythagoras (b. *c.* 582 BC). The Pythagoreans devoted themselves to mathematics, and believed that almost everything is numerically expressible. They observed that the pitch of musical notes depends on a simple numerical ratio in the length of the chords struck. This ratio, they thought, corresponded to the distance of the heavenly bodies from the centre of the Earth. Thus mathematics, astronomy, philosophy and music came to be closely related. In the seventeenth century the new style of experimental philosophy, which derived in particular from the writings of Francis Bacon, caused the study of music, and hence of sound, to be placed on a scientific footing.

Following Bacon's principle of testing all natural observations by experiment, the public lecture-demonstration achieved great popularity in the eighteenth century. But the science of sound was not sufficiently advanced to find a place among the subjects studied, which included mechanics, pneumatics, hydraulics and optics. Only two demonstrations relating to sound were included in the curricula of these lectures. One was that of an alarm clock under a bell-jar, from which the air was removed by an air-pump; the clock bell then became inaudible [1].

[2] The vibration of a glass bell to demonstrate the nodes.
c. 1870. *Deschanel, p. 786.*

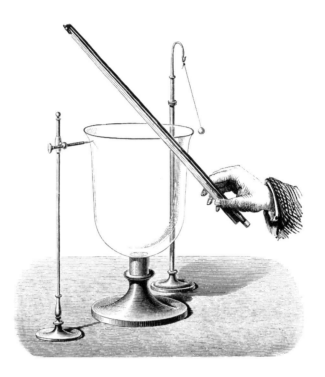

The other demonstration was of an upturned glass bell, with a series of pith-balls hung from strings to touch the sides of the bell [2]. When the bell was struck, the still nodes and the moving parts could be clearly seen from the stationary and jumping balls. But the main study, and hence the apparatus to demonstrate effects to do with sound, belong to the nineteenth century.

MUSICAL NOTATION

In the study of sound, it is customary to use the notation introduced by Helmholtz when referring to musical tones. Here the octave from bass C to middle C is written: $c\ d\ e\ f\ g\ a\ b\ c'$. The octave above is denoted by two accents, and the next by three. The octave below is shown by capital letters, and the one below that with subscript marks. The standard pitch for musical instruments and for concerts has varied between countries, so for scientific work the standard frequency is taken as $c = 128$ cycles per second (cps). Thus middle $c' = 256$ cps, and treble $c'' = 512$ cps. The French notation, which will be found on Koenig apparatus, is different, and corresponds as follows:

(64 cps)   (128 cps)

C	D	E	F	G	A	B	c
Ut_1	Re_1	Mi_1	Fa_1	Sol_1	La_1	Si_1	Ut_2

French tuning forks are marked with double the true frequency, so that Ut_2 is stamped 256.

[3] The sound of a watch ticking at the focus of a parabolic brass reflector can be distinctly heard at the focus of a similar mirror some distance away.
c. 1870. Deschanel, p. 807.

THE PHYSICS OF SOUND

A noise is produced by a disturbance of the air, which is first compressed followed by a rarefaction, so that the pressure is first high, then low. The same effect happens in solids such as wood and iron, and in liquids such as water. The sound travels as a pressure wave until its energy is gone. The wave is called a longitudinal wave, as it proceeds by a knock-on effect, whereas waves on water are transverse waves, because any point oscillates up and down, and water does not move forward away from the source, only the shape of the waves on the surface moves forward. Light is also a transverse wave motion.

Being a wave motion, sound has a velocity which is different for air, wood, water, and so on; if there is no material in its path, then it cannot proceed, so in a vacuum there can be no sound. This was discovered in about 1654 by Otto von Guericke after he had invented the air-pump. The velocity of sound in dry air at 0°C is about 331 metres per second; in water it is about four times greater, and in iron about fifteen times greater than in air.

When there is a quick succession of sounds, then a note is heard by the ear. Such a musical sound is made by the vibration of a stretched string, or the vibration of a column of air in a pipe. When making experiments, a tuning fork is commonly used, which is a U-shaped piece of steel whose prongs will vibrate when struck, giving a note of a definite pitch; by pitch is meant the frequency of vibration. The lowest note that can be heard by the average human ear is sixteen vibrations per second, and the highest about 24,000 vibrations per second, but this varies considerably, according to age, among other factors.

The wavelength of a sound wave is the distance between successive points of maximum pressure. It can be calculated using the formula

$v = f\lambda$, which means velocity equals frequency multiplied by wavelength.

Sound can be reflected from a flat surface, just like light from a mirror. An echo is produced by the reflexion of sound from a hard surface, such as a cliff or a wall. Sound can be refracted as is light by a lens. Acoustic lenses can be made from gases or liquids. If the air close to the ground is colder than the air above, then there is a lens effect, and a sound will carry a long way, and in the summer when the ground is hot, the sound will be refracted upwards because the upper air is cooler. This phenomenon was studied by Osborne Reynolds, who described his findings in 1874.

Other effects are diffraction, which may be experienced by the reflexions from a fence of equally-spaced rods, and interference. This occurs with two notes of the same frequency (pitch) which may reinforce each other to increase the loudness; or, if they are out of phase, that is the peak pressure in one coincides with the maximum rarefaction of the other, then scarcely any sound will be heard at all. If a tuning fork is sounded, there are four positions where it is nearly inaudible when turned around, because of the interference of the sound waves generated by the two prongs. If two tuning forks of very slightly different frequency are sounded together, then the sound is successively reinforced or diminished as the waves coincide or not. The result is a slow pulse known as beats. If one fork is sounding at 256 vibrations per second, while the other (loaded with a small piece of wax to slow it down) has a frequency of 252, then four beats per second will be heard, the difference between the two frequencies.

Another subject for study is the quality, or timbre of a musical note. It is obvious that the same note played on a piano or a clarinet sounds

[4] The production of harmonics on a sonometer, by touching the string, while bowing. Paper riders fall off at the anti-nodes, and remain in place at the nodes. *c.* 1870. *Deschanel, p. 833.*

[5] Sonometer stamped: RUDOLPH
KOENIG A PARIS. One wire is fixed and
the other can be weighted via the pulley. A
metre scale divided into centimetres allows
the bridge positions to be noted. Board
1300 × 140 mm; height 215 mm.
c. 1870. *Teyler's Museum (265)*.

differently; the tones are different, which is called a difference in quality.
Musical instruments do not give tones that are pure, that is, composed
of a single frequency. There are several frequencies blended together.
The strongest frequency is the fundamental, the others being the harmonics or overtones, and it is these that determine the quality of the
musical sound.

The two areas for the basic study of sound naturally relate to musical
instruments and their divisions into strings and pipes. For experiments
on vibrating strings, a monochord, or sonometer [4 & 5] is used. This
is a long sounding box or board, with a wire fixed by a peg at one
end, running over a couple of bridges to a pulley at the other end.
Weights can be hung on the wire at the pulley end, and the bridges
adjust the length of the vibrating wire. Strokes with a violin bow at
the middle will send waves to each end to be reflected back, forming
a stationary wave. With the wire vibrating as a single segment, the
pitch of the note is the fundamental. If the wire is touched lightly at
the mid-point, and bowed at the quarter of its length, the two segments
will each vibrate half the total length of the wire, and the note will
be the octave of the fundamental. In this case, the wire will be stationary
at the centre point (the node), and will be at its maximum displacement
at the quarter positions (the antinodes).

A vibrating wire or a tuning fork makes a feeble sound when by
itself, so, to enhance the strength of the note, a sounding-board or

[6] Bell and adjustable resonator, signed on a plaque: W. M. Logeman *HAARLEM* 1848. When the bell is bowed, the volume of the resonating cylinder is adjusted by the screw to maximum loudness. Base 270 × 154 × 38 mm; overall height 200 mm; bell diameter 78 mm. 1848. *Teyler's Museum (272)*.

[7] Resonating table, with glass bell on pillar, and a wooden cover; unsigned. When the bell is bowed, the sound is amplified by the hollow table top, the air in which resonates. Table height 816 mm, top 730 × 514 mm; bell height 220 mm, diameter 275 mm. *c.* 1889. *Teyler's Museum (792)*.

[8] Apparatus to demonstrate Chladni's figures. Brass plate on a wooden stand, circular brass plate as an alternative. Two boxwood shakers for sand of different size, and a violin bow. When the plates are sprinkled with sand and then bowed, patterns are formed by the sand at the nodes. Brass plate 300 × 298 mm; overall height of wooden stand 250 mm; diameter of circular brass plate 300 mm.
c. 1870. *Teyler's Museum (269).*

sounding box is used. This is the principle of the violin and piano. When used for experimental purposes, a tuning fork is generally mounted on a box that will strengthen the loudness of the note. The box, in fact, resonates, and its size is chosen to give the maximum effect. A tuning fork can be held over the top of a closed tube; if the length of the tube is adjusted, the air in the tube can sound loudly, that is, resonate. A node is formed at the closed end, and an antinode at the top, the tube length being a quarter of the wavelength. With a tube open at both ends, there will be an antinode at each end, and a node in the middle, which implies that the length is half a wavelength. Here is the principle of the organ pipe. Air is forced through a narrow slit and strikes the lip, causing eddies, and the column of air in the pipe selects one of the frequencies which it reinforces, or resonates with, and the pipe emits a loud note. This is called a flue pipe, and it may be open or closed at one end. A reed pipe in an organ is conical in shape, and the column is set in resonance by a reed.

Ingenious apparatus was invented to discover and to measure the effects noted above, and then later to demonstrate them in the classroom. It is this apparatus and its originators that will be described below.

INSTRUMENTS AND THEIR INVENTORS

The work of Ernst Florenz Friedrich Chladni (1756–1827) heralds the nineteenth-century interest in sound. For most of his life Chladni was devoted to the study of sound, no doubt because he was an amateur musician. Because no one had studied the vibrations of plates, he developed a technique of supporting a plate of glass or brass at one central point, covering the surface with fine sand, and then stroking the edge with a violin bow. The sand collected along the nodal lines of zero movement, giving rise to striking geometric patterns [8 & 9]. Chladni visited the Académie des Sciences in Paris in 1808 to show his technique and the results, and subsequently the visible display of vibrations in solids, and even in gases, was used in teaching.

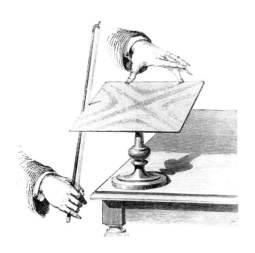

[9] The pattern of the Chladni figures on a square plate. The sand forms nodal lines.
c. 1870. *Deschanel, p. 787.*

[10] Siren to the pattern of Cagniard de Latour. The back view on the right shows the oblique air holes in the wind-chest and the count wheels.
c. 1870. Deschanel, p. 822.

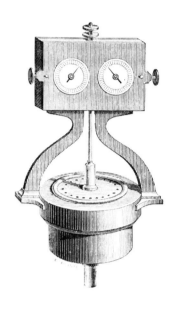
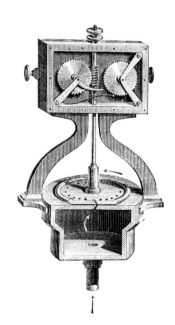

[11] Siren, signed: DELEUIL A PARIS. Air is forced into the wind-chest at the base, and it escapes through a set of holes, which turns a rotor as in a turbine. A note sounds according to the speed, which is calculated from the dials and a clock. Deleuil founded his firm in 1820, and it continued into the twentieth century. Overall height 150 mm; base diameter 59 mm.
c. 1850. Teyler's Museum (243).

Important innovations were made by Félix Savart (1791–1841) who worked on the physics of the violin while a medical student at the University of Strasbourg, and sent a paper on the subject to the Académie in Paris in 1819. The importance of the new subject was recognized in 1828, when he was appointed professor of experimental physics at the Collège de France, where he taught acoustics. He used Chladni's figures and air columns to study the elasticity of materials and gases. In order to work out the lowest and highest frequency that the human ear can detect, he devised the 'Savart disk'.

The Savart disk is a brass wheel with the edge cut into a number of teeth, as in a gear wheel. It is mounted so that it can be turned rapidly by a handle and gearing. A piece of card is held to the edge, and when this is struck by the teeth a note can be heard. The pitch can be altered by the rate of rotation to correspond with any other note. The frequency is worked out by the number of turns of the handle per second, the multiplication of the gear wheel, and the number of teeth on the outer wheel. To give an example: handle, one turn a second; gearing, 4 times; 80 teeth; result, 320 vibrations a second by the card. With this device, it was now possible to measure the frequency of any note.

An improvement to the Savart disk was the siren of Louis Friedrich W. A. Seebeck (1805–49). This consisted of a disk that could rotate in a vertical plane, and which was bored with a series of holes arranged parallel to the circumference of the disk. When the disk was set to rotate at speed, a small jet of air was directed at a ring of holes, so producing a note, which varied with the number of holes that passed the jet per second.

A more ingenious and more accurate siren was made by Charles Cagniard de la Tour (1777–1859) [10]. In 1819 he published an article on his siren in *Annales de chimie*, called, 'Sur la sirène, nouvelle machine d'acoustique destinée à mesurer les vibrations de l'air qui constituent le son'. This invention made Cagniard's reputation. Besides demonstrating the nature of sound, it made possible easy determination of the frequency of vibration of any sonorous body, by means of a speedometer which measured the rate of revolution. According to Cagniard's original design, there was no auxiliary motor. The apertures were arranged obliquely, so that the perforated disk would automatically rotate like a turbine when a jet of air was applied to it. The only disadvantage was that the pressure had to be increased in order to provide a sharper sound, so that the siren was soft for low notes, and shrill for high ones. This type of siren will also perform under water, when water instead of air is forced through the holes.

A modification of the siren by H. W. Dove (1803–79) made it possible to discover more easily the relations of different musical notes. In the fixed and rotating plates are four sequences of holes arranged in circles, and below are stops, so that any one ring of holes can be sounded or any combination of them, thus forming the fundamental chord. A further important development of the siren was made by Helmholtz, whose work is discussed in detail below. He added another windchest to the instrument, thus producing a double siren [12].

A device to demonstrate visibly the vibrations of strings was invented by Franz Emil Melde (1832–1901), professor of physics at the University of Marburg. A white string is attached to one prong of a tuning fork, and the other end weighted over a pulley. The vibrations, nodes, and antinodes can be seen by the contrast of the white thread against a black cloth.

A musical ear is needed to match notes when a siren is used. It was therefore desirable that a mechanical method should be devised to count the vibrations of a tuning fork. The revolving drum chronograph was described by Thomas Young in his *Lectures on Natural Philosophy* (1807). His apparatus was a metal cylinder round which was wrapped a sheet of paper coated with lamp-black. The cylinder was turned on its axis, and a bristle attached to a tuning fork placed to trace on the

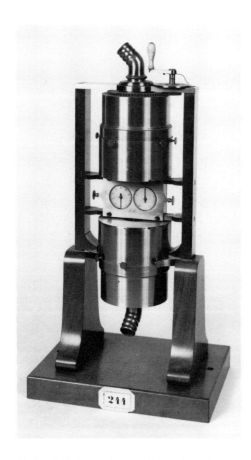

[12] Helmholtz double siren, signed: *F. Sauerwald in Berlin*. Base 207 × 152 mm; overall height 390 mm.
c. 1880. *Teyler's Museum (244).*

[13] The vibrations of a tuning fork are counted by the trace on a vibroscope.
c. 1870. *Deschanel, p. 824.*

[14] Phonautograph after Léon Scott. Unsigned, but the Museum records show that it is by Rudolph Koenig of Paris, and the date is given as 1865. The cylinder is fixed to the board, but the heavy iron mounting for the horn can be moved over the board. Base 840 × 730 mm; cylinder length 230 mm; diameter 180 mm; horn length 530 mm; mouth diameter 375 mm. 1865. *Teyler's Museum (275)*.

paper the movements of the vibrating prong. A closely similar device, called a vibroscope [13], was invented by a Frenchman, Jean-Marie-Constant Duhamel (1797–1872), who published an account of it in 1843. He used a stylus attached by wax to one prong of a tuning fork, and a screw was cut on the axis of the cylinder which enabled it to move horizontally, to extend the range of the trace. The cylinder can be turned so many revolutions in a given time, and the frequency worked out by counting the wave forms traced on the paper which had been given a smoke coating.

[15] Edison's tinfoil phonograph with flywheel, the middle of three models; it sold for 10 guineas in 1886. Base 200 × 150 mm.
c. 1886. *Science Museum (1887–29)*.

An extension of Duhamel's instrument was devised in 1857 by Léon Scott, and called the phonautograph [14]. It employs a conical chamber to collect the sound, which then causes an elipsoidal membrane stretched over the lower end to vibrate. At the centre of the membrane is attached a light stylus, and this records a trace on smoked paper fitted to a rotating cylinder. This instrument, which can register any sounds for analysis is clearly the precursor of Edison's phonograph of 1887.

The American, Thomas Alva Edison (1874–1931), invented an instrument for recording and reproducing sound which he called the phonograph [15], and which was at first intended as a scientific instrument. It consisted of a mouthpiece, closed by a thin metal disk with a small steel point fixed at the back. This point can transfer vibrations of the disk onto tinfoil wrapped around a cylinder. The surface of the cylinder has an accurately engraved helical groove that acts as a guide to the point. The cylinder is cranked by a handle, and a flywheel regulates the speed. The point impresses a series of indentations into the tinfoil. If the mouthpiece is replaced by a similar apparatus with an elastic membrane carrying the point, and a large horn, the indentations can be used to reproduce sound. The tinfoil does not reproduce a second time with clearness, but Edison's original instrument soon developed into the wax cylinder phonograph that became universally popular. The first man to devise disks as sound reproducers, in place of the wax cylinders, was the German-American inventor, Emile Berliner (1851–1929). His simple instrument, the gramophone [16] with disks only a few inches in diameter, was first produced as a toy, and played nursery rhymes and patriotic songs.

[16] Gramophone designed by Émile Berliner. Signed on a plate: GRAMMOPHON BERLINERS PATENT BREVETE DEUTSCHLAND 45048 OESTERREICH UNGARN 48887 FEBR. 24. 90. ENGLAND 15232 NOV. 8. 87. ITALIA 445 SEPT. 3. 89. ANGEM. FRANCE. The disk record was devised by Berliner as a toy, and the simple drive is by a hand wheel, spring drive to another wheel which rotates the horizontal turntable by a rubber friction wheel. The sound box has a needle to fit in the grooves of the disk, and a horn amplifier of papiermaché. Length 320 mm; mouth diameter 165 mm; base 300 × 145 mm; record disk diameter 121 mm.
c. 1890. *Teyler's Museum (814)*.

[17] Telephone to the 1861 design of Johann Reis. The transmitter is at the top, the receiver is below. This is the first instrument to transmit speech, the first in the sequence to the ubiquitous telephone of today. Baseboard 318 × 267 mm; overall height 150 mm.
c. 1865. *Teyler's Museum (289).*

The word 'telephony' was coined in 1861 by Johann Philip Reis (1834–74) of Friedrichsdorf. Although Charles Wheatstone had transmitted signals by wire in 1837, Reis experimented with producing musical sounds at a distance. His telephone transmitter had a mouthpiece in the side of a small box with a taut membrane at the top of the box [17 & 18]. When the membrane vibrated, a small piece of platinum fixed at its centre made and broke an electrical circuit. The receiver consisted of a coil of wire around an iron rod fixed on a hollow sounding box. An iron rod expands slightly when it is magnetized, and when the current is interrupted the rod resumes its normal length. Thus the longitudinal vibrations of the rod will be communicated to the sounding box, and become audible.

After this, little progress was made until Alexander Graham Bell (1847–1922) and Elisha Gray (1835–1901) took up the subject in the 1870s. Bell patented his design in 1876. Bell's second instrument incorporated an electromagnetic microphone, similar to ear-phones still in use today. The diaphragm is a disk of iron just in front of an electromag-

[18] Engraving showing the working of a Reis telephone; transmitter to the left, and receiver to the right. From Rudolph Koenig, *Catalogue des Appareils d'Acoustique*, p. 59.
1889. *Royal Scottish Museum (photograph 4825).*

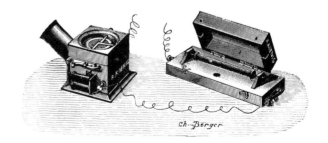

[19] Telephone, signed: THE
GENERAL TELEPHONE AGENCY
COMPANY (LIMITED) *223 GRESHAM
HOUSE* OLD BROAD STREET LONDON
EC. This instrument, a demonstration pair
mounted back to back, was purchased in
1880 for Dfl. 306.20. Baseboard
360 × 400 mm; overall height 400 mm.
1880. *Teyler's Museum (298)*.

[20] Telephone, signed: E. MALDANT &
C^{IE} 21 RUE D'ARMAILLE PARIS. This
demonstration pair (the second apparatus is
behind the board) cost, in 1880, Dfl. 150.
Baseboard 380 × 162 mm; overall height
525 mm.
1880. *Teyler's Museum (297)*.

netic coil. This is modulated by the voice, causing the diaphragm to
vibrate. In Britain the first commercial telephone company was
launched in 1878, and the first exchange established in London the following year. Thomas Edison found that carbon would change its electrical resistance with pressure. He made a microphone with specially
prepared carbon between plates of platinum near the vibrating diaphragm, and this improvement was introduced in 1878.

Herman von Helmholtz (1821–94) was a native of Potsdam, and
originally studied medicine and chemistry. In 1849 he took up the appointment of professor of physiology at the University of Königsberg,
and turned his attention to the study of physiological acoustics and optics. His first invention, in 1851, was the ophthalmoscope. He moved
to Heidelberg in 1858, and it was there that he wrote and published
his monumental treatise on sensory acoustics as the basis for the theory
of music. His great achievement was his formulation of the resonance
theory of hearing. It had been discovered during the 1850s that the
structure of the ear includes rod-like features of varying length. Helmholtz likened these to the strings of a piano, and conceived them as
acting like tuned resonators. He devised an instrument that was of considerable help in his research. In order to test the presence or absence
of a particular harmonic in a given musical tone, a resonator in tune
with the harmonic is put to the ear, and if the resonator 'speaks', it
proves that the harmonic is present. The Helmholtz resonator [21],
or resonance globe, is a hollow globe made out of thin brass, with an

[21] Helmholtz resonator and tuning forks mounted on resonance boxes. Brass resonator inscribed M I₃ and with R K monogram; box stamped: R U D O L P H K O E N I G A P A R I S, and U T₃. Box 300 × 118 × 69 mm. Large fork stamped U T₄ 1024 V S, and R K; box stamped: R U D O L P H K O E N I G A P A R I S, and U T₄. Box 148 × 83 × 48 mm. Smaller fork stamped: G 400 V I B /P A R S E C O N D E A C A V A I L L E - C O L L F E C I T; box (unsigned) 197 × 78 × 52 mm.
c. 1870. *Teyler's Museum (1041, 787, 249)*.

[22] Helmholtz sound synthesizer, stamped: R U D O L P H K O E N I G A P A R I S. A mahogany baseboard carries eight resonators with their electrically maintained tuning forks and a master tuning fork. Before each resonator is a clapper, or stop, which is moved by strings attached to the keyboard. All the resonators are marked with the R K monogram, a number (1 to 8), and the resonating note: 1/ U T₂, 2/ U T₃, 3/ S O L₃, 4/ U T₄, 5/ M I₄, 6/ S O L₄, 7/[nil], 8/ U T₅. The master energizing fork has contacts that can dip into mercury cups. It is stamped U T₂ 256 and has the R K monogram. Note: U T₂ corresponds to base *C* (in the Helmholtz notation), which has a frequency of 128 cycles per second (cps). It is marked with double this number, according to French practice, to count the pulses not the cycles. Board 1040 × 794 × 72 mm; largest cylindrical resonator, length 218 mm, diameter 177 mm.
c. 1875. *Teyler's Museum (248)*.

opening at each end across the diameter. The larger hole admits the sound, and the smaller, pip-shaped, fits into the ear. The air in the globe has, like an organ pipe, a particular fundamental note of its own which depends on the size of the globe. Sometimes the resonators are made in cylindrical form, but the action is identical.

The Helmholtz resonators enabled sounds to be analysed into their constituent frequencies [IX, facing p. 160], with benefit to music and to speech theory. But this was not all; Helmholtz also synthesized sound, that is, he reproduced a given sound by combining the individual sounds composing it, as shown by his resonators. The synthesizing

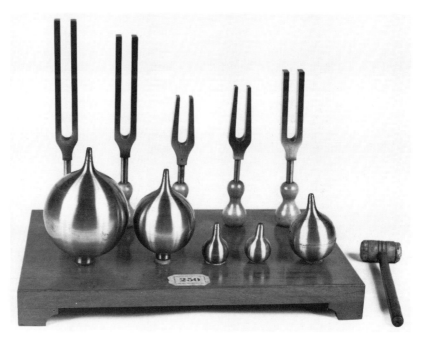

[23] Set of five Helmholtz resonators and five tuning forks. The forks are stamped *left to right*: OU, O, I, E, A. All stamped with the signature: RUDOLPH KOENIG A PARIS. The brass resonators have the R K monogram; they sit on cork, to be taken up and placed to the ear to amplify sound from the appropriate fork. The forks are sounded by striking with a hammer; one has cork ends, the other cloth and chamois leather. Base 350 × 215 × 37 mm; height of largest fork 225 mm; largest resonator diameter 88 mm.
c. 1870. *Teyler's Museum (250).*

[24] Singing flame apparatus after Schaffgotsch; signature plaque missing. A gas jet burning inside the long glass tube sounds the air in the tube in the manner of an organ pipe. Base 203 × 131 mm; overall height brass stand 382 mm; overall height to top of tube 590 mm; tube length 442 mm; diameter 33 mm.
c. 1860. *Teyler's Museum (238).*

apparatus [22] consisted of eleven tuning forks, the first in *c* (128 cps), nine others its harmonics, and the last serving as a make/break to the electro-magnets driving the tuning forks. Beside each fork is a resonator to enhance the sound. When the bank of forks is wired to an electrical supply, no current will pass until the controlling fork is bowed, when the contacts attached to it will be activated, and all the electro-magnets in the bank will attract their respective tuning forks. In front of each resonator is a stop disk on an arm; with the stop in place the sound from the fork is scarcely audible. With strings attached to each arm, that lead to a small keyboard, the stops can be moved away from the holes of the resonators, and the notes can be made clear. By pressing down all the keys, the sound of an open pipe is produced. Helmholtz was able to show that the different timbre or quality of sounds is due to the different intensities of the harmonics which accompany the primary tones of these sounds. This may be described as studying the colour of sounds.

A particularly interesting figure in the development of apparatus for research and teaching in the physics of sound is Karl Rudolph Koenig (1832–1901). A native of Königsberg, he took his doctorate there in physics, studying with Helmholtz. In 1851 Koenig moved to Paris,

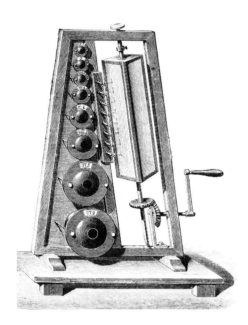

[25] A bank of eight Helmholtz resonators, with their small ends each connected to a separate manometric capsule which acts on a gas jet. When the rectangle of mirrors is rotated, it is easy to see the flame that is vibrating, so that a sound can by analysed.
c. 1870. *Deschanel, p. 857.*

and took the unusual step for an academic of apprenticing himself to a violin-maker by the name of Vuillaume. At the end of his time, in 1858, he formed a business as an inventor and maker of apparatus for the study of sound. He made an unrivalled reputation for novelty and accuracy, and much fundamental work was done in laboratories in Europe and America, employing his equipment.

Koenig adapted a device known as the singing flame [24], or chemical harmonica, to produce his manometric flame to analyse sounds. In the singing flame apparatus, a jet is formed by a narrow tube of glass, and a supply of hydrogen, or coal gas, is lit. An open glass tube is lowered over the jet, and a musical note is heard which varies with the dimensions of the tube; the flame reaches about a quarter of the way up the tube. The note is the result of resonance in the tube brought about by the combustion process. In order to observe the flame, another piece of apparatus was devised, the rotating mirror. This was a cube with mirrors on each side, rotated on a vertical axis near the flame. The image of the flame is then drawn out horizontally, when it can be seen that it is oscillating up and down.

In his manometric flame apparatus, Koenig used a sort of speaking tube to transmit the sound to a membrane, on the other side of which a gas supply fed a jet. Variations in sound pressure on the membrane (acting like a microphone in a telephone handset) were transmitted to the flame, which jerked up and down according to the nature of the sounds received. To make the flame shape clearly visible, Koenig's cube of mirrors was used. Today, this would be effected by using a cathode ray oscilloscope (which is like a television screen).

[26] Apparatus for experiments on the interference of sound, signed: P.J. KIPP & ZN DELFT; on the manometric capsules RUDOLPH KOENIG A PARIS. From a single entry pipe, air is forced through both tubes to manometric flames (not shown). The flames can be made to interfere when the frequencies are similar, giving rise to beats. One tube is fixed and the other can be moved (as in a trombone) and the distance measured by a millimetre rule reading to 360 mm. This apparatus was devised by Koenig in 1872. Overall height 850 mm; overall width 430 mm.
1889. *Teyler's Museum (7.91).*

[27] Engraving showing the experiment on the interference of sound, from Rudolph Koenig, *Catalogue des Appareils d'Acoustique,* p. 88.
1889. *Royal Scottish Museum (photograph 4824).*

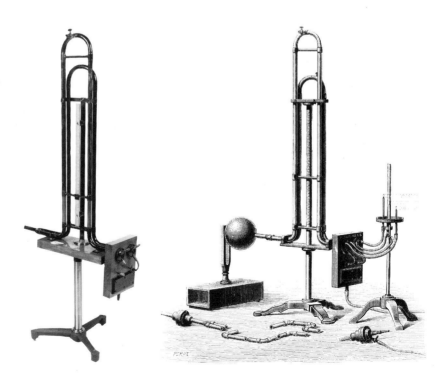

[VII] Jet cart, signed: *HAAS & CO., LONDON*. The copper sphere is partly filled with water which is heated to boiling point. A plug allows pressure to build up, and, when removed, the steam jet propels the cart. This is a variant on the aeolipile, first described by Hero of Alexandria. Sphere diameter 153 mm; overall height 250 mm.
c. 1800. *University of Pavia (1781).*

[VIII] Model of a Watt beam engine, signed: WATKINS & HILL, 5 CHARING CROSS, LONDON. This is a working model, powered by burning charcoal. It was used in lectures at the Clarendon Laboratory, Oxford. Base board 1000 × 370 mm; height to top of chimney 685 mm; beam 360 mm. *c.* 1840. *Museum of the History of Science.*

[28] Lissajous' figures, unison, octave and fifth.
c. 1870. *Deschanel, p. 849.*

[29] Part of the apparatus to show Lissajous' experiment by reflecting a spot of light from mirrors attached to the tuning forks. *Left:* a support of beechwood for a horizontal fork; a disk of speculum metal is attached to one prong and a counterweight to the other. *Middle:* vertical fork on stand, stamped 3/2 on the fork, and on the base block: LEREBOUR et SECRETAN A PARIS. *Right:* two forks mounted vertically on a stand. A spot of light is directed to the horizontal fork and the other, vertical forks are brought into the reflected beam in turn, to give the different figures. Beechwood support overall height 635 mm, base 300 × 300 mm; overall height of vertical fork stand 516 mm, base 300 × 300.
c. 1870. *Teyler's Museum (278/1, 2, 3).*

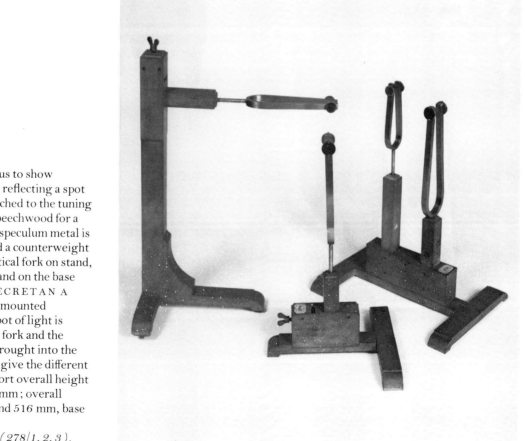

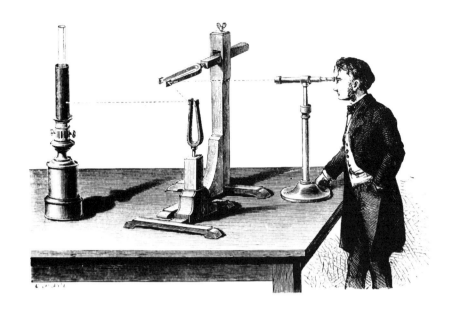

Koenig applied the manometric flame technique to demonstrate to a class of students the analysis of sounds by resonators. A bank of six resonators, whose notes have frequencies proportional to 1, 2, 3, 4, 5, 6, are fixed in a frame with their small holes attached each to a gas jet via a membrane. Alongside the jets is an elongated set of four mirrors. When a sound is made, the appropriate gas jets vibrate, and the effect is seen in the mirrors as they rotate [25].

Koenig's newly invented manometric flame apparatus was displayed at the International Exposition held in London in 1862, where it won a gold medal. Another gold medal was awarded to him at the Philadelphia Centennial Exposition of 1876. He not only supplied superb apparatus, but also made a fundamental contribution to science on his own account, culminating in his book of 1882, *Quelques experiences d'acoustique*. The clock tuning fork was, perhaps, his greatest contribution to precision in the study of sound. The tuning fork acted the role of a pendulum, and it could then be used as the standard for comparison with other forks.

A fascinating and aesthetically pleasing illustration of the frequency ratios between two tuning forks is given by the vibration figures known as Lissajous figures [28]. Jules Antoine Lissajous (1822–80) devised his demonstration apparatus by fitting two tuning forks with a small, plane mirror on one prong. One fork is then mounted vertically, and the other horizontally [29 & 30]. A converging beam of light is shone onto one mirror, from which it passes to the next mirror, which directs the light beam on to a screen. On this screen will be seen the pattern traced by the spot of light, which can be seen as a whole because the eye retains an impression of the image on the retina for a fraction of a second (the persistence of vision effect which is the basis of the cinema). If the first fork alone vibrates, the image is a straight line, and if the second only vibrates, the result is a horizontal light image. If both vibrate with equal frequency, the figure is an elipse, while if one is the octave of the other, a figure of 8 is formed. Lissajous first published the results of his experiments in 1857.

9 · Light

If we call light *those rays which illuminate objects, and* radiant heat *those which heat bodies, it may be inquired whether light be essentially different from radiant heat.*

William Herschel (1800)

The human eye is sensitive to a particular small region of the electro-magnetic spectrum, which includes gamma-rays, X-rays, ultra-violet, light, infra-red, radiant heat, and radio waves. This definition could only have been given at the beginning of the twentieth century, because only by then had the full range of the spectrum been investigated. Optics, the study of light, and by extension of the neighbouring parts of the spectrum, is generally divided into two parts: geometrical optics and physical optics. The former consists in tracing rays from a light source through different media, such as water and glass, from mirrors, and through lenses and prisms. Such studies are ancient; Renaissance artists and architects were well aware of perspective, and there were ray diagrams in the seventeenth century. By 1800 geometrical optics was fully established and changed little during the century, because it was mathematically based and not dependent on any theory of the nature of light.

Physical optics consists of theory and experiment on the nature of light, and the way it interacts with matter in many forms, for example transparent, reflective, and bi-refringent materials, crystals, and scattering by fine particles. Here it may be remarked that a number of important instruments were produced and used even before there was full theoretical understanding of the principle on which they were based; for example the spectroscope and the polarimeter.

The seventeenth century marks the beginning of the serious study of the nature of light, after which there was a quiescent period until the 1800s. What was known during the seventeenth century is summarized as follows:

1. Light appears to travel in straight lines, casting sharp shadows and not bending round corners (but see 5 below).
2. Light will pass through some kinds of matter (transparent), be absorbed by others (opaque), be reflected back by others.
3. When light is reflected from a surface, the angle at which it strikes the surface is the same as that at which it is reflected.

[1] Achromatic lens and prism, signed: *Soleil à Paris*. Jean Baptiste François Soleil (1798–1878) produced and sold a wide variety of optical instruments. He was succeeded by his son-in-law, Duboscq, in 1849 (see plate 3). Overall height 170 mm; lens aperture 55 mm; prism edge 25 mm. *c.* 1840. *Museum of the History of Science.*

[2] Prism on telescoping stand, signed: W. LADD LONDON. The prism is adjustable on two axes. A typical demonstration prism to reproduce Newton's experiment, this once belonged to Edward Chapman, Science Tutor at Magdalen College, Oxford, from 1868 to 1894.
c. 1868. Museum of the History of Science.

[3] Refraction goniometer, signed: *J. Duboscq à Paris.* This apparatus is intended to verify the sine law of refraction of light through a transparent liquid (Snel's Law). Sunlight is directed through the liquid in a narrow beam, and a radial arm is turned to receive the refracted beam. The movable horizontal bar is divided directly into sines. Jules Duboscq (1817–86) was a pupil and son-in-law of Soleil and succeeded to his business in 1849. From 1849 to 1883 it was J. Duboscq at 21 rue de l'Odéon, and from 1883 to 1886 it was Duboscq & P. Pellin; after 1886 it was Pellin alone. Height to top of circle 475 mm.
c. 1865. Pavia University (2097).

4. When light passes from one transparent medium to another, it is bent or refracted. The law of refraction was discovered in 1621 by Willebrord Snel (1580–1626).

5. In the 1650s Francesco Maria Grimaldi (1618–63) discovered diffraction of light, that is the bending of the wave around an edge into the region of the shadow. This is visible in water waves, but as light has such a short wavelength (as we know) the diffraction of light is extremely hard to detect.

6. The 1670 lectures of Isaac Newton (1643–1727), the result of work done since 1665, showed that white light can be split into colours by passing it through a prism. He also discovered the interference colours in thin films, such as flakes of mica, and in the air film between two plates of glass – Newton's rings [7].

[4] Heliostat for use in optical experiments, unsigned, but attributed to Meyerstein. Overall height 225 mm; base 114 × 114 mm.
1856. Teyler's Museum (310).

[5] Engraving showing the use of a heliostat and a prism to reproduce Newton's experiment on colours. 1869. J. H. Pepper, *Cyclopaedic Science*, p. 107.

[6] Hollow glass prism in brass case, signed: *Mᵒⁿ. Jules Duboscq à Paris*. This allows the dispersion of liquids to be measured. Overall height 460 mm; depth of case 100 mm.
c. 1865. Private collection.

7. In 1669 Erasmus Bartholin (1625–98) discovered double refraction in Iceland spar (calcite), which had been brought back to Copenhagen by an expedition of the previous year.

8. In 1676 the Danish astronomer, Olaus Roemer (1644–1710), showed that light has a finite velocity, and is not transmitted instantaneously, as had been thought.

9. Polarization of light by a calcite crystal was discovered in 1677 by Christiaan Huygens (1629–95).

Also during the seventeenth century, two rival theories as to the nature of light were formulated. One was the corpuscular, or emission, theory, which Newton elaborated and clung to. In this theory light was regarded as a flight of material particles emitted by the source, the sensation of sight being produced by their mechanical action on the retina of the eye. A wave theory of light was first expressed by Huygens in 1678, and he was able to account for all the phenomena except polarization in calcite. This was a crucial test for the rival theories, but as Huygens thought light waves to be longitudinal (as in sound), not transverse, he could not form an explanation – and neither could an emission theory. The theorems used to explain interference and diffraction apply to all kinds of wave motion, but polarization is quite another matter. Light waves are transverse, as was ably proved by Thomas Young and by Fresnel (see below).

After this, the theories about light became highly mathematical and complex. James Clerk Maxwell (1831–79) showed in 1860 that light was an electromagnetic phenomenon, and Hendrik Antoon Lorentz (1853–1928) suggested that an oscillator of atomic proportions could account for the high frequency waves. Max Karl Ernst Planck (1858–1947) introduced in 1900 the concept of light quanta, that is,

[7] Apparatus to demonstrate Newton's rings. *Left:* for transmitted light, signed: *J. Duboscq à Paris; right:* for reflected light, unsigned. *Left:* base 160 × 100 mm; aperture 60 mm: *right:* aperture 65 mm. In 1853 the Museum purchased a collection of instruments from Duboscq for Dfl. 107. *c. 1853. Teyler's Museum (402, 403).*

the waves are emitted in packets called quanta, which effectively combined the wave theory with the emission theory.

Interference

The first careful observation of coloured interference fringes was made by Newton, and became a popular demonstration under the name 'Newton's rings' [7]. When two pieces of glass with clean surfaces are brought into close contact, coloured fringes can be seen surrounding the point where contact between them is closest. These colours are similar to those produced by a drop of oil on water, and, in general, a very thin film of any transparent substance (a soap bubble) or a thin air gap, will produce interference fringes. Thomas Young (1773–1829) was a supporter of the wave theory of light, and he believed that the waves should interact in the same manner as water, or sound waves. He made an experiment with two pin-holes in a card, so that beams of light could be viewed coming from two distinct sources. Where the two bands of light crossed, he observed dark bands, and he took this to be confirmation of the wave theory. Young's experiments were made in 1802, and some ten years later, Augustin Jean Fresnel (1788–1827) was carrying out similar experiments, though with the aim of excluding diffracted light. He achieved his two beams of light by reflecting rays from a slit source of light off two mirrors, inclined towards each other at a very small angle, thus producing two virtual images very close together. In the region where the rays from the two sources overlap, interference is seen in the form of bright and dark bands. The dark bands are the places where the waves of light from the two sources are half a wavelength apart, and destroy each other; at the bright bands, the waves coincide, and produce reinforcement. Fresnel also used two shallow prisms that provided two interfering beams from a slit source of light. Fresnel's mirrors and prisms became key demonstration pieces for students [8].

[8] Fresnel bi-prisms for demonstrating interference of light. The adjacent prisms provide a double light source from the single slit. Probably of French manufacture. *c. 1870. Museum of the History of Science.*

[9] Engraving of cast-iron optical bench, 1200 mm long, with adjustable slit, a lens, bi-prism, and Ramsden eyepiece. Below are three diffraction objects, slit, hole, and a single edge. The whole sold for £28. 10s. Wooden optical benches were simpler and much cheaper. *c*. 1900. *Griffin, p. 574.*

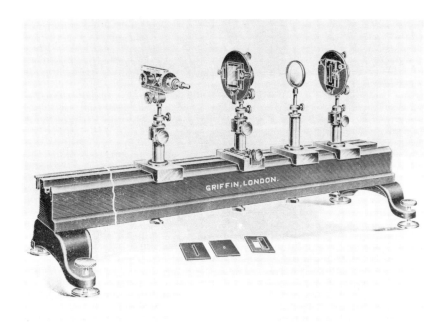

[10] Wave demonstration apparatus designed by Charles Woodward and published in 1851. The name-plate is missing, but most likely made by Watkins & Hill, London.
c. 1860. *Museum of the History of Science (BTS).*

To show the results of interference between waves, there is a demonstration devised in the 1860s by Charles Woodward, president of the Islington Scientific Society. This is composed of some 70 moveable rods in a wooden bar, the tops of which, finished with white knobs, arrange themselves in the form of a wave [10]. If the bottoms of the rods are pressed upwards by a wave template cut in wood, they move in such a way that the whole process of interference between one wave and another can be graphically demonstrated.

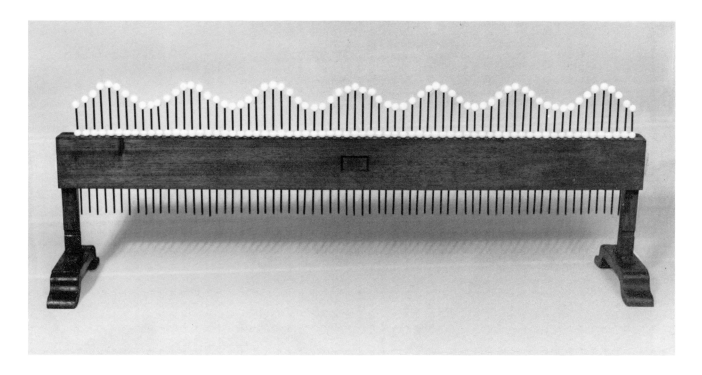

[11] Foucault mirror to measure the velocity of light, signed: *Froment à Paris*. The protectors for the mirror are lying on the base-board. The Museum paid Dfl. *296* for this 'luchtturbine' in 1863. Overall height 205 mm; base 200 × 140 mm. 1863. *Teyler's Museum (299)*.

Velocity of light

Roemer made his estimate of the velocity of light by observing and timing the eclipses of a satellite of Jupiter. His estimate was remarkably good, only twenty-five per cent too low on present-day figures. The velocity is enormous; light can travel in one second a distance equal to more than seven times the circumference of the Earth. In the middle of the nineteenth century, two Frenchmen decided to make an accurate measurement of the velocity of light actually on the surface of the Earth. Fizeau managed it over a distance of 8.66 kilometres, while Foucault achieved his measure within the laboratory.

Jean Bernard Léon Foucault (1819–68) collaborated with Armand Hippolyte Louis Fizeau (1819–96) from 1844 to 1850, when, after a dispute, they continued their experiments separately. Both tried the rotating mirror technique, first used by Charles Wheatstone (1802–75) in 1834, in an attempt to measure the speed of an electric spark. Foucault decided to improve on the original Wheatstone rotating mirror, but Fizeau used a fixed mirror a considerable distance away from a source of light, and a toothed wheel. The idea is that when the wheel rotates in front of the source, it will pass a beam of light through a gap between the teeth which will be reflected back by the distant mirror. If meanwhile the wheel has advanced so that a tooth now blocks the reflected beam, the observer will see nothing. From the velocity of the wheel and the number of its teeth, it will be possible to calculate the time taken for the beam of light to cover the distance to and from the mirror.

In Foucault's experiment, the central element was a rotating mirror, at which a beam of light was directed [11]. This was reflected to a concave mirror, which returned the light to the rotating mirror. If this

[12] Polariscope, signed: *Barbanti in Torino. 1831.* This type of instrument was developed by Étienne Malus in 1810 to demonstrate polarization by reflexion. The rectangular (below) and the circular (above) sheets of plain glass can be tilted at any angle, and the upper one rotated. The viewing aperture at the top is fitted with a selenite crystal, which pre-dates the use in 1835 of a nicol prism as analyser by Johann G. C. Nörrenberg (1787–1862). Base 174 × 166; overall height 440.
1831. *Museo di Storia della Scienza (3123).*

[13] Polarizing apparatus. *Left*: tourmaline forceps, length 130 mm (*c.* 1880); *centre*: nicol prism, 20 × 20 × 45 mm (*c.* 1830); *right*: quartz wedge with micrometer adjustment, signed: *J & A Duboscq à Paris*, length 112 mm (*c.* 1880). It is thought that the nicol prism was made by William Nicol (1768–1851), who invented the technique of construction in 1828. *Museum of the History of Science (64–288)*.

is rotating extremely fast there will be a slight displacement between the incident and reflected beams from the spinning mirror, so, knowing the speed of rotation and the displacement, and path length, of the beam, the velocity can be calculated. Foucault announced his findings in 1850, and then set about improving his apparatus, which was made by Paul Gustav Froment (1815–65). Foucault first of all used his apparatus to show that light travels more slowly in water than in air, so proving the wave theory. After announcing this theory in 1850, he went on to measure the velocity of light, having made some improvements in the mechanical design of his rotating mirror. His figure, published in 1862, was 298,000 km/second, whereas the modern figure is 299,792.5 km/second. The uniformity of rotation was checked by a siren on the spindle of the mirror, the note from which was compared with a tuning fork. Teyler's Museum in Haarlem, The Netherlands, always in the forefront with new experimental demonstration apparatus, purchased from Froment one of these rotating mirrors in 1863 for Dfl.296.

Polarization

The phenomenon of the polarization of light was discovered in 1690 by Christiaan Huygens, while he was experimenting with calcite crystals. Polarization means that the vibrations are restricted to one particular plane. In a calcite crystal, when the light passes in a certain direction, the beam is split in two, both parts being plane-polarized.

Research in this department was not continued until the early nineteenth century, when a prize was offered by the French Institut (previously the Académie des Sciences) for a study of the theory of double refraction. The prize was won in 1810 by Étienne Louis Malus (1775–1812), but, while working on the subject, he found that light could be polarized by reflexion from a transparent medium at a certain angle; he also discovered total refraction. This new phenomenon was published in 1808, and as part of his description, Malus coined the word 'polarization', as he considered the 'particles' of light to have sides or poles, which were lined up in the course of the reflexion. Arago and Biot in France were immediately attracted to the new study (see Chapter 12), and in Britain, David Brewster (1781–1868) took up the

[14] Projector for polarization effects, signed: *J. Duboscq à Paris.* Similar to a solar microscope; the mirror is backed by black glass. Fixing plate 227 × 227 mm; mirror frame 280 × 124 mm.
c. 1853. *Teyler's Museum (418).*

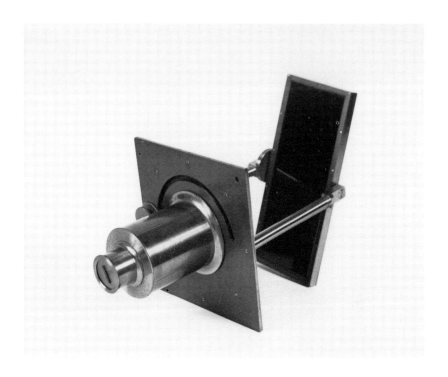

work with mirrors. This led him to formulate, in 1815, Brewster's Law of polarization by reflexion: the index of refraction is the tangent of the angle of maximum polarization. By using two mirrors, it is possible to produce complete extinction of light, and by rotating the mirrors, the light intensity can be varied.

Demonstration apparatus – the *polariscope* [12] – was soon available to show the Malus effect, and to prove Brewster's Law, apparatus that has changed little to the present day. To show this intriguing phenomenon, with unexpected effects for the novice, demonstrators used calcite crystals, plates of tourmaline, mica films, and stressed glass, to give figures and colours when interposed in a beam of polarized light. Special projectors, using sunlight or the carbon arc, were made to show these effects to large audiences, as spectacular colour changes can be guaranteed to capture an audience.

The first convenient way of obtaining polarized light was to use a nicol prism, named after its inventor, William Nicol (1768–1851), the Edinburgh geologist, who thought of it in 1828 [13]. It is made by splitting a calcite (Iceland spar) crystal along its shorter diagonal plane and cementing the parts together with Canada balsam. A beam of light is doubly refracted on entering the crystal, and one of the two rays is totally reflected at the balsam surface, while the other passes straight through. With two such prisms, the light entering the first, called the polarizer, passes on to a second, called the analyser. When crossed at right angles no light passes out of the second. When strained glass, or other birefringent material, is placed between the crossed nicol prisms, figures, or colours, or both, can be seen. Such pairs of prisms

[15] Polarimeter, signed: Franz Schmidt & Haensch BERLIN N.° 1142. An optically active solution in a long narrow tube placed between the nicol polarizer and analyser makes one half of the field light and the other dark. Rotation of the analyser restores a uniform field, to give a measure of the optical rotation.
c. 1870. *Museum of the History of Science.*

[16] Compression machine for stressing glass and other materials to show stress birefringence. Probably of German manufacture. The scale is from 0 to 200 kilo. Overall height 270 mm; base 77 × 78 mm.
c. 1865. *Teyler's Museum (409).*

[17] Plaster models to represent sections of the ray surfaces in uniaxial and biaxial birefringent crystals, made by J. G. Hofmann, Paris. Double cone: height 158 mm; diameter of ends 81 mm. c. 1860. *Teyler's Museum (409).*

were frequently supplied with microscopes to show the effects in geological samples and other crystals.

Polarization may be plane, eliptical, or circular, and crystals can give a variety of configurations to the patterns seen, because of the different symmetries of crystals: triaxial, uniaxial, trigonal, etc. As these symmetries are never easy to explain mathematically to students, three-dimensional figures were made to aid teaching, and one such set, in plaster, is shown here [17].

Phosphorescence

The name arises from the greenish glow seen during the slow oxidation of white phosphorus in air, though phosphorescence now means the light given out by a substance after it has been irradiated by light of a lower wavelength (higher frequency, implying higher energy). In modern terminology, the word luminiscence is used to include phosphorescence and fluorescence; the latter term indicating an extremely short afterglow.

The pioneering work on this subject was performed between 1839 and 1859 by Alexandre Edmond Becquerel (1820–91). His monograph, published in 1859, described the phosphoroscope invented to measure the time for which a substance would continue to glow after having been irradiated by a brilliant light. The instrument was a round metal box with a pair of rotating disks that had four apertures in each, arranged so that no light could pass directly through the box [18]. The substance was viewed through the front aperture after it had been illuminated by the Sun through the back aperture. By varying the speed of rotation of the shutters, the time of the afterglow could be measured. Becquerel-type phosphoroscopes were later made to be attached to projectors using carbon arcs, which give out a great deal of ultra-violet, usually a most effective irradiation source for generating luminescence.

[18] Becquerel phosphoroscope, signed:
J. Duboscq à Paris. The sample crystal is
shown just before insertion. Invented by
Alexandre Becquerel in 1859. Overall
length 300 mm; diameter of chamber
111 mm. *c.* 1865. *Teyler's Museum (399).*

[19] Spectroscope signed: *John Browning
London*. In this instrument the spectrum is
formed by six prisms arranged in a ring,
which means that the collimator with a slit
at the end is close to the telescope through
which the spectrum is viewed. The
spectrum is spread out to make it easier to
distinguish the lines from each other. Such
multi-prism spectroscopes were used by
astronomers. *c.* 1870. *Museum of the
History of Science (31–120).*

[20] Spectroscope, signed: *Spencer Browning & Co. London PATENT*. Also engraved: *Crookes spectroscope*. William Crookes (1832–1919) worked on spectroscopy during 1860–63, discovering thallium in 1863, for which he was elected to the Royal Society. Spencer Browning & Co. operated at 111 Minories, London, from 1840. They took patents for spectroscopes in 1861–2.
c. 1862. *Teyler's Museum (390)*.

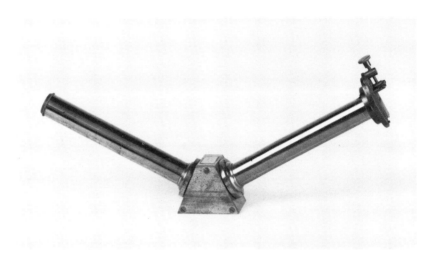

Colour

The human brain interprets light received on the retina of the eye in terms of colour. Artists had known for centuries that the so-called three primary colours, red, yellow, blue, give any hue when mixed. Thomas Young proposed a theory of colour vision based on three receptors in the eye, each receptor being predominantly responsive to red, green, and violet. This theory was revived by James Clerk Maxwell, who began experiments on colour mixing in 1849 at Edinburgh, the year before he went as a student to the University of Cambridge. Maxwell used a spinning disk – a sort of top – with adjustable sectors of coloured paper, and he was able to work out quantitative colour equations using red, green, and blue as primaries. For demonstrations, the colour disks are mounted on frames [XI, facing p. 161], and white and black disks are added to the coloured ones to adjust the intensity. With these in appropriate proportions, any colour may be matched. It is also worthy of note that Maxwell projected the first three-colour photograph in 1861.

Spectroscopy

The discovery of line spectra was of great importance in furthering the understanding of matter and of light. With the belief that light was the result of vibrations in 'the luminiferous ether', how could there be a separate, sharp line, representing a quite definite frequency of vibration? The new discovery presented difficulties in theorizing that were not overcome until the latter part of the nineteenth century, and finally in the twentieth. But this did not prevent the new spectroscopes being used for chemical analysis, although this, too, took a while to be realized (see Chapter 12).

The first recorded observation of lines in the spectrum from the Sun was published in 1802 by the English physicist, William Hyde Wollaston (1766–1828). He had been measuring refractive and dispersive powers of glasses, and noticed that there were some dark bands crossing the colours produced by his prism, with the light source in the form of a narrow slit. Wollaston completely misunderstood the implications, for he thought the bands were the divisions between the 'fundamental' colours – a distinctly Aristotelian view. The man who made the vital connexion – though not explanation, that came much later – was Joseph von Fraunhofer (1787–1826), who noticed, while making his study of optical glass, hundreds of fine lines crossing the Sun's spectrum. His paper, published in 1817, was entitled: 'The determination of the refractive and the dispersive powers of different kinds of glass, with reference to the perfection of achromatic telescopes.'

Fraunhofer made the vital connexion of the double dark line in the yellow-orange part of the spectrum with the bright line pair in the light emitted by sodium, when salt is put into the flame of a lamp. This line of research was taken up soon after by David Brewster and John Frederick William Herschel (1792–1871), but both men were quite unaware of the work of Fraunhofer until after their own publications, which were in 1822. Five years later, Herschel made the proposal that the lines from the Sun and stars were produced by absorption of light by the same elements as the corresponding bright lines in emission spectra, and that here was a sort of 'fingerprint' for the molecules and atoms. Although the mechanism proposed by Herschel was not the final one, he had encouraged other investigations, notably that of Foucault who published in 1849. It also encouraged the development and use of prism spectroscopes to analyse the light from stars, and so started the new division of astro-physics. Some of the instruments were large, employing up to ten prisms to increase the dispersion [19].

Science proceeds by leaps of the imagination, by accident, and by the sheer hard work of making exact measurements. It was the last approach that has made the name of Ångström known throughout the scientific world. Anders Jonas Ångström (1814–74), a physicist and astronomer at Uppsala University, Sweden, showed, in 1853, that the spectrum of an alloy consisted of the combined spectrum of the constituent metals. He also equated emission and absorption spectra by using the mathematics of resonance. Having become interested in this branch of physics, he spent the years 1861–8 in a most meticulous study of the dark lines in the Sun's spectrum, mapping over 1000 lines, and determining the wavelength of each one. For this work he used diffraction gratings made by the German technician Friedrich Adolph Nobert (1806–81). The grating allows exact calculation of a wavelength, which the prism does not. The gratings consisted of some thousand lines ruled on glass by a diamond in the space of 25 mm square. The wavelength of a spectral line is then proportional to the repeat distance between the rulings on the grating, and to the angles of incidence and diffraction of the light passing through the grating. Ångström expressed his measurements of wavelength in the units of one ten millionth of a metre, so that the sodium lines are 5896 and 5890 angstrom units (which is the internationally accepted name for the unit).

These measurements of wavelength, being so fine and exact, showed up the need for highly accurate basic standards of measure. It was found that the standard metre at Uppsala University was slightly longer than

[IX] Helmholtz resonator bank. All the brass resonators are stamped with the Koenig monogram R K, and they are numbered from 2, the largest, to 20, the smallest. They are also stamped with their resonating tone: e.g. numbers 2, 3, 4 – UT_2, SOL_2, UT_3; number 9 – RE_4; number 20 – MI_5. Base 980 × 345 × 150 mm.
c. 1870. *Teyler's Museum* (247).

[X] Uranium glass used to form candlesticks (height 220 mm), goblet (height 150 mm), discharger (length 300 mm), and cube (31 mm). They fluoresce in daylight and by an electric discharge.
c. 1865. *Teyler's Museum* (396).

[XI] Colour disks, and machine to rotate them. Probably made in Italy for use at Pavia.
c. 1865. *Pavia University (2035).*

[21] Direct vision spectroscope, signed: *Adam Hilger London*. Designed by George D. Liveing (1827–1924) and Sir James Dewar (1842–1923). The micrometer wheel is divided 0–100 by ones. Calibration for wavelength is made by using a standard spectrum, such as iron. Height to trunnions 400 mm; overall length 455 mm. *c.* 1880. *Whipple Museum (1253)*.

was thought; it was assumed to measure 999.81 mm, but in fact it measured 999.94 mm. This discrepancy becomes very important when measuring to the atomic scale, and it is nowadays avoided by taking the standard of length as the wavelength of a particular line in the spectrum, and working upwards rather than downwards. (See Chapter 3.)

The name particularly associated with the grating is Rowland. Henry Augustus Rowland (1848–1901) was professor of physics at

[22] Achromatic telescope, signed:
DOLLOND LONDON. The telescoping
struts are to prevent tremor of the image.
Overall length 1120 mm; aperture 70 mm.
c. 1820. *Musée d'Histoire des Sciences*
(770).

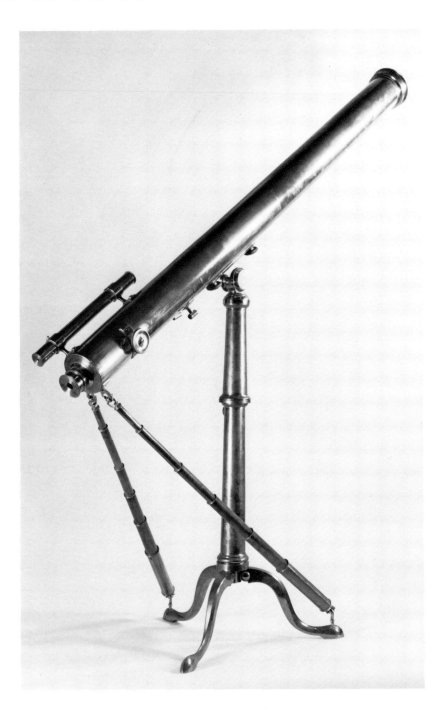

Johns Hopkins University, Baltimore, where, after 1880, he concentrated his efforts on the problems of ruling extremely fine gratings on metal. He remapped the solar spectrum, with wavelength measurements ten times more accurate than before. In 1890, at the Paris Exposition, he was awarded a Gold Medal for the gratings and the map. More than a hundred of the gratings were sold at cost to physicists throughout the world, and there were also replicas made for demonstration purposes. A brilliant innovation made by Rowland was to rule the gratings on a concave metal surface, which focused the spectra, giving better sharpness than a lens, and being equally effective for ultra-violet and infra-red. The Rowland gratings became the standard instruments for spectroscopic work throughout the world.

The Telescope

The refracting telescope and the compound microscope were invented in about 1600 by spectacle makers working in Middelburg, a town in The Netherlands. Their development was hampered by the poor quality of the glass available for making lenses. This was frequently marred by air bubbles, and was difficult to make completely homogeneous, because the temperature of the furnaces could not be raised sufficiently high. In addition, specific techniques for producing high quality optical glass had to await development in the early nineteenth century by Joseph von Fraunhofer, working in Munich, and, in the 1880s, by Otto Friedrich Schott (1851–1935) in Jena. A completely different defect in the quality of the image seen in the telescope and microscope was produced by the use of lenses themselves. A straightforward convex lens will produce coloured fringes round the image, a defect known as chromatic aberration. Because the surface of a lens is part of a sphere, spherical aberration also occurs. The problem of chromatic aberration in the objective lens of the telescope was solved in 1758 by John Dollond (1706–61). He discovered that a correction could be made by using two lenses to form the objective, composed of crown glass and flint glass. These two types of glass have different refractive indices, and different degrees of dispersion, and, when combined in a certain way, the coloured fringes are cancelled. In theory, the same correction was possible for the microscope, but the tiny lenses used as objectives presented technical problems that were not solved until the 1800s. Because of the problems of poor quality glass, as well as image blurring, the most effective telescope during the eighteenth century was the reflector, which used mirrors of polished metal, hand-shaped to the correct curvature.

By paying particular attention to the quality and choice of glass, and the way in which it was ground and polished. Fraunhofer was able to make powerful refracting telescopes in the years around 1820, and he also made some remarkable compound microscopes. His improvements were vital for instruments used by astronomers, but less important for the majority of users. There was a large professional market for telescopes, that were needed by seamen, coastguards, soldiers, and in particular by the French in their semaphore telegraph service. Towards the end of the century hand-held binocular telescopes were popular, because they were less tiring to use, and were practical for explorers and for military reconnaissance. The so-called Galilean type of refracting telescope, which has only two lenses, one positive and one negative, developed in the nineteenth century into binocular opera glasses and field glasses, some of the former being very ornate.

[23] Three naval telescopes, signed: *P. J. Kipp en Zn te Delft*. Three-drawer, brass, covered in leather. There is a pull-out shade for the objective. After the death of the founder in 1864, the firm took the above name. Length closed: 260 mm; aperture 38 mm.
c. 1870. *Teyler's Museum (356)*.

[24] Reading telescope, signed: *Steinheil in München*. N° 2645. The right-angled prism makes use easier when reading scales with the telescope horizontal. Karl August Steinheil (1801–70) founded an optical workshop at Munich in 1854. Overall length 223 mm; height 205 mm; aperture 27 mm.
c. 1860. *Teyler's Museum (359)*.

[25] French binocular telescope made of aluminium and covered in black leather. The objectives (25 mm) are triplets, each signed in ink on the rim: Lemaire. The eyepieces are Huygenian, and there is a further plano-convex erecting lens. Founded in 1847, the firm was named Baille-Lemaire by the end of the century. Overall length closed, 210 mm; open for use, *c*. 295 mm.
c. 1890. *Museum of the History of Science* (*78–20*).

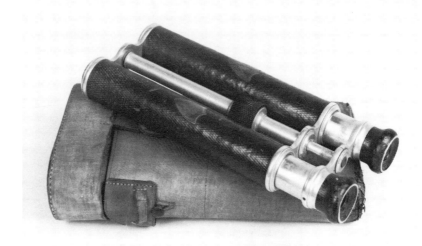

The Microscope

The job of a microscope is to reveal fine detail to the eye. The aim is to be able to see two small spots, or two lines that are very close together, as separate entities, and not as one larger spot or one wider line. It is the distance apart of the spots or lines which is called the resolution distance. The early compound microscope could resolve no better than 10 micrometres (0.01 mm), whereas the limit of the modern optical microscope is about 0.2 micrometres, or 50 times better. Magnification is necessary, but is not the complete story, as beyond a certain point magnification alone will not help to increase resolution. If the lens system is not well designed, then 'empty' magnification will result.

Early in the nineteenth century there occurred a great deal of progress in improving machine tools, and in the accuracy of scientific instruments. The microscope was an exception, for it had fallen behind the telescope through failing to benefit from the improved achromatic lenses introduced by Dollond in 1758. Such composite objective lenses were first produced commercially for the microscope by Harmanus van Deijl (1738–1809) in Amsterdam, during the first decade of the century, and during the second decade by firms in Paris and London [26]. At about this time important developments were taking place in Germany. In 1806 Fraunhofer joined the scientific instrument-making firm of Utzschneider, Reichenbach & Liebherr; by 1809 he was manager

[26] Compound achromatic microscope, signed: *Harm*. *van Deijl Inv: et fecit Amsterdam*. Harmanus van Deijl (1738–1809) made the first commercial achromatic microscopes, and only six are known to exist. The Museum paid Dfl. 200 in 1808 for this instrument. Overall height 353 mm.
1808. *Teyler's Museum (368)*.

[27] Reflecting microscope, signed: *S:I: Rienks, Provincie, Vriesland. 1825.* Signed on the back of the mirror: S.I.R. 1822. Syds Johannesz Rienks (1770–1845) was well-known for his telescopes. Height 545 mm; barrel diameter 105 mm.
1825. Teyler's Museum (330).

[28] The barrel cap and the primary mirror (diameter 102 mm) from the Rienks reflecting microscope.

of the optical workshop and, by 1811, director of glass-making and a partner in the firm. The initial success of his improvement of optical glass was in the design and manufacture of large objective lenses for the telescope, but this was soon followed by improvements to microscope lenses. What Fraunhofer was producing around 1817 was at least a generation in advance of English microscopes of the same period.

Some microscopists had, however, despaired of bettering the compound microscope, and other possibilities were being explored. One of these was the reflecting microscope, produced by Giovan Battista Amici (1786–1868) in Italy, by Syds J. Rienks (1770–1845) in the Netherlands [27 & 28], and by John Cuthbert (1783–1854) in London, all in the mid-1820s. Another scheme was to obtain more powerful

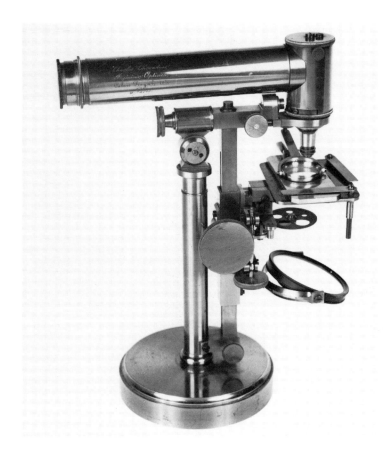

[29] Horizontal microscope, signed:
Microscope Achromatique Universel
*Inventé par Charles Chevalier Ingenieur
Opticien*, Palais Royal 165 *à Paris*. Charles
Chevalier (1804–59) succeeded his father
in 1841 and continued to produce similar
microscopes. Height 250 mm; base
diameter 118 mm.
c. 1845. Whipple Museum. (908)

[30] Inverted compound microscope,
signed: *Microscopio di F. Pacini A. Poggiali
Esegui Firenze*. Filippo Pacini (1812–83)
graduated in medicine in 1840, and from
1859 he taught microscopical anatomy at
Florence. He designed his own
microscopes, including an inverted one in
1868 for chemical use. Height 250 mm.
*c. 1868. Musée d'Histoire des Sciences
(461)*.

simple lenses by making them of materials of high refractive index, such as diamond and sapphire. Such lenses had limited success until the situation was transformed by the patient work of Joseph Jackson Lister (1786–1869), a wine merchant in the City of London, and the father of Lord Lister, the surgeon. Joseph Lister's years of experiment led to a paper on the design of objective lenses that was published by the Royal Society in January 1830. The improvements he proposed meant that the compound microscope could forge ahead as a scientific tool.

The microscope manufacturers of London were, by the mid-nineteenth century, the most highly skilled in the world, due in large measure to Lister's empirical work, which resulted in the first design of an optical system that was scientifically based. Naturally there were a number of microscope makers working in London, and a great many who retailed, both in the capital and in the provinces. Nevertheless, there were three makers who were pre-eminent, and who started firms that continued right through the century, and even beyond it. These three men were: Andrew Ross (1798–1859), Hugh Powell (1799–1883), and James Smith (d. 1870). Ross established his business in 1830, and by 1837 had an address at 33 Regent Street, Piccadilly. From this date until 1841, the signature on his microscopes runs: 'Andw. Ross & Co.', the 'company' being J. J. Lister, who collaborated

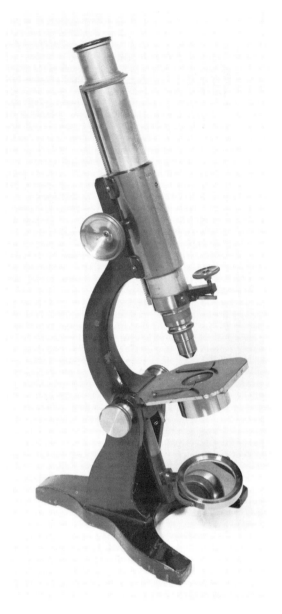

[31] Compound microscope, signed:
J. Spencer Maker *13 Aungier St. DUBLIN.*
Height 440 mm.
c. 1870. Private collection.

[32] Compound microscope, signed:
TOLLES BOSTON. The foot and limb are
of iron coated with black enamel. Robert B.
Tolles (1825–83) was in charge of the
Boston Optical Works, Massachusetts,
from 1867 to 1883. Overall height 400 mm.
*c. 1875. Museum of the History of Science
(B443).*

with Ross in the design of the new $\frac{1}{8}$ inch objective. This objective was composed of three achromatic doublets, arranged at specific distances from one another, so that spherical aberration was eliminated. Because such lenses were capable of much greater resolution and clarity of image, the optical tube had to be much more firmly mounted to avoid tremor. This led to a transformation in the design of the microscope stand [XII, facing p. 176].

In the 1870s the Jena University professor, Ernst Abbe (1840–1905), who worked closely with Carl Zeiss (1816–88), the Jena microscope maker, studied the formation of the image in the microscope, following the new principle of physics that regarded light as a wave motion. Abbe worked out a formula for the resolution of fine

[33] Compound microscope, signed:
SEIBERT & KRAFT WETZLAR. Height
closed *c.* 350 mm.
c. 1880. *Musée d'Histoire des Sciences*
(*119*).

[34] Petrological microscope, signed:
THURY & AMEY GENEVE. Fitted for
studying crystals under polarized light.
Height 370 mm.
c. 1890. *Musée d'Histoire des Sciences*
(*701*).

detail that is now famous: $d = \dfrac{\lambda}{2n \sin \theta}$

d = separation of detail; λ = wavelength of the light used; n = refractive index of the space between the object and objective (for air = 1); θ = half the angle of the light cone entering the objective. The product of $n \sin \theta$ is known as the Numerical Aperture (NA for short). The NA is the measure of the resolving power of a lens, and it is the figure engraved on all modern objectives, together with the magnification; for example, 40× (magnification), 0.65 (NA). As a guide, the minimum total magnification for a good modern objective has to equal 265 times the NA, otherwise full resolution will not be achieved.

If a fluid is put between the object and the objective (and the same fluid must be placed between the condenser and the underside of the preparation slide), then the refractive index will be greater than 1, and the NA thereby increased. For water, $n = 1.3$; for oils, $n = 1.4$ to 1.6. Abbe's theory, published in 1877, showed the reason for using oil immersion to get the most out of high-power objectives, and specially made objectives for use with oil have been available since about 1880.

[35] Ophthalmometer or keratometer, signed: NACHET ET FILS *17, rue St. Séverin, Paris.* This type of instrument was the invention of Jesse Ramsden (1735–1800), to examine the cornea of the eye and its accommodation. There is a head support and a microscope (short-focus telescope). Later, the instrument was used to measure the radius of curvature of the anterior corneal surface. Camille Sébastien Nachet (1799–1881) founded his firm in 1839 and he moved to the above address in 1863. Length of microscope: 220 mm; overall height 430 m.
c. 1870. *Museum Boerhaave (3084).*

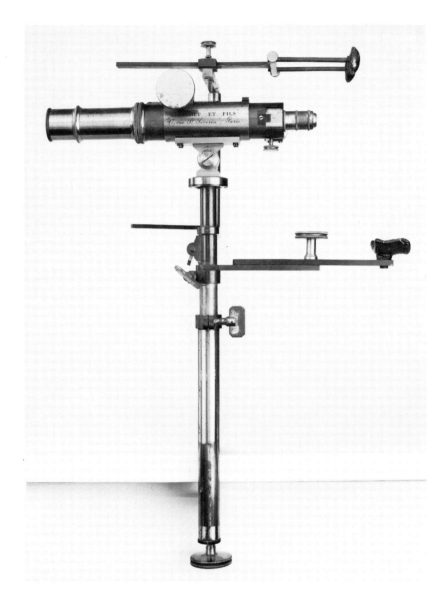

It was as a result of the remarkable combination of Abbe, Zeiss and Schott, an outstanding optical scientist and two outstanding technologists, that Jena became the centre of the optical instrument-making trade, especially for microscopes, from the late nineteenth century until World War II.

Photographic Instruments

Without photographic emulsions a great part of modern science could not exist. To the astronomer, photography is essential for the detection of very faint stars and of movement between stars, while the microscopist needs to record his images without the interpretations and omissions of drawing. The scientist is indebted, therefore, to the popular appeal of photography in the second half of the nineteenth century which helped to develop the subject so rapidly. The popularity widened the

[36] Solar microscope, signed: *Haas, Lisboa*. 1840. The sun was the most convenient, intense source for projecting microscope preparations until the introduction of oxy-hydrogen gas, and the electric arc. J. B. Haas (1753–1828) moved to Lisbon from London in 1800 and his business was continued after his death by his nephew, João Frederico Haas, until 1865. Plate 159 × 158 mm; overall length of tube from plate 420 mm.
1840. *Teyler's Museum (1229)*.

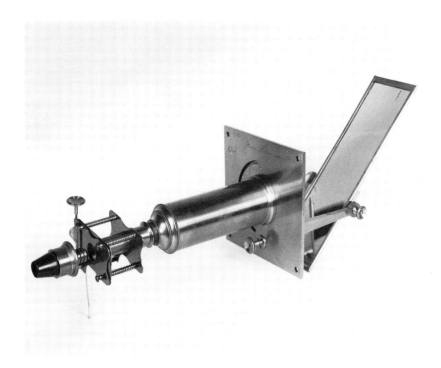

market for optical glass and lenses, which were made by the same factories as telescopes and microscopes.

William Henry Fox Talbot (1800–77) made his first experiments in photography using a camera obscura (see Chapter 16). This was an ancient instrument, used for drawing. It gave a name to the modern camera, which differs very little from the original in principle. Photography depends much more on photo-chemistry than on optics and optical instruments, so the history from 1840, after the first successful

[37] Engraving of a 'Scientific and Experimental Lantern No. 1 by W. C. Hughes, Kingsland'. This is intended for projecting demonstrations onto a screen, hence the erecting prism.
1888. *The 'Indispensable Handbook' to the Optical Lantern*, edited by W. D. Welford and H. Sturmey, p. 127.

[38] Signed: The NATURALISTS'
CAMERA Rowland Ward & Co.
Naturalists to the Court 166 PICCADILLY
LONDON. Made of mahogany and brass,
the camera takes 12 glass plates,
30 × 30 mm, which are held in a magazine.
Front 127 × 90 mm; depth 95 mm.
*c. 1885. Museum of the History of Science
(66–175).*

permanent images were demonstrated, is that of improvements in the sensitive emulsions that were to receive the image. In 1851, Frederick Scott Archer (1813–57) invented the wet collodion process, which lasted for some 40 years. The next step was rather slow; the gelatin dry plate was invented in 1871, but it was not sufficiently effective until the late 1880s. After this came the new era of the hand-held camera and the snap-shot; the first Kodak box camera with celluloid roll-film was manufactured in 1888.

10 · *Magnetism*

Our doctrine of the loadstone is contradictory of most of the principles and axioms of the Greeks. Nor have we brought into the work any graces of rhetoric, any verbal ornateness, but have aimed simply at treating knotty questions about which little is known in such a style and in such terms as are needed to make what is said clearly intelligible.

William Gilbert (1600)

The greatest scientific achievement of the nineteenth century was the discovery of electro-magnetic phenomena, and the theoretical explanation of them. This led to the production of electric power and electric light, to the electric telegraph, and eventually to radio – indeed it was the basis of modern technology. The essential unity of magnetism and electricity was proved experimentally in the 1820s (see below). However, the topics will be split between two chapters for practical convenience, even though, for most of the century, any distinction is bound to be arbitrary.

Up to the end of the eighteenth century electricity and magnetism could legitimately be regarded as separate studies. Electricity was the effect produced by friction, usually by rubbing glass with leather pads. The word itself derives from the Greek, 'elektron', meaning amber, and it is generally held that Thales of Miletus in about 600 BC was the first of the Greek philosophers to discover the attractive power of rubbed amber, that will cause small, dry particles to stick to it. Such was the phenomenon of static electricity, which was known about, but remained unexplained until the nineteenth century. By the end of the previous century, current electricity had also been discovered (see Chapter 11). Knowledge of magnetism is also ancient; the name is thought to derive from an area in eastern Europe where magnetic rock, which was called lodestone, was known to exist. Lodestone attracts iron, and this effect again was familiar, but inexplicable, to classical philosophers, who regarded it as magical.

The first scientific study of magnetism was published in 1600 by William Gilbert (1540–1603), physician to Queen Elizabeth I of England. This work, entitled *De Magnete*, the product of eighteen years of experiment, is a classic of scientific methodology. Gilbert made a model of the Earth in lodestone, which he called a terrella, and he was the first to apply the name, poles, to the ends of the compass needle,

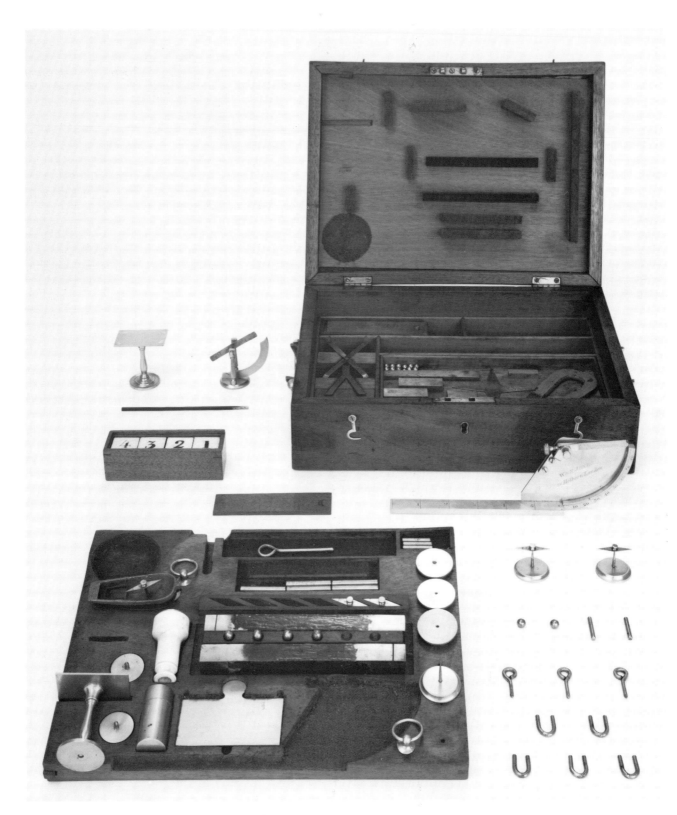

[1] Magnetic cabinet, signed: *W. & S. JONES 30 Holborn London.* The equipment follows closely that described by George Adams, Jr, in his *An Essay on Electricity* (1784) and *Lectures on Natural and Experimental Philosophy* (1794).
c. 1810. *Science Museum (1936–441).*

because they pointed to the Poles of the Earth. In 1576 Robert Norman constructed the first dipping needle, which was able to measure the vertical component of the Earth's magnetic field (see Chapter 14). The scientific term for lodestone is magnetite, or magnetic iron oxide (Fe_3O_4), which has a strong attractive power for iron, and was therefore a mysterious and fearful force that obviously lent itself to demonstration. The demonstration is that of supporting weights, the bigger, the more dramatic. A piece of magnetite will support its own weight of iron, and so a large piece will support the weight of a man. It was also discovered that artificial magnets could be made by using magnetite to give permanent magnetic power to pieces of ordinary iron, and this was the method generally followed in the production of magnetic needles for compasses (see Chapter 14). The familiar horse-shoe-shaped magnet brings the two poles adjacent to each other, and thus increases the attractive power and the weight-supporting capacity. In the late eighteenth century powdered iron came to be used in the making of magnets. Apart from the important geodetic and navigational use, magnets in bar form were sold in kits for teaching and demonstration. One of these was to show what were called the lines of force. A piece of stiff paper, or a sheet of glass, was laid over a bar magnet, and on the surface iron filings were scattered. These then arranged themselves in symmetrical and well-defined lines and curves, which Faraday called lines of force, corresponding to the lines of force of the Earth itself, as established by the use of the dip-needle in field experiments.

ELECTROMAGNETISM

The branch of physics that deals with the relationship between electricity and magnetism, whereby a magnetic field is produced by an electric current in a wire, is called electromagnetism. What proved to be one of the most far-reaching discoveries in the world originated from the observations of the Danish professor of natural philosophy, Hans Christian Oersted (1777–1851). It must be pointed out that Charles Augustin Coulomb (1736–1806) in the 1780s had 'proved' that electricity and magnetism were two quite distinct types of matter of fundamentally different natures. There was no question of one turning into the other, so to speak. Oersted, through absorbing the philosophical ideas of Immanuel Kant (1724–1804) thought in terms of the conversion of forces. He predicted in 1813 that a fine wire carrying an electric current would have a magnetic field, but his professorial duties prevented him from designing an experiment to test the possibility (a delay of seven years that seems rather extraordinary). The actual discovery was made in the spring of 1820, during a lecture demonstration. The current produced by a battery was led through a very thin platinum wire, which was placed over an ordinary compass, in its glass case. When the current was switched on, the needle moved. He made further tests, and found that a current-carrying wire is surrounded by a circular magnetic

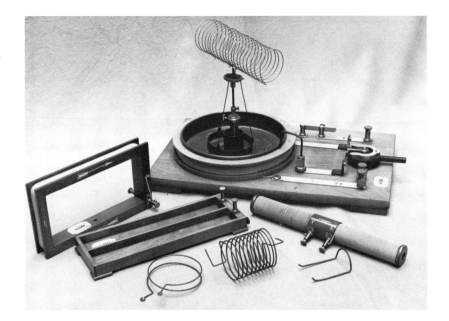

[2] Collection of apparatus to demonstrate the discoveries, during 1820–25, of André Ampère (1775–1836) on the electromagnetic properties of a current in a wire. Signed: *E. Ducretet à Paris.* 1892. *Teyler's Museum (830).*

[3] Electromagnetic terrella, known as Barlow's globe, signed: *C. Dell'Acqua a Milano.* The model Earth is wound with copper wire along parallels of latitude. When connected to a battery a magnetic field is formed, which can be detected by compass and dipping needles. Overall height 410 mm; diameter of sphere 185 mm.
c. 1840. *Pavia University (1961).*

[4] Apparatus to show the effect of a magnetic field on the electric discharge in a rarefied gas. The coil magnetizes the soft-iron core, which protrudes into the glass vessel called 'an electric egg'. This demonstration is due to the Swiss physicist, Auguste Arthur de La Rive (1801–73), to show the behaviour of the Aurora Borealis. Purchased by the Museum in 1859 for Dfl. 54.90. Base 270 × 176 mm; overall height 660 mm.
1859. *Teyler's Museum (694).*

OPPOSITE:
[XII] Compound microscope, signed: AND^W. ROSS & C^O, *OPTICIANS 33 Regent St. Piccadilly.* The first of the modern microscopes, with corrected multiple-lensed objectives, a firm support to the body tube, and accurate focusing controls. Andrew Ross (1799–1859) was at this address from 1837 to 1841, while he was in partnership with J. J. Lister, which accounts for the '& Co.' in the signature. Overall height 520 mm.
c. 1838. *Museum of the History of Science (C 69).*

field. This result was published in a paper dated 21 July 1820. From this simple-looking experiment soon followed the epoch-making ideas of Ampère and Faraday.

The true founder of electrodynamics, and the man who coined this name for it, was André Marie Ampère (1775–1836). Immediately inspired by the discovery of Oersted, Ampère conducted a series of brilliant experiments, the results being published in 1822 in *Recueil*

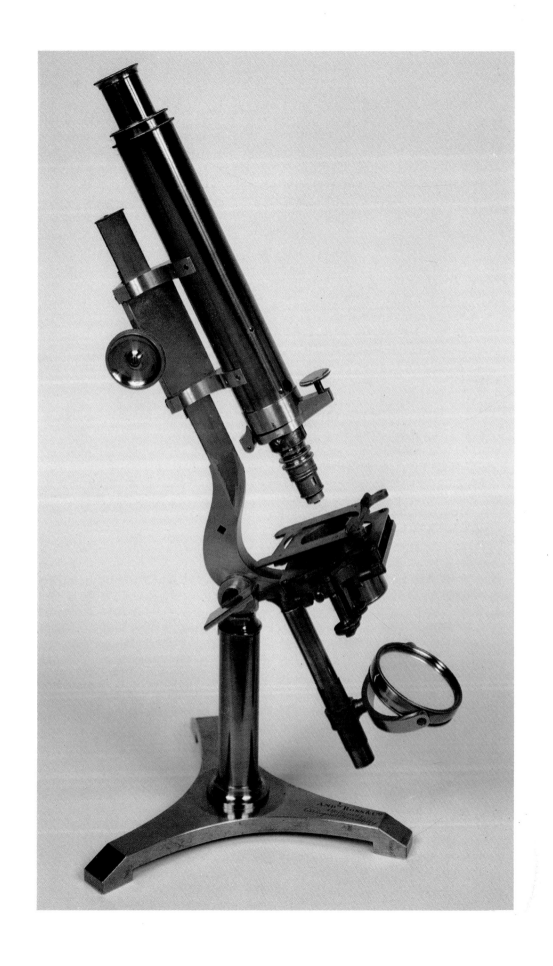

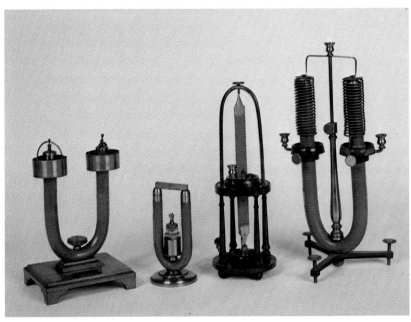

[5] Magnetic sparkler, signed: *C. Dell'Acqua fecit in Milano nel 1840* [No.] *3.* Also labelled: *Calamita scintillante di Nobili.* The coil is oscillated rapidly between the poles of the pair of magnets, and induced currents produce a spark discharge. Leopoldo Nobili (1784–1835) was professor of physics at Florence from 1831. Width across back 510 mm; depth excluding handle 380 mm; height 270 mm. 1840. *Pavia University (1997).*

OPPOSITE:
[XIII] Projection microscope, signed: WRIGHT & NEWTON'S PATENT *SOLE MAKERS NEWTON & C⁰. OPTICIANS TO THE QUEEN 3, Fleet Street,* London. The four objective cans are signed: GAS MICROSCOPE *Newton & C⁰.* An accompanying pamphlet is headed: The New Patent Lantern Microscope, for Oxyhydrogen or Electric Light. Base board 520 × 225 mm; overall height 460 mm; overall length 800 mm. *c.* 1885. *Teyler's Museum (780).*

[XIV] Group of apparatus to illustrate Faraday's and Ampère's laws (numbered from left to right): 1. Horseshoe magnet with a pair of Ampère's buckets, signed: M. LOGEMAN fecit AMSTERDAM. The 'buckets' are small galvanic batteries that rotate round the poles of the magnet by which they are supported. Overall height 190 mm; base 120 × 99 mm; 2. A demonstration of the effect of heat on magnetization. Overall height 125 mm; base diameter 60 mm; 3. A revolving magnet, which is turned by the current circulating in the central coil. A demonstration after William Sturgeon (1783–1850) described in 1832. Overall height 250 mm; base diameter 85 mm; 4. A pair of copper-wire helices that contra-rotate around the poles of the supporting horseshoe magnet. Overall height 298 mm. *c.* 1840. *Teyler's Museum (659, 471, 660, 658).*

d'observations électrodynamiques. The Académie des Sciences in Paris had received the news from Denmark on 4 September 1820, and the members could scarcely believe the truth of the report, chiefly because of Coulomb's long-established 'proof' of the impossibility. Ampère did believe, and performed his experiments, coming back to the Académie on 18 and 25 September and 9 October. He showed:
1. that two parallel wires carrying currents behave like magnets;
2. that a solenoid, which is a wire coiled into a cylinder, behaves just like a magnet, and will suck an iron needle into the middle of the coil;
3. that a current-carrying wire will behave like a magnetic needle;
4. and that the magnetic effect in a bar of iron is the result of currents of electricity around the molecules, and that these molecules could be aligned (this followed a suggestion from his friend, Fresnel).

Between 1820 and 1825 Ampère produced his electrodynamical theory of the nature of electricity.

The law relating the resistance in a circuit, and the voltage and current strength, was formulated in 1827 by the German physicist Georg Simon Ohm (1787–1854). Ohm's law, taught in every school, is that the current is proportional to the voltage and inversely proportional to the resistance, expressed thus: $I = E/R$. For measuring the strength of electric currents and for verifying Ohm's laws of flow, Servais Mathias Pouillet (1790–1868) introduced the tangent and sine galvanometers in 1837. With the current flowing in a copper hoop or in a coil of wire, a compass needle at the centre was deflected by the magnetic field associated with the current in the hoop or coil. The strength is proportional to the tangent of the angle of deflection [xv, facing p. 192]. In the case of the sine galvanometer [6], the coil and scale are rotated to keep the needle at zero. The current is then proportional

[6] Sine galvanometer, signed: *W. M. LOGEMAN Fecit, HAARLEM.* This type of instrument was devised in 1837 by Pouillet for measuring electric currents. The needle is kept at zero by rotating the coil, the angle being read off a scale on the base plate. The current is proportional to the sine of this angle. Overall height 440 mm; base diameter 220 mm.
c. 1848. *Teyler's Museum (635).*

to the sine of the angle of rotation. This form can be made more sensitive than the tangent. In 1840 Wilhelm Eduard Weber (1804–91) defined the absolute electromagnetic unit of current in terms of the deflection of the magnetic needle of a tangent galvanometer. The term 'weber' was agreed internationally in 1933 for the practical unit of magnetic flux.

The nineteenth century has a number of self-taught inventors and scientists, and among those whose contributions were significant in the field of electromagnetism, were Sturgeon, Barlow, Faraday, and Gramme. William Sturgeon (1783–1850), son of a boot-maker and apprenticed in that trade, and later a soldier, who studied science off-duty, while stationed in the artillery at Woolwich, acquired the technical skills to make apparatus, and to lecture to a variety of audiences. In 1825 he received a medal from the Society for the Encouragement of the Arts and Manufactures for apparatus to demonstrate effects in electromagnetism, and, in particular, for his invention of the electromagnet. Sturgeon took the wire cylinder or solenoid of Ampère and inside it he placed a bar of soft iron, which became strongly magnetic while the current flowed in the coil of wire. By putting the iron in the form of a horse-shoe, the lifting power was increased. In America, Joseph Henry (1797–1878) began his researches on electromagnetism in 1827 by improving the insulation and windings of such a magnet to the point where it would lift 3000 pounds weight. In 1832, independently of Faraday, he discovered self-induction.

Peter Barlow (1776–1862) was from a well-to-do family, but was self-taught scientifically. His work on magnetism led to his election to the Royal Society in 1823, and in 1825, he attempted to make an electric telegraph, but the insulation was not effective. Barlow's name is associated with a demonstration piece known as Barlow's wheel [7].

[7] Barlow's wheel, to show the principle of the electric motor. The star wheel dips into a mercury trough between the magnet, so that when a current flows through the wheel it rotates. Named after Peter Barlow who devised it in 1822. Purchased in 1856 by the Museum for Dfl. 15.60. Base 160 × 78 mm; height 168 mm.
1856. *Teyler's Museum (589).*

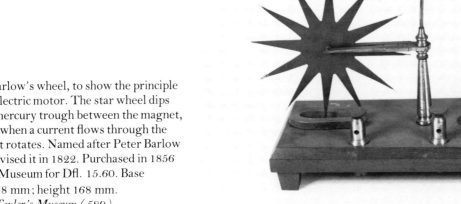

[8] Wheatstone's electric telegraph, signed: W A T K I N S & H I L L 5 C H A R I N G C R O S S L O N D O N. *Left*, the communicator; *Right*, the alphabet dial telegraph. This form of apparatus was an improvement made in 1840 to the original of 1837. It was favoured by teachers; see J. H. Pepper, *Cyclopaedic Science* (1869), p. 429. *Left*: base 178 × 100 mm; height 160 mm. *Right*: base 204 × 123 mm; height 240 mm.
c. 1844. *Teyler's Museum* (676, 675).

This consists of a light copper disk cut with star-shaped teeth. This rotates in a vertical plane, and the teeth just dip into a trough of mercury which lies between the poles of a horseshoe magnet. When the wires from a battery are connected to the support for the disk, and to the mercury, the toothed wheel rotates, and the direction depends on the direction of the electric current. This apparatus illustrates the action of some of the electromagnetic machines, such as Gramme's.

The time was ripe for the development of the electric telegraph. Not only did the rudiments of the technology exist, but there was also a powerful economic need in the form of the railway network that was begun in Britain in about 1830, and which, by 1860, had covered most of the country. The race was won by two men who, having started separately, came together in 1837 to patent and develop the first practical electric telegraph [8]. These were Charles Wheatstone (1802–75) and William Fothergill Cooke (1806–79). The first line was laid into the new Euston station, and opened in 1837, the year Queen Victoria came to the throne. Thirty years later, there were 90,000 miles of telegraph wires, and 3000 public telegraph offices, transmitting six million messages a year. London and Paris were linked by 1852, India joined the network in 1864, and America in 1866.

The Wheatstone-Cooke telegraph works by using a battery of chemical cells to provide the current, a circuit-breaking key to be used by the sender, a transmission wire, and a receiver that consists of an electromagnet. This is energized by the sender's signals, and moves a pointer. With a system of short and long key contacts, or by reversing the current to swing a needle to the right or left, a code was built up to represent the alphabet and the numerals.

Quite independently of Wheatstone, the American artist, Samuel Finley Breese Morse (1791–1872) acquired an interest in things electrical, and, on returning home from Europe in 1832, he thought of a scheme for an electromagnetic telegraph. After a long period of solo development, he constructed a working model that could be exhibited in New York in 1837. He returned to London the next year to patent his device, but his application was successfully opposed by Wheatstone. What he did achieve, and vindicated in legal action, was his invention of the electromagnetic recording telegraph. His name will always be remembered for the Morse code, the arrangement of short and long signals transmitted along wires, and later used in wireless telegraphy.

The first electric telegraph capable of transmitting speech was the 1861 design of Johann Reis. This has been described, together with later developments, in Chapter 8.

The electric clock (see Chapter 2) also employs an electromagnet, and the first electric time-telling device was patented in 1841 by Alexander Bain (1810–77).

Michael Faraday (1791–1867) was the son of a blacksmith [9]. He was apprenticed as a bookbinder, and, while repairing a copy of the *Encyclopaedia Britannica*, he read the article 'Electricity', which awoke a keen interest in science. He then began to teach himself, and was fortunate to be able to attend the meetings and lectures given at the City Philosophical Society in London. By a lucky chance, he was recommended as a temporary assistant in 1812 to Humphry Davy at the Royal Institution, and eventually obtained a permanent position there. Though his interests were wide, he always kept his attention on electrical phenomena, and was therefore particularly struck by the discovery of Oersted. Faraday was able to demonstrate electromagnetic rotation, the conversion of electrical into mechanical energy, and this momentous discovery was published on 21 October 1821, in a paper, 'On Some New Electro-Magnetical Motions, and on the Theory of Magnetism'. In 1831 he invented the electromagnetic generator, and with it the modern electrical engineering industry. Using a large, permanent magnet, he mounted a copper disk to spin vertically between the poles. Two spring contacts pressed against the axle and the edge of the disk. When the disk was rotated, an electric current was generated in the circuit connecting the contacts. During the next six years, Faraday went on to elucidate the laws of electrochemistry, and specific inductive capacity, and he laid the foundations of field theory.

Faraday made the further surprising discovery of the connexion between magnetism and light (often called the Faraday effect). William Thomson (1824–1907, who became Lord Kelvin in 1892), wrote to Faraday on 6 August 1845, suggesting that he should try experiments with polarized light. On 13 September, just five weeks later, Faraday had found that if a piece of glass was placed between the poles of a powerful electromagnet, and if polarized light was passed through the glass, then the plane of polarization was rotated when the power was switched on, and the amount of the rotation depended on the strength of the magnetic force.

The foundation of electrical theory so ably laid by Faraday was built upon by the Edinburgh and Cambridge mathematician, James Clerk

[9] Michael Faraday in the 1850s. He established the common identity of all forms of electricity distinguished in his day: voltaic, common, magneto-electric, thermo-electric, and animal. By 1831 he had laid the foundations of the electrical industries of the world. *Museum of the History of Science.*

[10] Example of the first electromagnetic generator, signed: *Pixii Rue de Jardinet No. 2 à Paris*. The design is that of Antoine Hippolyte Pixii (1808–35), who made the first model in his father's workshop in 1832. Base 615 × 380 mm; height 1.18 m. *c.* 1833. *Museo di Storia della Scienza (552).*

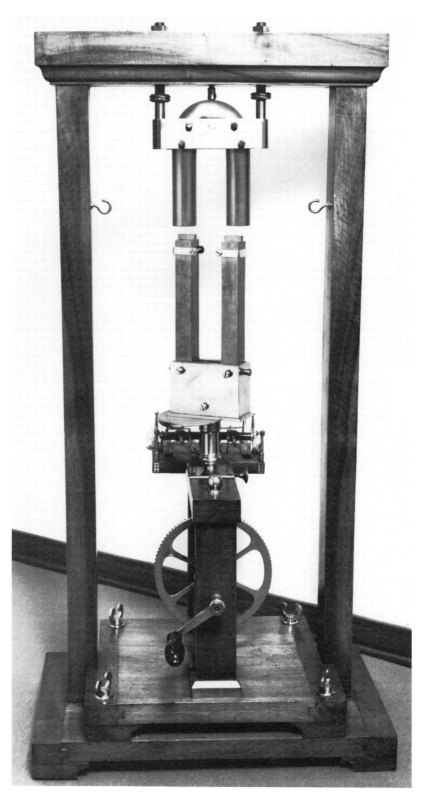

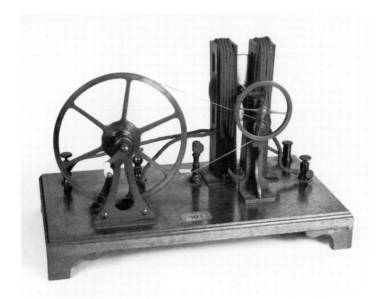

[11] Electromagnetic generator, signed: WATKINS & HILL 5 CHARING CROSS LONDON. This form follows that of Faraday's discovery of 1831. Francis Watkins published in 1838 a paper on 'electromagnetic motive machines'. He was from 1828 curator of philosophical apparatus to London University, as well as a partner in the firm of Watkins & Hill. Base 408 × 224 mm, height 255 mm. *c.* 1844. *Teyler's Museum (701).*

[12] Electromagnetic motor, signed: WATKINS & HILL 5 CHARING CROSS LONDON. Two armatures, each of four coils, are mounted on the same axle between four cylindrical permanent magnets. Base 265 × 175 mm; overall height 235 mm. *c.* 1844. *Teyler's Museum (679).*

Maxwell (1831–1879). One of the most brilliant of theoretical physicists, Maxwell's tragically short career fell into two distinct parts. During the first 14 years of his working life, he collected together all the electromagnetic forces in physics within one unifying theory, which he published as a *Treatise on Electricity and Magnetism* in 1873. Having achieved this, he attempted to extend this unification to the entire field of natural science, thus proving himself the forerunner of Einstein.

After Faraday had established the possibility of electric motors and generators, various inventors and instrument makers began producing different designs for practical machines, and also demonstration set pieces for teaching. The first electromagnetic generator was made in 1832 by Antoine Hippolyte Pixii (1808–35) [10], and consisted of a horseshoe magnet rotated under a pair of fixed coils. An alternative design had a fixed magnet with coils that rotated, and was devised by Edward Montague Clarke (fl. 1804–46), an instrument maker in the Strand, London. William Ladd constructed, in 1867, a dynamo-electric generator with two revolving armatures, and Charles William Siemens (1823–83) published his version in the same year, and in 1879 invented the electric furnace. But the most efficient machine, a generator producing direct current, was the invention of the Belgian joiner and model-maker, Zénobe Théophile Gramme (1826–1901), in 1869 [13]. Some years later, he devised the continuous current dynamo

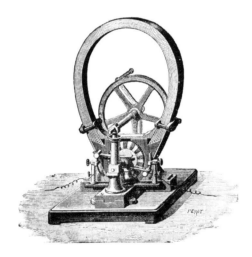

[13] The Gramme electromagnetic generator, producing direct current. Presented to the Académie des Sciences in July 1871, this model became the classic laboratory generator, capable of producing 6 volts and 28 amps. This wood engraving appears in the sixth edition of *Deschanel* (1881), and in the 1892 *Catalogue* of E. Ducretet et L. Lejeune, who offered it at 650 francs.

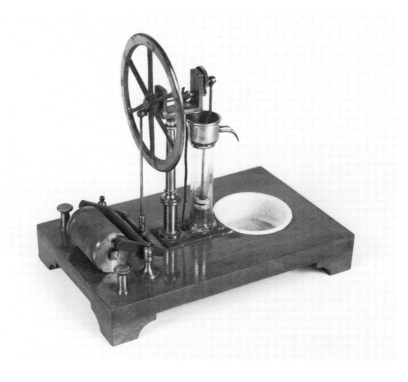

[14] Electromagnetic model pump, signed: TECNOMASIO MILANO. The electromagnet attracts a bar that cranks the wheel to the lift pump. Reciprocating motion is maintained by a make-and-break switch. Base 205 × 118 mm; overall height 190 mm.
Late 19th century. *Pavia University (1958)*.

[15] Induction coil for electro-medical or other uses, signed: WATKINS & HILL 5 CHARING CROSS LONDON. The solenoid primary circuit is attached to a battery; the interrupter at the top is turned, so inducing a high frequency current in the secondary coils. Base 151 × 152 mm; overall height 260 mm.
c. 1850. *Teyler's Museum (698)*.

[16] Ruhmkorff induction coil, signed: E. DUCRETET ET L. LEJEUNE 75, RUE CLAUDE BERNARD PARIS. This design is capable of generating very high voltages, and can produce a spark 100 mm in length. Ducretet founded the firm in 1864. Base 478 × 211 × 85 mm; height to top of terminals 265 mm; coil diameter 115 mm. c. 1892. *Teyler's Museum (854)*.

driven by steam power and used to produce electric light, and so became the inventor of long-distance transmission of direct current electricity. A forerunner in electric light generation was Henry Wilde (1833–1919) who, in 1864, made a dynamo-electric machine which produced powerful electric arc light, and which found an application in the search-light. The word dynamo should be reserved for a generator where part of the winding magnetizes the soft-iron core, known as auto-excitation.

The Induction Coil

The induction coil consists of two separate coils of wire one inside the other wound around a cylinder with a central core of soft iron rods. When a current is passed through the first, primary coil, current is induced in the secondary coil. If, then, the first coil is of thick wire, about 2 mm in diameter, and the second is of thin wire, about 0.2 mm, then the secondary can accommodate many more turns of wire to produce the same thickness of coil. The induced voltage is in proportion to the number of turns by which the secondary exceeds the primary, so it is possible to obtain a thousand volts from the secondary when a six-volt battery is put across the primary. The induced current occurs only when the current first flows, so a soft-iron armature is fitted that is attracted by the core when it becomes magnetized by the switched-on current. This pulls a make-and-break device similar to that used on an electric bell, cutting off the current so that the core loses its magnetism for a moment. The process thus oscillates, and a high-frequency, high-voltage current is induced, which can produce a long spark between terminals.

In 1851 the German, Heinrich Daniel Ruhmkorff (1803–77), made

[17] Electro-medical induction apparatus, signed: RUHMKORFF *MÉCANICIEN*, 15, Rue des Maçons Sorbonne, Paris. By holding the brass parts on the handles, the patient receives a tingling shock. The batteries are mercury sulphate cells. Case 262 × 116 × 37 mm.
c. 1856. Teyler's Museum (696).

[18] The signature panel in the lid of the case shown in plate 17.

the first successful apparatus of this type, which was therefore given the name, Ruhmkorff's coil [16]. Ruhmkorff settled in Paris in 1840 as a precision instrument maker, and his firm was continued after his death by J. Carpentier. The induction coil was exhibited at the Paris Exhibition of 1855, after which it became very popular for energizing discharge tubes, and was used in the production of X-rays at the end of the century.

Electricity has been applied for medical purposes, often in quack medicine. The use of electrical high voltage discharges will be referred to in the next chapter. Induction in coils can be employed, and a popular electro-medical machine used this method for giving patients tingling shocks [17, 18, 19]. The electricity from two small batteries is led to a pair of coils with a vibrating contact breaker across their poles. The power of the shock is regulated by sliding copper cylinders over the coils. Later, the same sort of device was powered by a hand-turned generator.

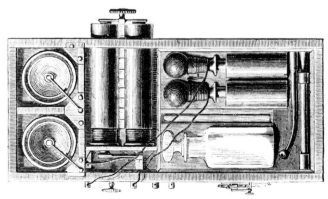

[19] Engraving showing the Ruhmkorff electro-medical induction apparatus.
c. 1870. Deschanel, p. 778.

[20] Electro-medical induction coil, signed: MACAULAY AND SON, 39, Redeness Street, YORK. The plaque advertises this as: 'Dr. Simpson's' apparatus. See plate 21. Base diameter 200 mm; overall height 185 mm. Mid-19th century. *Whipple Museum (1301).*

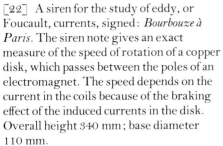

[22] A siren for the study of eddy, or Foucault, currents, signed: *Bourbouze à Paris.* The siren note gives an exact measure of the speed of rotation of a copper disk, which passes between the poles of an electromagnet. The speed depends on the current in the coils because of the braking effect of the induced currents in the disk. Overall height 340 mm; base diameter 110 mm.
Late 19th century. *Private collection.*

[21] The plaque on the induction coil shown in plate 20. The doctor is possibly Sir James Young Simpson (1811–70), the son of a baker, who took a doctor of medicine degree at Edinburgh in 1832, thereafter specializing in midwifery.

Induced currents in a conductor tend to flow so as to produce a magnetic field that will oppose the field producing them. Such induced currents are known as eddy currents, or Foucault currents, after Léon Foucault (1819–68). Eddy currents can, therefore, produce a braking effect, which provides many applications, including the electric supply meter, where the rotating element stops immediately when the current flow ceases. The energy generated by eddy currents in a conductor reveals itself as heat, and this can therefore reduce the efficiency of a motor.

[23] Eddy current machine, signed: *Ruhmkorff à Paris*. A copper disk (diameter 75 mm) is rotated rapidly between the poles of an electromagnet, making the disk hot through induced currents. The heat is measured by a thermopile (behind the disk). Eddy currents are also called Foucault currents, after J. B. L. Foucault (1819–68) who invented this type of apparatus in 1855. A similar model was offered for sale in 1892 by Ducretet at 450 francs. H. D. Ruhmkorff died in 1877. Base 380 × 343 mm; overall height 420 mm. 1855–77. *Pavia University (1960)*.

11 · Electricity

Dr Priestley has well observed, that electricity has one advantage over most other branches of natural philosophy: it furnishes matter of entertainment for all persons promiscuously, while it is also a subject of important speculation for the most philosophic minds. Neither the air-pump, nor the orrery, nor any experiments in hydrostatics, optics, or magnetism, &c. ever brought together so many, or such great concourses of people, as those of electricity have singly done.

George Adams, Jr (1794)

Some simple electrical phenomena have been known since antiquity, the classic being rubbed amber attracting light particles, such as chaff. The word electricity derives from the Greek name for amber. William Gilbert (1544–1603), who is best known for his work on magnetism, also investigated rubbed amber, and he invented a crude indicator to demonstrate the attraction. Otto von Guericke (1602–86) constructed a sulphur-ball frictional generator in 1660, but he did not see his investigation in the same terms as the electrical experiments that were to develop in the eighteenth century, but rather in the context of his ideas about the universe.

The real founder of the empirical science of electrics was Francis Hauksbee Senior (*c.* 1666–1713), who began his studies in 1705, having been appointed Curator of Experiments to the Royal Society in the previous year. Newton had already shown that rubbing glass produced the amber effect, and Hauksbee constructed a machine with a globe of glass that was rotated, and rubbed by a pad of sheepskin. The globe had been evacuated by an air-pump, and a glow discharge was seen inside the globe, the forerunner of discharge lamps of the nineteenth and twentieth centuries. In 1709 Hauksbee published his findings in *Physico-Mechanical Experiments on Various Subjects, Containing an Account of Several Surprising Phenomena Touching Light and Electricity*. For most subsequent investigations, this was the foundation document.

The electrostatic generator was at first Hauksbee's globe, but by the 1750s it consisted of a disk of glass [1 & 2], which was more efficient and safer, as it could not explode through over-heating. A cylinder electro-static generator was patented in 1782 by the instrument maker, Edward Nairne (1726–1806), which he called a 'Medico-Electrical

[1] Electrostatic friction generator, English-type plate machine, Cuthbertson's final pattern. Base 255 × 128 mm; overall height 361 mm; plate diameter 228 mm. *c.* 1810. *Whipple Museum (1361).*

[2] Electrostatic friction generator, French-type plate machine, sometimes called Ramsden's pattern. It has a pair of large, brass prime conductors. Base 620 × 320 mm; overall height 550 mm. Mid-19th century. *Musée d'Histoire des Sciences (525)*.

Machine'. It was compact and portable, for the treatment of patients [3]. This medical application of static electricity was largely bogus, and inspired by the sheer wonder of the extraordinary effects produced by electrostatics. At the very beginning of the nineteenth century, the commonest generator was the disk, or plate machine, which could have one or two rotating disks of glass. This was followed by the Nairne-type cylinder machine, and these two forms continued unchallenged into the middle of the century.

Naturally, there were variations in design to obtain greater efficiency and larger voltages. One inspiration had been the extremely large, double, plate machine made by the Englishman, John Cuthbertson (1743–1821), working in Amsterdam for Martinus van Marum (1750–1837), director of the Teyler's Foundation in Haarlem. This machine was delivered in 1784, and was improved until 1791. The disks were over 6 feet in diameter (1650 mm), and the voltage, producing a spark of 24 inches (610 mm), was about 330,000 V.

After the generator itself, the next really important discovery was that of the Leyden jar [4 & XVI, facing p. 193]. It is named after a town in Holland where little original electrical research was done. The true inventor of the jar is now thought to have been Ewald Georg von Kleist (*c.* 1700–48), the German experimenter who found out about the effect in 1745. It was only a few months later that the

[3] Painting showing electrical treatment. Oil on canvas, 641 × 876 mm, signed: David Henry Friston. The woman, sitting on an insulated chair (note the footrest) is probably being treated for 'nervous headaches'. The electrostatic friction generator is of the Nairne cylinder type.
c. 1860. *Geffrye Museum, London, E2.*

[4] Leyden jar, signed: HARVEY & PEAK LONDON (diameter 95 mm). *Below,* an insulated footstool, to isolate a person from the ground. While standing on such a stool a person's hair will stand on end if he touches a prime conductor. Top (308 × 250 mm; height 150 mm. Mid-19th century. *Whipple Museum (2016).*

discovery was made, probably independently, in Leyden, by Pieter van Musschenbroek (1692–1761). By electrifying a glass jar containing water, an enormous shock was received. This is the earliest form of condenser, or capacitor, and was manufactured with electrodes of foil on the inner and outer surfaces of the glass jar. When it was used with a frictional electrical machine, very large voltages could be obtained, and consequently, very long spark discharges in air. The larger the jar, the better, and great batteries of jars produced correspondingly more spectacular effects. Van Marum even exploded metal wires, a technique used much later in spectroscopic analysis.

To make measurements of the capacity of Leyden jars, a sort of crude electrometer was devised, which bore very little relationship to the later instruments such as that of Coulomb. The early measuring instruments consisted of spheres of brass mounted on insulating glass rods, and moved against a ruler, or used with a micrometer. With these, it was possible to compare the quality of different Leyden jars, by setting a gap, and seeing how long it would take for a particular jar to spark at a given gap [5].

The nature of the electric spark discharge was naturally itself of interest, and various experiments were undertaken, one of which was to try to determine the speed of the electric spark. An attempt was made in the mid-nineteenth century to use a stroboscopic disk [6], an adaptation of the invention of Professor S. Stampfer of Vienna (see Chapter 16). Since we now know that a spark travels in about one millionth of a second, there was, in fact, no hope of measuring its speed in the nineteenth century.

A curiosity, especially suitable for lecture-demonstrations, was the hydro-electric generator invented by the engineer, Sir William George

[5] Spark measurers (electrometers).
Left with a plane scale; *right* with a
micrometer screw.
Mid-19th century. *Teyler's Museum (551,
552)*.

[6] Rapidly rotating disk to demonstrate
the duration of an electric discharge. The
disk has segments blue/white and on the
reverse black/white. When rotated the
impression is a grey; a spark makes the
sectors stand out sharply. As a discharge
occupies about 1 millionth of a second, this
disk cannot possibly give a measure of the
effect, merely an illustration. Base
120 × 70 mm; diameter of disk 180 mm.
c. 1865 *Teyler's Museum (522)*.

[7] Armstrong's hydro-electric frictional
generator. Water drops driven by steam
issuing from the jets at the top, become
electrically charged by friction in the jet.
Purchased in 1852 for Dfl. 387. Overall
height about 1 metre.
1852. *Teyler's Museum (514)*.

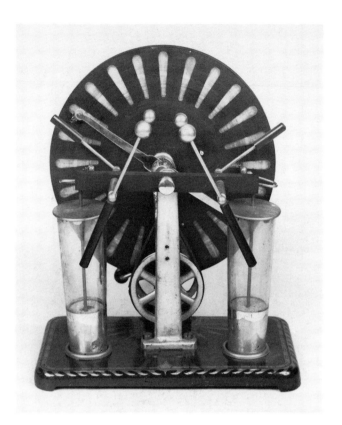

[8] Wimshurst electrostatic induction generator, unsigned, but made in Germany. The instruction pamphlet shows kits of accessories. James Wimshurst had produced such a machine by 1880. Base 240 × 130 mm; height 280 mm; plate diameter 213 mm.
c. 1900. Private collection.

[9] Electrostatic induction generator, Holtz type, signed: TECHNOMASIO ITALIANO MILANO. Devised in about 1870 by Wilhelm Holtz (1836–1913), the induction machine produced high voltages readily. The horizontal plates contra-rotate at high speeds, and at the start a sector of vulcanite is held over the upper plate opposite a bottom comb. After a few seconds the sector can be removed. Base diameter 585 mm; overall height 530 mm; plate diameter 430 mm.
Late 19th century. *Pavia University.*

Armstrong (1810–1900), in 1840 [7]. This device was a steam boiler mounted on four glass legs for insulation, and from which steam was ejected through a group of jets, directed at a metal comb connected to an insulated conductor. The charge was generated by the friction of drops of water against the sides of the jets, the steam forcing the drops out. Perfectly dry steam does not produce the effect. At the Royal Polytechnic Institution in London, a large machine of this type was built, with a boiler $6\frac{1}{2}$ feet in length and $3\frac{1}{2}$ feet in diameter (1980 mm, 1067 mm), with 46 jets. It was constructed under Armstrong's supervision, and that of the lecturer in natural philosophy, Dr Bachoffner, and was capable of producing sparks of 22 inches (558 mm). As was observed: 'The working of the machine is necessarily accompanied by the disengagement of an enormous quantity of steam, which, besides causing a deafening noise, has the mischievous effect of covering with moisture everything within reach. Accordingly, though very interesting in itself, it is by no means adapted to the general purposes of an electrical machine.'

The most powerful machine invented in the nineteenth century for the generation of static electricity was the Wimshurst induction machine [8]. It was the invention of the English engineer, James Wimshurst (1832–1903). Produced by 1880, it consisted of two contrarotating glass (or ebonite) disks, each carrying narrow strips of tinfoil. Two conductor bars at the front and back have small metal brushes at the ends that touch the strips as they move round. At each side are

[XV] Large tangent galvanometer, signed: *W. M. Logeman HAARLEM*
1848. This instrument, with three circuits, was designed by the lawyer and
amateur scientist P. Elias (1804–78) and made by W. M. Logeman
(1821–94). The current in a hoop is proportional to the tangent of the angle
by which the compass needle is deflected. Overall height 1250 mm; maximum
width 785 mm.
1848. *Teyler's Museum (636).*

[XVI] Battery of four Leyden jars (diameters 80 mm). Wooden stand 240 × 240 mm; height to top of pillar 265 mm.
Mid-19th century. *Pavia University*.

[XVII] Electric discharges in rarefied gases; the Frontispiece to the English edition of *Deschanel* (1872), printed by Blackie & Son. *Left*: an electric egg with alcohol vapour; *centre, from the top*: fluorescence of calcium sulphide, hydrogen, fluorescence of uranium glass, fluorescence of strontium sulphide; *right*: fluorescence of uranium glass and of quinine.

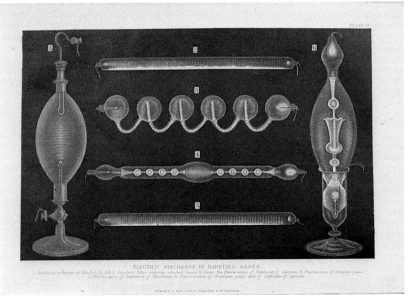

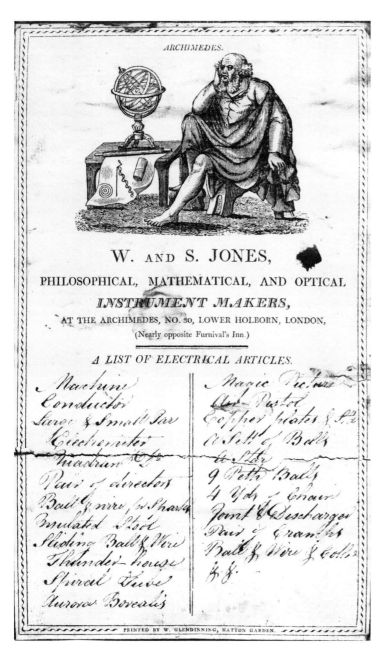

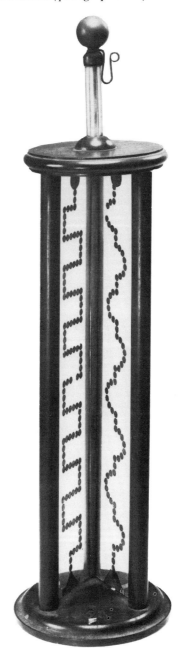

[10] The firm of W. & S. Jones was at 135 Holborn until 1799, after which the address was 30 Holborn to 1838, when Samuel died. *c.* 1810. *Science Museum (photograph 6289).*

[11] Electric bomb or mortar, made of ivory sitting in a wooden cup. A discharge in the cavity blows the ball out, which shows the expansion of the air, as with thunder. Base diameter 43 mm; diameter of ivory ball 18 mm. Mid-19th century. *Pavia University (1849).*

[12] Scintillating glass panels. A discharge sparkles between each small tin-foil spot, exhibiting what was called 'electric light'. Base diameter 110 mm; height 420 mm. Mid-19th century. *Musée d'Histoire des Sciences (365).*

collecting combs attached to Leyden jars and discharging electrodes. Each strip of foil has a charge induced by the oppositely charged strip of the other disk in the pair, so both positive and negative charges are collected by the combs. The Wimshurst machine quickly found a place in most schools and colleges, and even toy models were made. Large, robust machines were made for generating X-rays, after these were discovered in December 1895 by Professor Wilhelm Conrad Röntgen (1845–1923). One model, with twelve 26-inch glass plates, giving 15-inch sparks, was sold in 1910 for the high price of £50.

The electrostatic generator served a purpose in providing phenomena that led to the establishment of theories of electricity, and to the identification of lightning as an electric discharge no different from that obtained by the machines. For the general public, the generators produced a variety of spectacular tricks for domestic entertainment. Kits for this purpose were produced from 1800 by such firms as W. & S. Jones [10] and remained in production until the early twentieth century. The accessories included: the electric cannon or mortar [11]; the thunder house, and fire house; electric chimes, or 'gamut of bells'; the electric windmill; the electric swing; scintillating panels [12], and aurora flashes; the doll whose hair stands on end; dancing pith figures, and many more.

ELECTRIC DISCHARGES IN GASES

Jean Picard (1620–82) noticed, in 1676, a glow at the end of a barometer tube, when it was being carried at night. This phenomenon was later explained by Francis Hauksbee Senior as caused by friction between the mercury and the glass wall, and the same effect was noticed by others when working with evacuated glass vessels. Van Marum proposed that the Aurora Borealis was produced by an electrical discharge in rarified air; the effects are, in fact, most pronounced when the pressure in the vessel is between 1 and 10 torr. Later, Benjamin Wilson

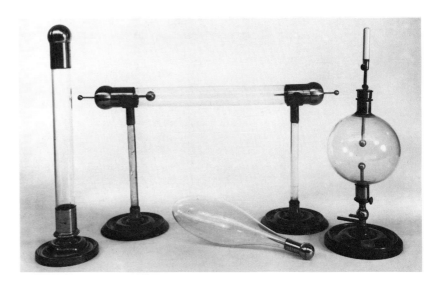

[13] Aurora flasks and tubes. *Left to right*: luminous conductor to show the falling star effect; aurora tube with ball and point at opposite ends to show the character of the discharge if the conductor is positive or negative; aurora flask; aurora globe or electric egg.
Early 19th century. *Science Museum (1927–1440; 1927–1176; 1927–1439; 1927–1274).*

[14] Long and elaborate Geissler tube. Johann Geissler (1815–79) was a mechanic at the University of Bonn, and a particularly fine glassblower. He made these discharge tubes from the late 1850s onwards. *c.* 1875. *Science Museum (1876–22).*

(1721–88) discovered that there is no luminous discharge in a strong vacuum. The name aurora tube, or aurora flask [13], was given to the wide range of glass containers of different shapes made to demonstrate the glow effect of electrical discharge in a partial vacuum.

Johann Heinrich Wilhelm Geissler (1815–79) belonged to a family of glassmakers, and practised his skill as mechanic at the University of Bonn, making chemical and physical instruments, and learning from the scientists with whom he worked. Anxious to achieve a stronger vacuum, he devised his own mercury air-pump in about 1855 (see Chapter 6), and by its use he was able to make rather small glass tubes with electrodes melted into the ends, filled with rarefied gases . The technology of Geissler tubes [14], as they came to be called, helped to introduce a new branch of physics, leading directly to the discovery of cathode rays. There is an interesting practical application that was discovered and put to use for the Geissler tube. The light produced by the discharge was found to be a safe method of illumination in mines [15], where the danger of using any form of naked flame was ever-present. The apparatus was all contained in a portable leather case, and consisted of a battery with an induction coil, causing a steady discharge in a Geissler tube, contained for greater safety in an outer glass

[15] Electric, miner's safety lamp. A Geissler tube inside a sealed glass cylinder is energized by a battery and an induction coil. Lamp 253 mm; diameter 45 mm. *c.* 1865. *Teyler's Museum (911).*

[16]   *Left*: a Puluj electric radiometer where the vanes are moved by the off-centre cathode ray stream. *Right*: a Crookes tube for showing that the cathode stream is deflected by a magnet; it is made visible on a fluorescent screen. Height 240 mm; 140 mm.
c. 1895. *Museum of the History of Science*.

tube. This miner's lamp was described in *The Applications of Physical Forces*, by Amédée Guillemin, translated by Mrs Norman Lockyer (London, 1877).

The name cathode ray was first used by Eugen Goldstein (1850–1930), though the phenomenon was first discovered by Julius Plücker (1801–1868), who worked with Geissler. Goldstein was using a small, evacuated discharge tube and very high voltage from an induction coil, and he described the glow from those particles emitted from the cathode (negative terminal) under a high electric field. The colours depend on the gases or vapour in the tube [xvii, facing p. 193]. Investigation of cathode rays was continued by Sir William Crookes (1832–1919). He examined them at various gas pressures, and then considered the effect of a magnetic field on the stream of negatively charged particles, or cathodes. He found that a bar magnet forms the beam of cathode rays into a spiral, while a horseshoe magnet produces a curve. The so-called Crookes' tubes are intended to show how the cathode stream is deflected by a magnet. A novel extension of Crookes' radiometer (see Chapter 7) was devised by another physicist who worked on secondary cathode rays, Johann Puluj. He devised an electric radiometer [16] that showed the mechanical effects produced by cathode rays, namely, that they will push round the vanes of a radiometer, and published his discovery in 1877. At the very end of the nineteenth century, work on cathode rays by the great Cambridge physicist, Joseph John Thomson (1856–1940) led to his discovery of the electron.

[17] Early Voltaic pile, composed of a total of 49 pairs of plates. The discovery was published by Alessandro Volta (1745–1827) in 1800. Baseboard 220 × 220 mm; overall height 250 mm. Early 19th century. *Teyler's Museum (575).*

[18] Early Voltaic cell. In Volta's original paper of 1800 two different techniques for producing a current are described. One was a pile of plates and the other was a *'couronne de tasses'*. Each cell had a copper and a zinc plate dipping into brine. Height to top of lid 150 mm.
Early 19th century. *Teyler's Museum (574).*

[19] Example of Crosse's water battery, which resembles a *'couronne de tasses'*. Zinc and copper strips dip into 48 glass cells containing water. The cells are insulated by paraffin wax in a porcelain dish. Dish 345 × 265 mm; diameter of cells 27 mm. Late 19th century. *Musée d'Histoire des Sciences (1199).*

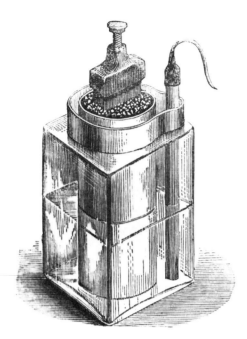

[20] A Leclanché cell, with a carbon cylinder in a porous pot that stands in a glass jar containing sal ammoniac. The positive pole is a rod of zinc. The Leclanché cell originated in 1867.
c. 1880. *Negretti & Zambra, p. 394.*

[21] Carbon arc lamp with clockwork regulator, signed: *J. Duboscq à Paris Brevete S.G.d.G.*. Also engraved: Nº 1. As the carbon is consumed, the rods are moved slowly by the clockwork to maintain a constant arc length, a technique invented by Léon Foucault (1819–68), in 1849. Overall height 830 mm.
c. 1850. *Teyler's Museum (620).*

[22] Bifilar torsion electrometer, signed: Saverio Gargiulo Napoli 1856. The museum records this as after Palmieri. Luigi Palmieri (1807–96) was director of the physical observatory, Naples, from 1854, and he invented a number of devices for meteorological use. In 1885 he published a book on the laws of atmospheric electricity. Overall height 510 mm; diameter of cell 165 mm.
1856. *Pavia University (2209).*

CURRENT ELECTRICITY

Electrostatics – the study of electricity produced by friction – had reached a dead end at the close of the eighteenth century. The phenomena had been fully examined, ever larger sparks had been produced, but the discovery that electricity could be produced in some other way was needed to rejuvenate the whole subject. The road that led to the production of current electricity – the most ubiquitous and accessible source of power in the modern world – began with the work of Luigi Galvani (1737–98), Professor of Anatomy at Bologna University. He was studying the effects of electrical discharge on animal muscle, when he observed that muscle contractions in the legs of frogs he was working with occurred even when there was no electrical discharge being applied. This led him to postulate his theory of 'animal electricity' which he believed was released within the organism when it came in contact with two different metals. The theory was further investigated by Alessandro Volta (1745–1827), who became sceptical of any animal basis in the electrical effect. He decided that it was the combination of two

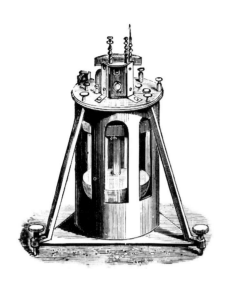

[23] Lord Kelvin's standard electrometer, catalogued at £36.
c. 1900. *Griffin*, p. 670.

distinct metals with moisture that produced electricity. In March, 1800, Volta wrote to Sir Joseph Banks, describing what later became known as the Voltaic pile [17], a combination of copper and zinc plates, with cloth moistened by salt water between them, which was the first electric battery. Then began the race to produce electric batteries that were increasingly compact, durable and safe. Many scientists all over Europe applied themselves to the problem, but the work of two men was particularly significant. The first was John Frederic Daniell (1790–1845), Professor of Chemistry at Kings College, London, who also devised a hygrometer (see Chapter 13). Daniell's battery consisted of a cylinder of zinc and copper, separated by a porous earthenware tube, with salt water, or diluted sulphuric acid, in contact with the zinc, and sulphate of copper in the other cell. This battery produced a steady, uniform current, and was found excellent for use in such processes as electro-plating, gilding and electrotyping.

Another highly efficient battery that also had the merit of cheapness, was devised by Georges Leclanché (1839–82). Its element was a cylinder of carbon inside a porous pot, closely surrounded by a mixture of ground-up manganese peroxide and coke, the top sealed with wax. This unit was then placed in a glass bottle, with a rod of zinc as the positive terminal, and the bottle half filled with a solution of sal ammoniac [20]. In 1841 Robert Bunsen (1811–99) had introduced carbon instead of the more expensive copper, as the negative pole, and Leclanché's cell, first produced in 1867, was a further improvement on the same lines.

The Carbon Arc

Humphry Davy (1778–1829) made important contributions to electro-chemistry, giving a series of Bakerian Lectures to the Royal Society on the subject, from 1806. He had enthusiastically entered the field opened up by Nicholson and Carlisle (see Chapter 12), and he published papers in Nicholson's *Journal* during the autumn of 1800. Davy invented the electric arc, and was able to demonstrate the carbon arc lamp at the Royal Institution in 1801, using a battery of 2000 plates. But for its further development and any practical applications, arc lighting had to await the development of powerful chemical batteries, such as that of Daniell, and of dynamo-electric machinery, particularly the Gramme machine of 1871 (see Chapter 10). The arc lamp is an important source of intense illumination, for use with projectors, in microscopy, in street lighting, and for lighthouses. But it is almost dangerously intense, being capable of damaging the eyesight, and cannot therefore be used domestically. The discovery that made the carbon arc capable of sustained use in street lighting and lighthouses was that of Jean Bernard Léon Foucault (1819–68) who found a method of increasing its durability by regulation [21]. His self-regulating arc lamp used clockwork to keep the two carbon electrodes at a constant distance apart, by moving their supports to keep pace with consumption. His lamp was first produced in 1849 (see also Chapter 9).

[24] Quadrant electrometer, with mirror, aluminium needle, hollow quadrants on insulating glass pillars and wire cage, offered for sale at £6.
c. 1900. *Griffin, p. 667.*

[25] A very sensitive quadrant electrometer, with quartz fibre suspension made conductive by a hygroscopic salt. A small mirror deflects a light beam onto a scale. The invention of the Hungarian, Friedrich Dolezalek (1873–1920). Offered for sale at £7. 10s.
c. 1905. *Griffin, p. 667.*

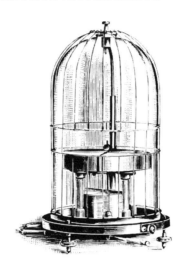

The Electrometer

The electrometer is the fundametal instrument for measuring potential difference (which is measured in volts), and depends on attraction or repulsion of charges on plates or wires. The measurement can be done by weighing, in which case the charge is recorded directly in terms of weight. Of the early electrometers, one of the most important was the torsion balance of Charles Augustin Coulomb (1736–1806). This was used in 1785 for experiments to determine the distribution of electric charge over conductors of different shapes, and in experiments to verify the law of inverse square of the distance. Faraday made improvements by providing protection from external influences. Accuracy was introduced into such measurements by William Thomson, Lord Kelvin (1824–1907) in 1853, by means of insulation, drying the air inside the instrument, and ensuring careful screening from external interference. This 'absolute' electrometer [23] was followed in 1857 by the 'divided ring' electrometer, of improved sensitivity, and the 'quadrant' electrometer [24 & 25] of 1867, which, at its most sensitive, could detect 0.01 volts and had a range of up to 400 volts.

The Galvanometer

This is a device for measuring electric current, and depends for its action on the current being run through a coil to make a magnetic field; this is based on Oersted's work on electromagnetism (see Chapter 10). The coil is wound onto a frame, and there is a divided circle, with a suspended needle. The current passes through the coil, making a magnetic field that deflects the needle. William Thomson, who did such important work on the mariner's compass (see Chapter 14), also devised a series of galvanometers. The first was his mirror galvanometer, planned for receiving signals through the Atlantic cable. The cable of 1858 had only three weeks of successful working, owing to defective insulation, and it was only by use of a mirror galvanometer on each side of the Atlantic that an exchange of messages was possible. Thomson also made an astatic version of the mirror galvanometer [27], the

[26] Galvanometer, signed: *J. Duboscq à Paris.* Also engraved: Nº 3. A current in the coils produces a magnetic field that deflects a needle suspended in a fine thread. Jules Duboscq was trading under his own name from 1849 to 1883. Overall height 240 mm; diameter of cell 118 mm.
c. 1860. *Teyler's Museum (1065).*

[27] William Thomson's astatic mirror galvanometer, signed: ELLIOTT BRO^S LONDON № 539. A silk fibre supports a short needle and a light concave mirror at the centre of a vertical coil. The mirror reflects a beam of light onto a scale. The curved, adjustable bar is a magnet to neutralize the Earth's magnetic field. Purchased in 1881 for Dfl. 146. Overall height 525 mm; barrel diameter 115 mm. 1881. *Teyler's Museum (645)*.

[28] Voltmeter and ammeter combined, signed: Ferdinand Ernecke BERLIN S.W. 46. The needle has an air brake and a safety catch. Base 190 × 88 mm; height 190 mm. *c. 1900. Teyler's Museum (1197)*.

[29] The signature plaque on the voltmeter in plate 28, which includes the name of the agent in Utrecht.

[30] Set of resistance coils, in a mahogany box with an ebonite top, of German manufacture. The plaque is engraved: *Neusilber regulirt* [sic] *bei 20 C.* Removal of a key brings in a resistance from 1 to 2000 Ohms.

Late 19th century. *Teyler's Museum (630)*.

first version being produced in 1857. In this, adjustable magnets formed an astatic system to neutralize the Earth's field.

For general purposes, there are a great many types of voltmeter and ammeter, depending on the range of voltage or current to be measured, and the level of sensitivity needed. For use in teaching, a piece of ancillary equipment is the ubiquitous resistance box, with which current can readily be varied in convenient steps.

12 · Chemistry

The causes of chemical change are as yet unknown, and the laws by which they are governed; but in their connexion with electrical and magnetic phenomena, there is a gleam of light pointing to a new dawn in science; and may we not hope that, in another century, chemistry having, as it were, passed under the dominion of the mathematical sciences, may find some happy genius . . . capable of unfolding its wonderful and mysterious forms.

Humphry Davy (1826)

Chemistry is the branch of science that is concerned with the composition of substances, whereas physics deals with the properties possessed by substances. The nineteenth-century physicist left the molecule alone, while the chemist broke up and re-arranged the molecules. For example, a physicist may heat a substance to measure the conductivity of heat, or to change a solid to liquid, but a chemist would heat it to change a metal into its oxide, a re-arrangement of, and an addition to the molecules. As George Fownes (1815–49) wrote in the Introduction to *A Manual of Elementary Chemistry, Theoretical and Practical* (1847):

> The Science of Chemistry has for its object the study of the nature and the properties of all the materials which enter into the composition or structure of the earth, the sea, and the air, . . . The highest efforts of Chemistry are constantly directed to the discovery of the general laws or rules which regulate the formation of chemical compounds, and determine the action of one substance upon another. These laws are deduced from careful observation and comparison of the properties and relations of vast numbers of individual substances; – and by this method alone. The science is entirely experimental, and all its conclusions the results of skilful and systematic experimental investigation.

A convenient, if not absolutely comprehensive, definition of organic chemistry is that it deals with hydrocarbons and derivatives. A vast number of compounds are made up of hydrogen and carbon, with one or more hydrogen atoms replaced by other atoms or groups of atoms.

Before the nineteenth century, there had been no clear demarcation between inorganic and organic compounds. Nicholas Lémery

(1645–1715) published in 1675 his *Course de Chymie*, where he classified substances as 'animal', 'vegetable' or 'mineral'. As would be expected, many of his allocations cannot stand today; nevertheless, his was an attempt at a more reasonable classification of the world's products. Even Lavoisier began with the Lémery classification, which was seriously questioned when the same compound was obtained from both vegetable and animal sources. So arose the division of organic chemistry, but it was still held that organic compounds could only be formed in the presence of a vital force, or life spirit. Thus it was thought to be impossible actually to synthesize in the laboratory an organic compound, a view that was given a death blow by the synthesis of urea in 1828 by Friedrich Wöhler (1800–82), who was then teaching at an industrial school in Berlin. It is also worthy of note that he was the first to isolate aluminium in 1827.

During the second half of the nineteenth century, the state of chemical knowledge was parlous, far behind that of physics. The classical, four-element theory – earth, air, fire, water – continued to persist because there was nothing to replace it; the calcination (prolonged heating) of metals, and the combustion of matter, were thought to be processes of decomposition, and the composition of both air and water was quite unknown. As for heat, the phlogiston theory held sway. Phlogiston (from the Greek, burn up) was the term given to an element, or substance, that was considered to exist in all combustible bodies, and was driven out by the process of combustion. The idea had been formulated by Georg Ernst Stahl (*c.* 1660–1743) in 1702, and it continued until 1775, when it was rejected by Antoine Lavoisier (1743–94). Joseph Priestley (1773–1804), on the other hand, lent his considerable reputation to support the phlogiston theory, though by 1800 it had been largely abandoned. The phlogiston theory was an attempt to explain experimental observations, and was, therefore, an advance. Like many theories it had to be discarded when more ingenious experiments were thought up, and more precise measurements made. According to the theory, hydrogen, which was called 'inflammable air', was loaded with phlogiston, because combustion was so rapid in its presence. Nitrogen, on the other hand, was called 'phlogisticated air', because it was not capable of supporting burning. 'Dephlogisticated air' was oxygen, and 'fixed air' was carbon dioxide. It must be remembered that the modern names were not in use, and the descriptive names were intended to convey what happened in certain experimental situations. It was Lavoisier who introduced the terms oxygen, nitrogen, and hydrogen in the 1780s. He also used the word gas (*gaz*) instead of the general term 'air', and the first use of gas in printed English was in 1779.

This French aristocrat, whose life was so tragically cut short by the guillotine during the Reign of Terror, revolutionized thinking in regard to chemistry. Lavoisier established the precision chemical balance as fundamental to chemical reasoning, following the first important quantitative experiments made by Joseph Black (1728–99), of Glasgow and Edinburgh Universities. From the beginning, Lavoisier had the idea that mass was conserved, which means that although chemicals can react to form new substances, the total weight remains constant. This principle of conservation has been tested in recent times to high orders of accuracy, far beyond the early balances. Clearly, seeking to test the theory provided an impetus to improve the balance, as well as to find other experimental techniques.

At the beginning of the nineteenth century an argument occurred between the two French chemists, Claude Louis Berthollet (1748–1822) and Joseph Louis Proust (1754–1826) about the proportions in which two elements would combine together to form a compound. Proust maintained that they always kept to the same proportions, and he maintained the law of constant composition. At this time, John Dalton (1766–1844), a Manchester teacher, explained his atomic theory published in 1808, where every element is made up of identical atoms, which are different from all other atoms. Moreover, the elements can be listed according to their relative weights.

Naturally, to test ideas of such far-reaching consequences, elements and compounds had to be made pure, probably in quite small quantities, so analytical techniques were developed, in addition to better balances. For analysis, the innovator was the great Swedish chemist, Jon Jacob Berzelius (1779–1848), who was to determine the atomic weights of nearly half the elements. For this work he analysed many thousands of compound substances.

Language is vital in conveying ideas; as a result of the work of Lavoisier, Berthollet, and Fourcroy, the reformed chemical terminology was published in 1787 as *Méthode de Nomenclature chimique*. Lavoisier continued his reformation with an introductory text for beginners: *Traité*

[1] Two copper distillation vessels. Distillation requires a heated vessel closed by a head in which the distillate condenses and runs out through a side tube. Both these stills have water-cooled heads, one exit spout for the cooling water, the other for the distillate. *Left*, of the type sometimes called a 'Moor's head', from the shape of the top; height 500 mm. *Right*, believed to have come from the laboratory of Antoine Baumé (1728–1804); height 500 mm. Late 18th century. *Museum of the History of Science* (78; 77).

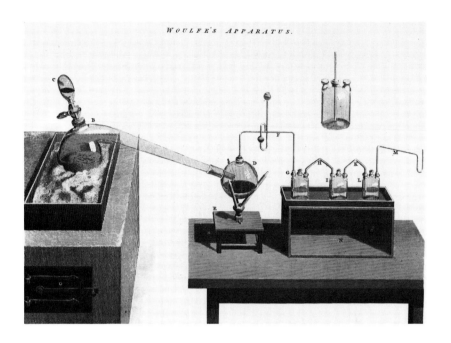

[2] Engraving from Abraham Rees, *The Cyclopaedia*, plates volume II (London, 1820), Chemistry plate VI. The engraving is dated 1 January 1803. The furnace heats a retort, set in a water bath, the distilled products passing through a receiver into a series of Woulfe's bottles. This form of bottle, with three tubulures, became a standard item in most chemical laboratories. It is named after the Irish chemist, Peter Woulfe (*c.* 1727–1803). 1803.

Elémentaire de Chimie (1789). It was in three parts, the first dealing with gases, oxidation, fermentation, putrefaction, the composition of air and water, acids, bases, and salts. The second part concerned the action of acids and salt-forming bases, and it included the first modern list of chemical elements. The third, and most considerable part of the book, discussed apparatus and the methods of chemical experimentation. This was a radical change over anything before, for little attention had previously been given to apparatus, since chemistry was done with pots and pans.

Some of Lavoisier's classic apparatus is preserved in the Conservatoire des Arts et Métiers, Paris, and that of his enthusiastic Dutch supporter, Martinus van Marum (1750–1837), is preserved in the Teyler's Museum, Haarlem. Van Marum was able to improve on the design of Lavoisier's apparatus, which he found difficult to acquire, and in any case expensive. He employed an expert mechanic, Frederic Fries, to make, during 1791 and 1792, the large, brass and glass apparatus for the combustion of hydrogen in oxygen to make water, which required a combustion chamber, a pair of gas-holders, and a pair of water cylinders. These were needed to maintain a constant, controlled rate of gas supply into the combustion chamber. Different chambers were made in which to burn phosphorous, oil, or carbon. What is remarkable here is the early employment of a laboratory technician to make apparatus, and chemical apparatus for one particular purpose only, to study and demonstrate the combustion process in relation to the phlogiston and subsequent theories. Normally, chemical apparatus is in units that are assembled in different arrangements to suit a particular experiment. It is this sort of apparatus, produced in some quantity, that may still be found, although much glassware and pottery will have been broken. Also, glassware is difficult to date, and, as shapes for certain uses continue for a long time, a relatively modern piece may be taken as older than it really is.

[3] Small, tin, portable still for determining the alcoholic content of wine, signed: *Alambic de Descroizilles l'Ingr Chevallier, Optician du Roi Place du Pont Neuf No. 15 Paris*. Jean Gabriel Augustin Chevallier had a shop from 1796 at the corner of Pont Neuf and Quai de l'Horloge. François Antoine Henri Descroizilles (1751–1825) was a dispensing chemist of Rouen. His still for wine analysis was produced by 1810. Overall length 460 mm; diameter 100 mm.
c. 1810. *Musée d'Histoire des Sciences (18)*.

[4] Dr Nooth's apparatus, designed for impregnating water with 'fixed air', i.e. carbon dioxide, to prepare medicinal waters. It resembles the Kipp's apparatus used in chemistry since the mid-nineteenth century. Invented *c.* 1780 by John Mervin Nooth (1737–1828).
c. 1800. *Science Museum (1927–1198)*.

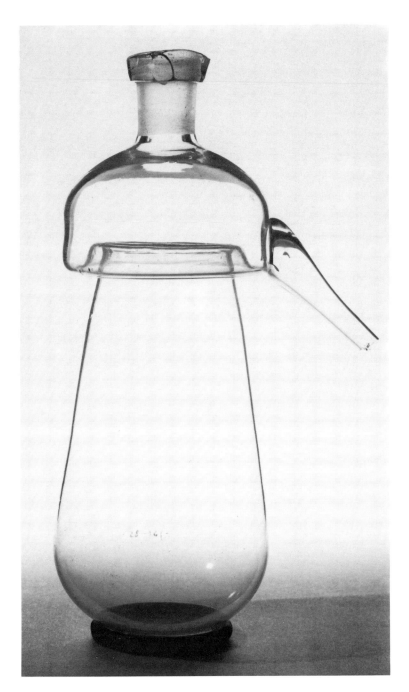
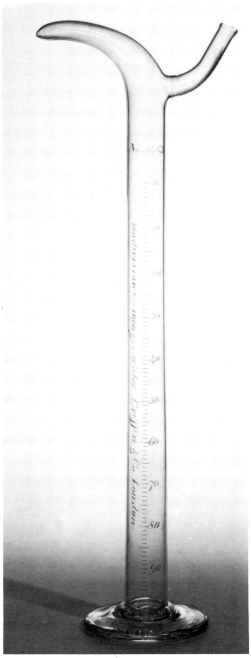

[5] Glass alembic, a term which properly implies the whole apparatus, but is sometimes used for the head only. This remained virtually unchanged for nearly 2000 years. The distillate condenses in the head and runs into the internal gutter and out through the side tube.
Early 19th century. *Science Museum (1951–356)*.

[6] A Bink's burette, signed: *Griffin & Co. London. No. 5463*. Used in volumetric analysis, a burette is a calibrated glass tube to deliver variable amounts of solution. A pipette delivers a fixed amount.
c. 1850. *Science Museum (1914–651)*.

An idea of the normal range of chemical apparatus used in the first quarter of the nineteenth century is given by an inventory made out for a new professor of chemistry at Oxford University. Charles Daubeny (1795–1867) was appointed in 1822, having studied at Edinburgh University. He was a passionate believer in the educational value of chemistry, and gave a lecture with the title 'On the Importance of the Study of Chemistry as a branch of Education for all Classes'. He was also a founder of the British Society for the Advancement of Science, in 1831. The apparatus that he inherited in 1822 consisted of the following, which have been roughly grouped into categories (omitting chemical substances) for convenience in listing.

1. Many dozen glass jars and bottles;
2. 15 dozen glass retorts, earthenware retorts, and retort stands;
3. Some 100 crucibles, evaporating dishes, pestles and mortars;
4. 3 dozen glass mattrasses (glass vessel with oval body and long neck, for distilling) and 3 dozen eudiometers (used in gas analysis);
5. Apparatus for decomposing water, a copper and tin gasometer;
6. Apparatus for the decomposition of animal and vegetable substances costing £40;
7. Woulfe bottles, Nooth's apparatus, 117 pounds of mercury;
8. 3 cast iron furnaces, 1 black lead furnace, blow-pipes;
9. 8 Argand lamps, 6 spirit lamps, 1 burning glass;
10. 2 precision balances (one costing £20), scales, weighing machines;
11. 3 air-pumps, and several receivers;
12. A plate, and a cylinder, frictional electric machines;
13. Electrometers, electrophorous, Faraday's magnetic apparatus, galvanic battery;
14. Barometer, hygrometers, thermometers, Bréguet's metallic thermometer;
15. A microscope.

[7] Group of chemical glassware, earthenware and porcelain retorts (top shelf) from the Chemical Laboratory of the University of Oxford, acquired for the use of Charles Daubeny (1795–1867), Professor of Chemistry from 1822. This apparatus was used for fractional distillation, one of the basic chemical processes from antiquity.
Mid-19th century. *Museum of the History of Science.*

[8] Davy's apparatus for the estimation of the carbonate content of soil. The equipment consists of a flask fitted with a dropping funnel, a delivery tube connecting the flask with a bladder, a vessel to hold water, with a spout, and a small beaker. A known weight of soil was treated with acid in the flask, the carbon dioxide given off inflated the bladder which displaced water into the beaker, from which it was measured. The volume of gas was thus known, and the carbonate in the soil could be calculated. From 1803 to 1813 Humphry Davy gave lectures to the Board of Agriculture, and described the use of such an apparatus. Overall height of flask 250 mm; height of displacement vessel 140 mm; height of beaker 85 mm. Early 19th century.
Museum of the History of Science (154).

The presence of electrical instruments and the air-pump shows that there was artificiality in identifying 'boundaries' between chemistry and physics, then as now.

At the beginning of the nineteenth century, instruction in chemistry was provided by private tutors, like Richard Kirwan (1733–1812), who taught in London and later in Dublin. Humphry Davy (1778–1829) lectured on chemistry at the Royal Institution in London (founded 1799), but this was not a systematic course suitable for training young men. The founder of systematic instruction was Justus von Liebig (1803–73), who was appointed in 1824 to the professorship of chemistry at the University of Giessen. He stressed qualitative and quantitative analysis, rigour in preparation of substances, and original research, the latter being a novelty in university teaching of science. Liebig had a huge success throughout Europe, and he has become known as the 'chemist breeder'. In England systematic teaching was founded at the College of Chemistry in 1845, which continues, with changes in name, to the present day as the Imperial College of Science and Technology. From mid-century, therefore, universities, and then schools, had to take notice of the educational and technical reasons for teaching chemistry, with the consequent requirement for very large quantities of apparatus.

If Liebig actualized a chemical school, he was not the first to propose it. This was done in 1820 by Thomas Thomson (1773–1852), a professor at Glasgow University, who wished to train young practical chemists. As he said: 'As an art, it is intimately connected with all our manufactures. The glass blower, the potter, the smith, and every other worker in metals, the tanner, the soap-maker, the dyer, the

[9] The billhead of Fredrick Accum, whose laboratory and shop was in Old Compton Street, Soho, London. This bill is dated, in ink: March 16th 1805. A number of items sold are shown, including a voltaic pile, retort, spark eudiometer, balance, spirit blowpipe, and Woulfe's bottles. 1805. *Museum of the History of Science* (*392*).

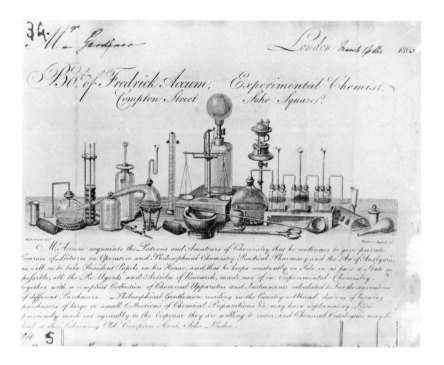

bleacher, are really practical chemists; and the most essential improvements have been introduced into all these arts by the progress which chemistry has made as a science.' Slowly, the chemist entered into manufacturing industry, to control quality and to devise novelties. In 1840 the numbers of 'manufacturing chemists' was a little over 1000; thirty years later, it had reached 14,000. Clearly, a great deal of analytical apparatus was being used.

The feeling that chemistry had come of age in Britain was a reason for the birth of the Chemical Society of London in 1841. Its objective was 'the advancement of chemistry and those branches of science immediately connected with it.' There were to be meetings, publications, a library and a museum. This formalized specialization within science was important in establishing the chemist and the profession of chemist in industry and in society. A leading figure both in the teaching of chemistry, and in its application to industrial processes and to public health, was Fredrick Christian Accum (1769–1828), who was born in Hanover, but moved to London in 1793. He set up premises in Old Compton Street, London, in 1800, where he gave lectures and demonstrations, and also sold chemical apparatus [9]. For a period he was in commercial partnership with Alexander Garden, and he supplied apparatus to such eminent chemists as John Dalton and John Gorham of Harvard University, Massachusetts. Two of the most influential of Accum's many publications were a *Practical Treatise on Gaslight* (1815) [XVIII, facing p. 240], and a *Treatise on the Adulterations of Food and Culinary Poisons* (1820). The latter helped to arouse public concern over the food supply of the nation. In 1850 a microscopical examination of ground coffee by Dr Arthur Hassall established for the first time

[10] Slide rule for chemical equivalents, signed: *W. Cary, 182, Strand, Jan. 1. 1814.* The printed table on the rule is that devised by William Hyde Wollaston (1766–1828). With oxygen as standard, at 10 on the scale, he calculated the combining proportions of various substances and listed them on the logarithmic scale from 10 to 320. William Cary (1759–1825) was a pupil of Jesse Ramsden. Dimensions 306 × 65 × 10 mm. 1814. *Museum of the History of Science (292).*

a satisfactory means of detecting adulteration. His research received wide publicity, and he was commissioned by *The Lancet* to extend his work to other foods. For the next four years the reports of *The Lancet* Analytical Sanitary Commission were regularly published, giving names and addresses of hundreds of manufacturers and tradesmen selling adulterated products. These revelations led to the setting up of a parliamentary committee, and, in 1860, to the Adulteration of Food and Drink Act, the first of a number of Acts to ensure the quality and purity of food in Britain.

The 1875 Food and Drugs Act required public analysts to be appointed throughout the country, to provide a systematic means of testing samples. By the end of the century, the firm of A. Gallenkamp & Co. of London, established as scientific equipment suppliers in 1880, was putting out a catalogue entitled: *Apparatus for the Equipment of Public Analytical Laboratories; For the Analysis of Milk, Water, Food, Gas, Sewage etc.* During the same period, a series of Public Health Acts made local authorities responsible for dealing with proper sewage disposal, the provision of a pure water supply, the inspection of manufacturing premises, including slaughter houses and dairies, and many other matters. All these measures, essential in a country with a rapidly increasing urban population, greatly extended the practical applications of chemistry. The chemist was needed, in increasing numbers, in government and industrial laboratories.

CHEMICAL APPARATUS AND INSTRUMENTS

Although some chemical apparatus and instruments were in use long before the nineteenth century, and continued to be used during that century, much that was new was developed in the period. A stimulus was the rapid progress in chemical theory, which became more systematic, and more numerical [10]. The reasons for this lie partly in the conceptual advances made by Lavoisier, John Dalton, and others, and partly in instrumental advances, particularly in the chemical balance, that became a precision instrument (see Chapter 3). This new, precision tool extended the limits of experimental corroboration of theory. As Humphry Davy wrote, in *Elements of Chemical Philosophy* (1812):

> Nothing tends so much to the advancement of knowledge as the application of a new instrument. The native intellectual powers of man in different times are not so much the causes of the different success of their labours as the peculiar nature of the means and artificial resources in their possession.

The new industries, such as gas-lighting, and railways, required chemists to control and develop products, and so employed men who worked in laboratories. The growth of specialist chemical apparatus manufacture was thereby created, with a gradual end to reliance on the individual craftsman. Early manufacturers were Accum, Knight,

[11] First page of a catalogue published by J. J. Griffin & Co. in 1850. The wood engraving shows a typical mid-century chemistry bench.
1850. *Science Museum (photograph 1101/72).*

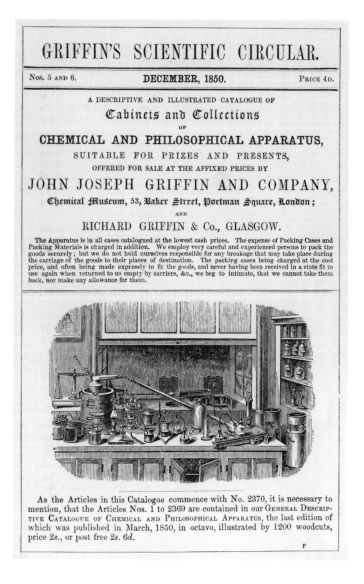

GRIFFIN'S SCIENTIFIC CIRCULAR.

Nos. 5 AND 6.　　　DECEMBER, 1850.　　　PRICE 4D.

A DESCRIPTIVE AND ILLUSTRATED CATALOGUE OF

Cabinets and Collections

OF

CHEMICAL AND PHILOSOPHICAL APPARATUS,

SUITABLE FOR PRIZES AND PRESENTS,

OFFERED FOR SALE AT THE AFFIXED PRICES BY

JOHN JOSEPH GRIFFIN AND COMPANY,

Chemical Museum, 53, Baker Street, Portman Square, London;

AND

RICHARD GRIFFIN & Co., GLASGOW.

The Apparatus is in all cases catalogued at the lowest cash prices. The expense of Packing Cases and Packing Materials is charged in addition. We employ very careful and experienced persons to pack the goods securely; but we do not hold ourselves responsible for any breakage that may take place during the carriage of the goods to their places of destination. The packing cases being charged at the cost price, and often being made expressly to fit the goods, and never having been received in a state fit to use again when returned to us empty by carriers, &c., we beg to intimate, that we cannot take them back, nor make any allowance for them.

As the Articles in this Catalogue commence with No. 2370, it is necessary to mention, that the Articles Nos. 1 to 2369 are contained in our GENERAL DESCRIPTIVE CATALOGUE OF CHEMICAL AND PHILOSOPHICAL APPARATUS, the last edition of which was published in March, 1850, in octavo, illustrated by 1200 woodcuts, price 2s., or post free 2s. 6d.

F

Button and Griffin [11]. Quantity production led to cheaper apparatus and increased trade. There was now the opportunity for innovation by the manufacturer who could make special apparatus for special needs.

The Great Exhibition of 1851 contained few entries under 'Chemical Apparatus', and about half of these were to do with electric batteries. Balances were in a different part of the exhibition. Praise was given to German glass-ware for its lightness and durability. A cabinet of analytical laboratory apparatus that was awarded a Prize Medal was shown by Knight & Sons of London. It comprised: 'graduated cylinders, jars, blow-pipes, an improved bellows, pneumatic troughs, chemical tests; lamps, retorts and other glass articles; apparati from iron and earthenware, arranging furnaces, mortars etc., being a complete set of articles in daily use by the practical chemist.'

[12] *Left*: a charcoal furnace made of refractory fireclay (height 160 mm, diameter 150 mm), and bound with iron straps, signed: MORGAN ENGLAND. *Right*: a crucible of fireclay, with a lid (height 330 mm, diameter 130 mm). Mid-19th century. *Museum of the History of Science (1; 235).*

[13] Six Bunsen burners. *Left to right*: brass tube adjustable for angle, cast-iron base embossed: TOWNSON & MERCER LONDON (11); copper tube, with metal gauge on top, cast-iron base, embossed: CAMBRIDGE INSTRUMENT CO. (9); brass rose-head to spread flame, cast-iron base (12); brass triangular flame-spreader, cast-iron base, embossed: BAIRD & TATLOCK (10); triangular, adjustable support at top, and air control tap; cast-iron base embossed: PAUL HAACK AUSTRIA (13); iron tube and cast-iron base; air intake by collar operated by a lever (7). The Bunsen burner was designed for heating, and so used a gas/air mixture. It was first made in 1855. Height 140–180 mm. Late 19th century or early 20th century. *Museum of the History of Science.*

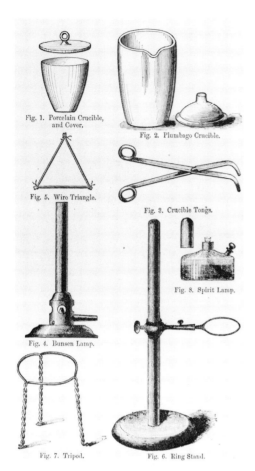

Fig. 1. Porcelain Crucible, and Cover.

Fig. 2. Plumbago Crucible.

Fig. 5. Wire Triangle.

Fig. 3. Crucible Tongs.

Fig. 8. Spirit Lamp.

Fig. 4. Bunsen Lamp.

Fig. 7. Tripod.

Fig. 6. Ring Stand.

[14] Illustration in C. R. Alder Wright, *The Threshold of Science* p. 5, which shows a Bunsen burner and associated apparatus. 1892.

Furnaces, Blowlamps and Burners

The new style of chemist needed a source of heat that was easy to manipulate, that was portable, and would heat up quickly. The fixed furnace, like the kitchen range, was superseded by the small, black lead and iron furnaces, that were portable. Another useful portable heat source was the Argand lamp (see Chapter 7), the invention of Aimé Argand (1750–1803). His lamp, which burnt paraffin, was patented in 1784. Later, gas burners were used, the most famous being the Bunsen burner [13 & 14], invented in 1855 by Robert Wilhelm Bunsen (1811–99). An important eighteenth-century innovation in the provision of heat was the intense, controllable source provided by a mouth blowpipe [15]. This became most important in mineral analysis, and

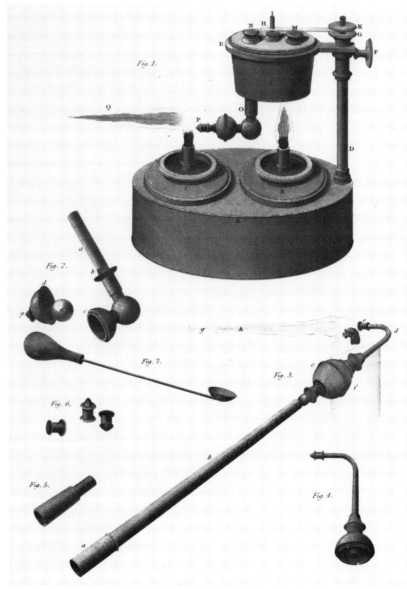

[15] Engraving from Abraham Rees, *The Cyclopaedia*, plates volume II (London, 1820), Chemistry plate XI. The engraving is dated 1811. A spirit lamp blowpipe above, and a mouth blowpipe below, of the Cronstedt pattern. The blowpipe came into use during the late 18th century to give an intense, controlled source of heat for mineral analysis. 1811.

[16] Blowpipe analysis kit, signed: MANUFACTURED BY J. T. LETCHER TRURO Cornwall. The kit, in a mahogany box, comprises a blowpipe, agate pestle and mortar, cobalt glass, magnet, steel anvil, spirit lamp, tallow candle, charcoal pastilles, platinum sheet and wire, porcelain block, wooden phials, and glass bottles with reagents. The London Society of Arts awarded a silver medal for such a kit. Box 270 × 120 × 80 mm.
Late 19th century. *Museum of the History of Science (16)*.

later in the study of chemical constitution generally. The blowpipe presented two problems; the desirability of finding a substitute for the human operator, and moisture condensing inside the tube. In the nineteenth century bellows were often used to operate laboratory blowpipes, and higher heat was achieved by employing oxygen, or a mixture of oxygen and hydrogen. The firm of J. Newman made a number of oxy-hydrogen blowpipes, including the well-known model devised by Goldsworthy Gurney, a chemical lecturer, who received a gold medal from the Society of Arts for his invention of 1823. However, in addition to these large and complex blowpipes, the small, simple version continued to be popular as the nucleus of portable kits for geologists and others [16 & 17].

Crystallography; the Goniometer

Up to now, we have been concerned with a more traditional conduct of chemical operations. During the nineteenth century there came into use pieces of apparatus and techniques borrowed from the physicist, who in some ways was more advanced in his subject than the chemist when the century opened, a time when there was scarcely any common ground between these two branches of science. It may be said that the chemical atomic theory of Dalton, propounded in the first years of the century, marks the watershed between qualitative and quantitative studies, where the physicist could join in through his interest in the internal structure of matter. Dalton had observed numerical regularities in the combining weights of elements, and others were to observe regularities in combining volumes. Crystallographers realized that crystals might look different, but that those of the same substance always had faces

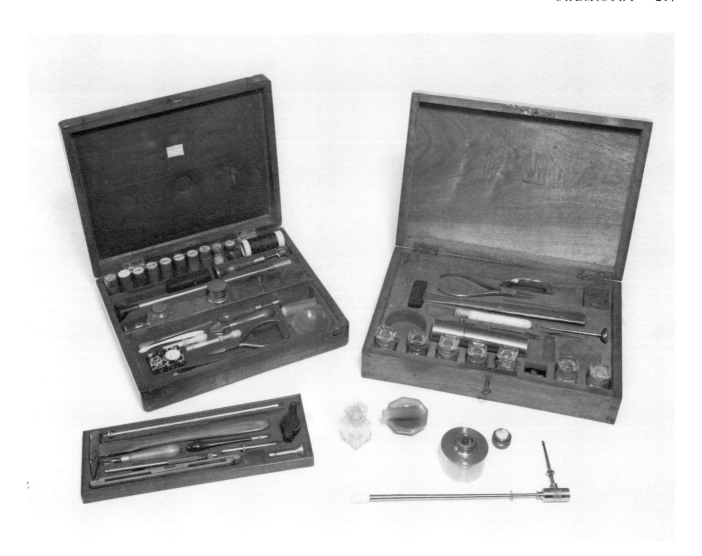

[17] Mineralogical prospector's kits, that on the left signed: C. Osterland Mechaniker in Friedborg Sachsen. That on the right is unsigned, but is of German manufacture for the French market. Mid-19th century. *Science Museum* (1973–287, 1964–504).

[18] Group of beechwood crystal models, made in Paris under the direction of René Juste Haüy (1743–1822) for Martinus van Marum (1750–1837) of Haarlem. Three in the top row show Haüy's ideas of how a crystal may be built up of a series of units, *molécule intégrante*.
1802–4. *Teyler's Museum* (nn).

[19] Two crystal goniometers, signed
left: *I. Newman 122 Regent Street
LONDON*; *right*: W. & [S.] Jones London.
The contact goniometer (*right*, radius
43 mm) is the pattern used by Haüy. The
full-circle goniometer (*left*, radius 50 mm)
is W. H. Wollaston's design of 1809. John
Newman (fl. 1816–1838) started at 7–8
Lisle Street, and moved to 122 Regent
Street in 1827.
c. 1830. *Museum of the History of Science
(64–219; 39–9).*

that kept exactly the same interfacial angles. The great French crystal-lographer, René Just Haüy (1743–1822), even proposed that the external appearance of the crystal's facets was a reflection of the internal structure, a series of building blocks which he called *molécules intégrantes* [18].

The goniometer measures the interfacial angles of crystals. The contact goniometer [19], used at the turn of the century by Haüy, consists of a small precision semi-circle, with adjustable arms to fit the angle between faces of a crystal. This was satisfactory for larger crystals, but the improvement of the instrument made by William Hyde Wollaston (1766–1828) extended the work to very small crystals. It consisted of a full circle [19], on the axis of which the crystal could be mounted; the interfacial angle was measured by a beam of light reflected off the faces.

Structure Models

Haüy's idea that crystal morphology is a reflection of crystal structure proved to be fundamentally correct, and led towards what is called stereo-chemistry, the study of structure in three dimensions. It is convenient, and instructive, to illustrate the arrangement of the atoms in a molecule by means of a spoke and ball model, a practice that continues in schools and colleges to this day. The first of such models to be produced were the 'glyptic formulae' kits [20 & XIX, facing p. 241], described originally in the first volume of the periodical, *The Laboratory*, published in 1867.

The Spectroscope

One of the most powerful analytical techniques invented in the nineteenth century was spectroscopy. It arose by accident from work on

[20] The explanatory chart attached to the box containing the molecular model kit, shown in plate xix, facing p. 241.

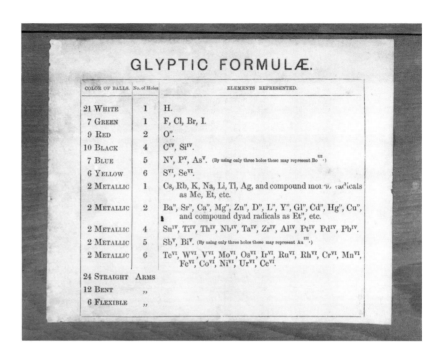

GLYPTIC FORMULÆ.

COLOR OF BALLS	No. of Holes	ELEMENTS REPRESENTED.
21 White	1	H.
7 Green	1	F, Cl, Br, I.
9 Red	2	O''.
10 Black	4	C^{IV}, Si^{IV}.
7 Blue	5	N^V, P^V, As^V. (By using only three holes these may represent Bo^{III}.)
6 Yellow	6	S^{VI}, Se^{VI}.
2 Metallic	1	Cs, Rb, K, Na, Li, Tl, Ag, and compound mon-ve radicals as Me, Et, etc.
2 Metallic	2	Ba'', Sr'', Ca'', Mg'', Zn'', D'', L'', Y'', Gl'', Cd'', Hg'', Cu'', and compound dyad radicals as Et'', etc.
2 Metallic	4	Sn^{IV}, Ti^{IV}, Th^{IV}, Nb^{IV}, Ta^{IV}, Zr^{IV}, Al^{IV}, Pt^{IV}, Pd^{IV}, Pb^{IV}.
2 Metallic	5	Sb^V, Bi^V. (By using only three holes these may represent Au^{III}.)
2 Metallic	6	Te^{VI}, W^{VI}, V^{VI}, Mo^{VI}, Os^{VI}, Ir^{VI}, Ru^{VI}, Rh^{VI}, Cr^{VI}, Mn^{VI}, Fe^{VI}, Co^{VI}, Ni^{VI}, Ur^{VI}, Ce^{VI}.
24 Straight	Arms	
12 Bent	,,	
6 Flexible	,,	

the dispersion of glass by Joseph von Fraunhofer (1787–1826), who, in 1814, noticed that the Sun's spectrum, as dispersed by a glass prism, was crossed by hundreds of fine dark lines. In 1826 William Henry Fox Talbot made the suggestion that the spectral light from burning a substance might be an aid to chemical analysis, but it was many years before the idea was developed. Although William Allen Miller (1817–70) published in 1845 a paper on spectrum analysis, he did not convince sceptical chemists of the practical usefulness of the spectroscope. This was fully proved by Gustav Robert Kirchhoff (1824–87) and Bunsen working at Heidelberg. Bunsen wrote in November 1859 to his former pupil, Henry Enfield Roscoe (1833–1915), now professor of chemistry at Manchester: 'Kirchhoff has made a most beautiful and unexpected discovery: he has found out the cause of the dark lines in the solar spectrum.' He went on to say that now the composition of the Sun and the stars could be determined, as well as all manner of chemical substances in the laboratory. This was because the atomic or molecular structure of a substance caused it, when heated, to emit light radiation in bands of colour strictly characteristic of that substance alone [xx, facing p. 241].

Roscoe was an enthusiastic supporter of the Kirchhoff-Bunsen technique in Britain, and he introduced a wide audience to the value of line spectra for chemical analysis, by lectures, by translating Bunsen and Kirchhoff's classic work, and by his own *Spectrum Analysis* (1869). The result of this was a demand for prism spectroscopes, and attempts were made to make them more sensitive by adding more and more prisms, even up to ten. The firm of John Browning, already in optical instruments, became well known for its spectroscopes (see Chapter 9).

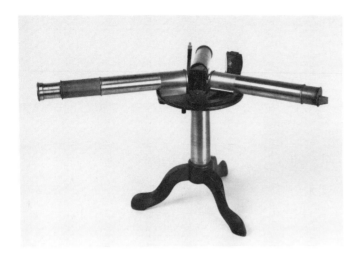

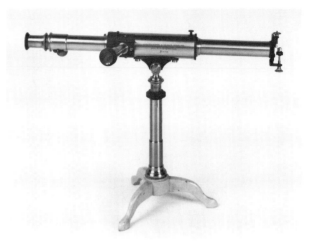

[21] Typical spectroscope, unsigned, probably French. The collimator on the right passes the light via a slit to the prism, which disperses the light and this is observed by the telescope on the left. The middle collimator projects a scale into the field of view, the illuminator being a gas flame (the burner is just visible). A second prism can be introduced at will for greater dispersion. Height 250 mm; length of telescope 230 mm.
c. 1870. *Teyler's Museum (391).*

[22] Direct vision spectroscope, signed: SPECTROSCOPE A VISION DIRECTE par J. G. Hofmann Paris. The side tube allows the spectrum from the Sun to be compared with the light from a sample. The dark Fraunhofer lines in the Sun's spectrum provide a wave-length standard to identify the emission lines in the spectrum from the sample. Overall height 340 mm; overall length 475 mm.
c. 1870. *Teyler's Museum (393).*

They were made for the chemist, the physicist, the astronomer, and for attachment to the microscope; and in addition to all these larger models, there were pocket-sized direct-vision spectroscopes [22].

The spectroscope is the oldest optical method of chemical analysis, and it has been argued that it has aided pure science perhaps more than any other instrument. It must be borne in mind that the theory behind the workings of an instrument does not have to be understood. The atomic origin of line spectra was not known, but once the pattern of lines revealed by the spectroscope was seen to be a 'fingerprint' of an element or compound, then the way lay open to analyse mixtures very simply.

During the course of his experiments, Kirchhoff had analysed a sample of the mineral water from the Durkheim springs. Among the familiar lines were two new blue ones. Using the facilities of a nearby factory, Kirchhoff was able to reduce 12,000 gallons of water to produce for him seven grammes of a new element, which he called Caesium, meaning 'sky-blue', the name being descriptive of the colour of the spectral line. He found yet another new element during the same process, for he collected ten grammes of Rubidium, so named because the spectral lines were dark red. These discoveries were made in 1860, and Kirchhoff thus increased the number of known elements to 59.

A mathematical formula that connected the frequencies of the lines in the spectrum of hydrogen was put forward in 1885 by the Swiss mathematician, Johann Jakob Balmer (1825–98), but the mechanism of light emission by hydrogen was still not understood. The real physical significance was discovered in 1913 through the theoretical explanation, involving quantum jumps in the structure of the atom, given by the Danish physicist, Niels Hendrik Bohr (1885–1962).

The Polarimeter

A similar example of an instrument being used for analysis, in advance of the theoretical understanding of the way it worked, is the polarimeter. This is an instrument that uses polarized light, which is passed

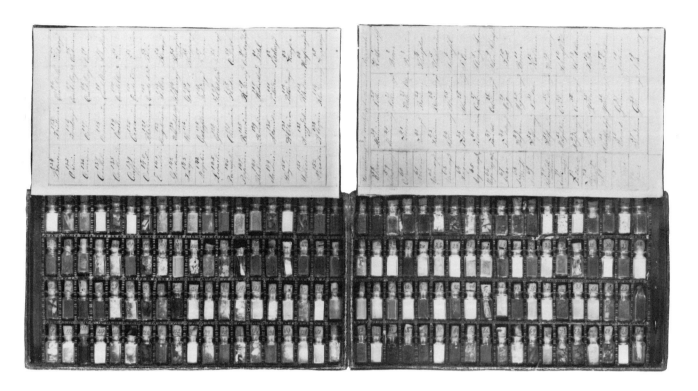

[23] Folding case of glass bottles
containing samples of the elements and
compounds. The key is handwritten in
German. Closed 220 × 120 × 30 mm.
Late 19th century. *Museum Boerhaave*
(S268).

[24] Saccharimeter, signed: Hermann &
Phister, Bern. A descriptive pamphlet with
the instrument is titled: *Anleitung zum*
Gebrauch des Wild'schen Polaristrobometer
(Saccharimeter, Diabetometer) in seiner
neusten, verbesserten Form (Bern, 1868). A
saccharimeter is a polarimeter adapted for
use with white light, and it measures the
optical activity of sugar solutions.
c. 1868. Teyler's Museum (428).

through a glass tube containing a liquid. Certain oils, sugar solutions, and so on, have the power of rotating the plane of polarization, and the number of degrees of rotation is a measure of the 'optical activity'. That polarization was a general property of light was discovered in Paris in 1808 (see Chapter 9) and one man in particular was attracted to the new possibilities for research. This was Jean Baptiste Biot (1774–1862), and he at first believed that only solid crystals could rotate the plane of polarization. In 1815, however, he found that a long tube containing turpentine acted like the solids, and thereby revealed that the property was inherent in the molecules, and not merely in the ordered arrangement found in a crystal.

Biot designed the first polarimeter, which incorporated a tube of standard length to contain solutions of known strength. In 1816, and again in 1833, Biot worked on sugars, and was able to show that cane sugar and beet sugar have the same optical activity and are therefore identical. This led to the invention of the *saccharimeter* [24], which is a special type of polarimeter adapted for use with white light rather than with the yellow, monochromatic sodium flame. The saccharimeter became widely used in breweries, to control processes and quality, and in the food industry generally. The modern physical explanation of rotatory polarization by molecules comes from the work of a number of physicists during the second decade of the twentieth century.

The Refractometer

This is an instrument devised for measuring the refractive index of transparent materials, in particular, glass [25]. Originally used in optics, it was adapted for use with liquids by Carl Pulfrich (1858–1927), who, in 1890, went to work with Ernst Abbe at the Carl Zeiss works in Jena, becoming head of the optical measuring instrument department. He designed an adaptation of Abbe's refractometer for the use of chemists in 1895. The Pulfrich refractometer measured the critical angle at the surface between a liquid and a glass prism whose refractive index was known. Pulfrich also adapted the instrument for use with butter fat, and other fats and oils, since its application to food testing quickly became apparent. The same principle was also used in his work on rare gases by John William Strutt (1842–1919), later Lord Rayleigh, who discovered argon, a rare gas, with William Ramsay, in 1894.

The Colorimeter

Crude colorimetric determinations were first made during the 1830s. This technique relies on the colour of a sample solution being compared with a standard solution of known composition. A. Jacquelain (1804–85) devised, in 1845, a method for the determination of copper, based on comparison of the colour of copper-ammonia salts. In 1853 A. Müller (1828–1906) described his 'Complementär Colorimeter', which had only a single container and adjustable tube. A second container and tube for the standard solution were added in 1863 by F.

[25] Refractometer for testing the purity of butter by its refractive index. Water at a constant temperature can be passed through the specimen chamber assembly. This is an Abbe refractometer adapted for a special purpose. *c.* 1890.

Dehm, and this arrangement was further improved by the French optician Jules Duboscq (1817–86) in 1870. His instrument became the most widely used colour comparitor, or colorimeter [26].

The Osmometer

During his investigations into the diffusion of soluble substances during the 1850s, Thomas Graham (1805–69) distinguished two sorts of substances: those, which he called crystalloids, that diffused into solution very quickly, such as salt and sugar; and colloids, such as gelatine and albumen, that diffused slowly. He discovered that if diffusion takes place through a membrane, like thin parchment, the crystalloids still diffuse quickly, but the colloids hardly at all. This study developed a method of separating solutions, called dialysis, that has become very important in medicine. Graham went on to study various types of animal and vegetable semi-permeable membranes that provide a barrier to colloids. The name given to the phenomenon of passage through a membrane is osmosis, and the osmometer [27] was devised to make measurements of the process.

[26] Colorimeter, signed: J. DUBOSCQ P. PELLIN PARIS. Also inscribed: colorimetre. In this, an improved model, the specimen holders move and the glass plungers are fixed. The light is reflected upwards by the mirror, passes through two containers holding the sample and the standard solutions, through two glass plungers, through prisms to the eyepiece. The solutions are moved relative to the plungers until the colour densities of both solutions are the same. Jules Duboscq (1817–86) was joined in 1883 by Philippe Pellin, who continued the firm alone after 1886. Base 176 × 178 mm; overall height 540 mm.
c. 1885. Private collection.

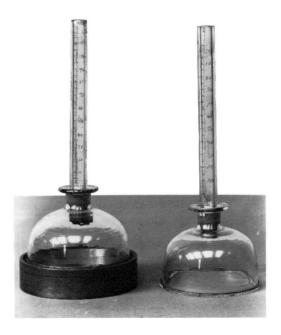

[27] Pair of osmometers used in 1854 by Thomas Graham (1805–69) for studying osmotic pressure. Osmosis is the passage of liquids through semi-permeable membranes, such as a pig's bladder. This was fixed across the base of the 'bell', with a salt solution inside the vessel. The whole is then placed in water so that the liquid levels inside and out are the same. The water gradually passes through the membrane and the column inside the calibrated tube rises. 1854. *Science Museum (1894–188e).*

[28] Group of chemical apparatus. *Left to right, front row*: porcelain pneumatic trough (length 170 mm) with gas-collecting cylinder to 17 cu. in. (height 171 mm) (*90*); a gas bottle with S-tube connects with it (*144*); a test glass, or precipitating glass (height 132 mm), conical, with lip, the forerunner of the test-tube (*187*); a test-tube (length 100 mm) in a walnut rack (base 170 × 53 mm; height 76 mm) (*197*); a retort in green glass, with a brass stop-cock (overall length 265 mm), the tap signed: KNIGHT FOSTER LANE (*138*). *Back row*: Hope's eudiometer (height 340 mm) (*114*); a spark eudiometer (height 293 mm) (*120*); a voltameter (overall height 160 mm) used for the electrolysis of water into hydrogen and oxygen (*398*).
Early 19th century. *Museum of the History of Science*.

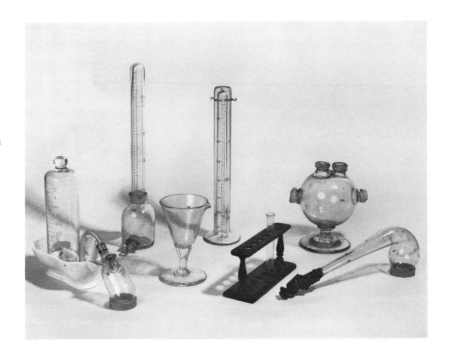

The Eudiometer

The purpose of this instrument is to measure the purity of air, that is, its oxygen content, information that was particularly significant for studies in respiration. There are certain substances that absorb oxygen without absorbing nitrogen, and these were used in eudiometry experiments. The method devised by Alessandro Volta (1745–1827), at the end of the eighteenth century, was to use hydrogen to absorb the oxygen in the air sample by means of an electric discharge. His so-called *spark eudiometer* [28] was described in two letters to Joseph Priestley in 1777 and 1778. Humphry Davy devised in 1830 a spark eudiometer on a spring-loaded support, that acted as a shock absorber when the gases were exploded. Bunsen, who worked on the combustion reactions of gases in the 1850s, also designed a spark eudiometer with platinum wires bent inside, close to the roof of the tube.

The eudiometer, devised by Thomas Charles Hope (1766–1844) and published by William Nicholson in his *Journal of Natural Philosophy, Chemistry and the Arts*, used a solution to absorb the oxygen [28], and was intended for analysing atmospheric air at lecture-demonstrations. It used an alkali sulphide solution to absorb the oxygen. This was contained in a bottle, into the neck of which the tube with the air sample was inserted. When the bottle was placed under water and its side stopper removed, the level of the water rising into the graduated tube showed how much oxygen had been absorbed.

The Voltameter

Electrolysis of water is the process by which water decomposes into oxygen and hydrogen when an electric current is passed through it.

In 1789 two Dutch chemists used static electricity for experiments on the electrolysis and synthesis of water. In 1800 William Nicholson (1753–1815) and Anthony Carlisle (1768–1840) observed that a bead of water on their voltaic pile, or battery, was producing bubbles, and the gas was later proved to be hydrogen and oxygen. Michael Faraday (1791–1867) found a practical measuring function for electrolysis by discovering, in 1834, that he could measure the power of his battery by the quantity of water that was decomposed in a unit time. He called the apparatus a Volta-electrometer [28], which was soon afterwards abbreviated to voltameter. This should not be confused with a volt-meter, which measures the tension of an electric current.

13 · Meteorology

An Instrument I contriv'd to shew all the minute variations in the pressure of the Air; by which I constantly find, that before, and during the time of rainy weather, the pressure of the Air is less, and in dry weather, but especially when an Eastern Wind blows, it is much more, though these changes are varied according to very odd Laws.

Robert Hooke, *Micrographia* (1665)

From earliest times, man as agriculturalist and navigator has observed and attempted to forecast the weather. The scientific study of changes in the atmosphere began in the mid-seventeenth century, arising from experiments to do with the existence of a vacuum, which was denied by the classical philosophers ('nature abhors a vacuum'). If a long tube is filled with water and inverted into a bucket containing water, then the column of water will fall until its weight is balanced by the pressure of air on the surface of the water in the bucket. There will then be a vacuum at the upper, closed end of the tube. With water, the height that the atmosphere can support is of the order of 30 feet (9.15 m). Using the heaviest liquid possible, the liquid metal mercury, the atmosphere will support a column of 30 inches (762 mm) only, because of the much greater density of the liquid. Therefore mercury proved to be the most convenient liquid for use in the barometer, the instrument devised to measure the weight or pressure of the atmosphere (the word is derived from the Greek word for weight).

The first man who made an instrument to show changes in the pressure of air was Evangelista Torricelli (1608–47), who was a Florentine pupil of Galileo. He described his experiments with a tube containing mercury in three letters written in June 1644. The variations in the height of a column of mercury can be shown and measured, and will record changes in atmospheric pressure. In fine, dry weather, the pressure will be high, and the column will be around the maximum height of 31 inches (787 mm); when it is rainy or stormy, and the pressure is low, the height of the column will fall below 29 inches (735 mm).

A demonstration apparatus to show the effects of heat was the thermoscope, devised by Galileo, which consisted of a column of water in a spiral glass tube that rose as air in a bulbous reservoir expanded when warmed. The thermometer is a descendant of Galileo's thermoscope, and is used to measure temperature. The problems in making a thermometer were to find a substance which would respond uniformly to changes in temperature, to produce a tube of uniform cross-section, and to devise a suitable scale for measurement. Daniel Fahrenheit of Amsterdam, working in the early years of the eighteenth century, was the first man to produce a thermometer of any accuracy. The mercury and the alcohol thermometers are used for meteorological (or medical) purposes. For the scientific study of heat, which requires the measurement of extremes of heat and cold, other devices are needed.

By the mid-eighteenth century, instruments had, therefore, been invented to measure the pressure of the atmosphere (the barometer) and its temperature (the thermometer). A third important quality, humidity, could also be demonstrated by a method usually attributed to Robert Hooke, and used in an instrument called the hygrometer. The beard of the wild oat was found to be highly responsive to dampness in the atmosphere; it forms a tight spiral when dry, but uncurls in response to humidity in the air. On barometers made post-1760, a hygrometer using this material, or occasionally catgut, is frequently found. From the end of the seventeenth century these meteorological instruments proved of particular importance to astronomers. The atmosphere acts like a great prism, bending the light received at the observatory from the heavenly bodies. Astronomical measurements required adjustment according to the pressure, temperature and humidity of the atmosphere. As it became possible for astronomers to make their measurements to increasingly finer standards of accuracy with the improvement of their mathematical instruments, they required a comparable accuracy in meteorological instruments.

It is thought that the oldest of all meteorological instruments is the rain gauge. Although of very ancient origin, it was not apparently used in Europe until an isolated experiment was recorded in Italy in 1639. Basically very simple, a container left in the open so that, after rain, the depth of water can be measured, its measuring capacity was refined in the seventeenth century. A wide funnel was used to lead the rain water into a narrow vessel, making it easier to record small quantities.

The most familiar of all meteorological instruments is the wind vane. A famous classical example was that fixed to the Tower of the Winds in Athens in about 50 BC. At the end of the sixteenth century in Italy, gearing was attached to a wind vane to turn a dial fitted conveniently in the interior of the building. Such a device became popular, and can be seen in many aristocratic houses, among them Blenheim Palace in Oxfordshire. The speed, as well as the direction, of the wind is of interest; the earliest anemometer is again attributed to Robert Hooke, and consisted of a swinging plate, rather like a shop sign, the level of swing being recorded in degrees on a quadrant mounted behind it.

Instruments were also made to record the length of time in which the Sun shines, and the level of heat it produces. J. F. Campbell devised in 1853 a sunshine recorder [1] which focused the Sun's rays through a glass globe filled with water, so that the burning point made a trace on a hemisphere of wood. This was later improved both by Campbell and Sir George Stokes (1819–1903) by using a solid sphere of glass, and a strip of paper to record the burning trace. To measure the Sun's heat on a given area, an instrument called a pyrheliometer was invented, which recorded the degrees of heat imparted to a quantity of mercury over a fixed period of time.

Apparatus also exists for testing the electrical state of the atmosphere; some is sufficiently sensitive to show the diurnal variations in atmospheric electrical charge. To record the amount of ozone (O_3 an isotope of oxygen, O_2) in the atmosphere, chemically impregnated paper was used; laboratory equipment also existed to produce ozone for experiments [2]. The barograph [3] and thermograph are automatic recording instruments, designed to provide a constant record of atmospheric changes, often by an ink trace on paper, moved by clockwork.

The scientific study of the weather inevitably remained limited until man, and hence instruments, became airborne, a process which began with the invention of the air balloon in 1783. A notable pioneer of meteorology was James Glaisher (1809–1903), who, as superintendent of the magnetic and meteorological department of Greenwich Observatory, organized observations in Britain for a quarter of a century. In 1862 he made a series of scientific balloon ascents which attracted much publicity. Throughout the nineteenth century, and until 1914, a range of specialist instruments was designed to make atmospheric observations, first from manned balloons, and, later, in kites and unmanned balloons. These latter made systematic recording much easier. After 1940, meteorographs, as they were called, were abandoned in favour of the radiosonde which transmits weather information by radio from a balloon.

[1] Sunshine recorder, signed: PILLISCHER 88 NEW BOND St LONDON. This form of instrument was devised in 1853 by J. F. Campbell, and modified by George Stokes in 1880 to take a strip of paper which records the burnt trace made by focusing the Sun by means of the glass sphere. By 1885 the latitude adjustment was fitted. The base is of black marble (267 × 268 × 38 mm); the axis of the glass sphere (diameter 102 mm) can be set for latitudes between 0° and 70°. c. 1890. *Private collection.*

[2] Ozone generator, signed: TISLEY'S OZONE GENERATOR TISLEY & SPILLER 172 BROMPTON ROAD LONDON. Ozone was first discovered by Martinus van Marum in 1785; it was named in 1840 by C. F. Schonbein. Ozone is a very powerful oxidizing agent, and its presence was considered important for health. Experiments were made to identify it in air, and this piece of apparatus was to produce the gas for laboratory use. There are two glass tubes one inside the other coated with tinfoil outside and in; a sort of Leyden jar. An electric discharge between the foils will ionize the oxygen in the air when passed through the tubes. Base 305 × 88 mm; diameter of glass tube 28.5 mm.

c. 1868. *Teyler's Museum (600)*.

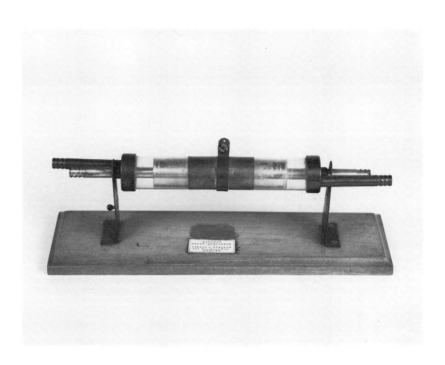

[3] Barograph for continuously recording barometric pressure by a pen on a cylindrical chart that is turned by clockwork. The movement of the aneroid barometer is amplified by a lever with a recording pen at its end. Signed: *Maison de l'Ing*ʳ *Chevallier Opt*ⁿ, *Avizard F*ʳᵉˢ *Suc*ʳˢ, *21 rue Royale, Paris* No. 237. Also inscribed: Baromètre holosterique. Overall dimensions 180 × 310 × 170 mm.

c. 1900. *Musée d'Histoire des Sciences (1057)*.

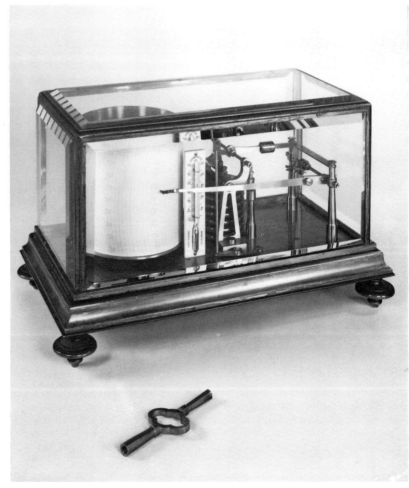

[4] Stick, or pediment, barometer, signed: *W. Cary, London*. The barometer tube is straight, and ends in a cistern. This form is the earliest design of barometer, which continues in the Fortin type. The case is of mahogany. Overall length 960 mm.
c. 1840. Museum of the History of Science.

THE BAROMETER

What made the barometer so popular for domestic use was the discovery in the seventeenth century of the connexion between alterations in air pressure and changes in the weather. The simplest form of barometer is a glass tube, under 3 feet (900 mm) in length, sealed at the upper end; the sealed end of the tube contains a vacuum, below which is a column of mercury, and the open end of the tube stands in a cistern of mercury. A variation is to have a bent or siphon tube, with the shorter section open. The pressure of air on the surface of the mercury in the cistern, or the open end of the siphon tube, is recorded by the rise and fall of the mercury at the top of the tube. Another development was to have the tube bent at an angle of around 80°, so that the movement of the mercury was magnified, and therefore easier to measure.

The most common type of barometer in the eighteenth century was the stick [4], in which the tube is held in a long, narrow mahogany case, often with an ornamental top. Others of this period have the bent tube, some with a mirror set within the angle, in a picture-frame mount. The wheel barometer was invented in the 1660s, and consisted of a siphon tube with a float on the mercury, and a pulley and weight system, to record the rise and fall of the mercury on a circular dial. The feature of this type is that the tube is invisible, while the dial is very prominent, an arrangement which became very popular in the early nineteenth century, when the so-called banjo barometers [5] could be found in many homes. Barometers were often associated with thermometers and hygrometers, and many also incorporated a vernier scale, for greater accuracy of measurement; another association was with clocks.

In the first half of the nineteenth century, an extensive trade in banjo barometers was conducted from London by Italians, who retailed them in hundreds of British towns. These decorative, domestic pieces are commonly made with mahogany veneered cases that hide the mercury tube, but give great prominence to the large circular scale plate. Below this is usually a small bubble level, and above a thermometer; at the very top can be a simple hygrometer. They bear the name of an Italian tradesman linked with the English place name where they were sold. One of the most famous of such Italian firms, one that is still in existence, is Negretti & Zambra, who were Opticians and Meteorological Instrument Makers to Queen Victoria, and to many State boards and observatories. This firm was responsible for the publication in 1868 of the important manual, *A Treatise on Meteorological Instruments, Explanatory of their Scientific Principles, Method of Construction and Practical Utility*. Enrico Negretti came to England in 1830, aged 12, and was later apprenticed to an instrument maker. By 1843 he was trading from Holborn, and in 1850 he took as partner J. W. Zambra. In the Great Exhibition of 1851 the firm took the only Prize Medal for meteorological instruments as a group.

Late Victorian and Edwardian barometers can be closely similar to

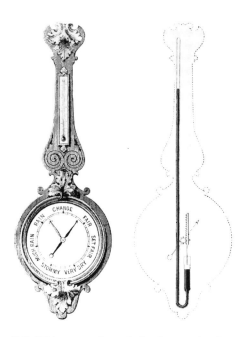

[5] This engraving of a banjo, or wheel, barometer shows at one side the form of the siphon tube and the float whose movements are indicated by the dial. Although described by Hooke in 1665, the siphon tube was scarcely used until the early nineteenth century in the banjo form of case. This form continued well into the twentieth century, and some that look the same may have an aneroid mechanism instead of a mercury tube. This type was made in extremely large numbers. *c.* 1870. *Deschanel, p. 155.*

earlier ones, but there are also elaborate Gothic models supplied to fit in with the styles of architecture in fashion. Being domestic 'weather glasses' they had to match the furniture of libraries and halls. At the time, the banjo pattern was called a 'dial barometer', and the stick a 'pediment barometer'. Of the latter type, two important varieties were produced from the 1860s onwards by Negretti & Zambra for non-domestic use. The 'Fitzroy Storm Barometer', or 'Fisherman's and Life Boat Station Barometer' was made for the Board of Trade and for the Royal Lifeboat Institution. The mercury was in a wide-bore tube, mounted in oak, and the register plate with scale and markings was of porcelain. Admiral Fitzroy (1805–65) had been responsible for setting up a storm warning system, when he was head of the Meteorological Office of the Board of Trade. Incidentally, Robert Fitzroy was also commander of HMS *Beagle* which carried Charles Darwin as naturalist.

This 'Sea Coast Barometer' is associated with Admiral Fitzroy's name, but it is not the same as the mass-produced 'Admiral Fitzroy's Barometer' (XXI, facing p. 256) that was made from the 1870s until the outbreak of World War II. This barometer consists of a wooden frame bearing a printed sheet at the back with the scale and weather lore. The simplest syphon tube holds the mercury, a thermometer is fitted, and there is also a 'storm-glass'. This odd device is a glass tube filled with a solution of camphor, potassium nitrate and ammonium chloride in alcohol and distilled water. It is supposed to show changes

[6] Three ornate banjo barometers, also called 'dial' barometers. The left and centre models were made in rosewood inlaid with pearl or metal, with dials of silvered brass. The centre one, with eight-day clock, cost £25. The right-hand model was offered in carved oak, mahogany, or walnut, at five, six or eight guineas. *c.* 1880. *Negretti & Zambra, p. 115.*

[7] Sympiesometer signed: *Patent Adie & Son, Edin^r.* No. 1463. R. Adie, *Liverpool.* The temperature scale is in centigrade and the barometer scale in millimetres, so this particular instrument will have been made for export. This type of instrument is, in effect, a much improved version of Hooke's air barometer, which is for use at sea. The thermometer allows an adjustment to be made for the effect of heat on the air or gas in the bulb. Adie & Son traded in Edinburgh from 1835 to 1880, and Richard Adie was in business in Liverpool from 1835 to 1875. Mahogany case 570 × 40 × 30 mm.
c. 1835. *Musée d'Histoire des Sciences* (*860).*

in the solubility of the crystals, and their rise and fall in the tube, according to the weather conditions: crystals at the bottom – frost in winter; rising crystals – wind; clear liquid – bright weather; dim liquid – rain. The use of this attachment is more amusing than practical.

The other practical instrument was the 'Farmer's Barometer', an ordinary stick-type, but with wet and dry bulb thermometers attached. The difference in reading between the two gives the humidity of the air, which helps to differentiate between wind and rain, both of which reduce the height of the mercury.

Making the stick barometer suitable for use at sea necessitated finding a means of preventing the mercury bursting its tube. This can be done by putting in the middle of the length of glass a constriction to prevent violent oscillations of the liquid. An instrument of this type was made by Edward Nairne (1726–1806) and taken on a Polar expedition in 1773 by Captain Phipps. When used on board ship the barometer is held by gimbals and a wall bracket. The first International Meteorological Congress was held in Brussels in 1853 to work out a way of improving observations at sea. The recommendations were passed on by the British government to the Kew Committee of the British Association for the Advancement of Science which worked at the Kew Observatory. In 1855 the Kew marine barometer was brought out. It used metal to protect the glass tube, which was considerably constricted. Traps to prevent air getting past the mercury were devised and the register plate bore no wording, as this was thought to be misleading. A vernier allowed readings to 5/100th of an inch. Improvements were made by Admiral Fitzroy, who became Meteorological Officer to the Board of Trade in 1854; in particular, he caused the glass tube to be packed with vulcanized rubber to check vibration caused by gun fire. The Kew marine barometer and the Fitzroy marine gun barometer used by the British Navy, were both made by Negretti & Zambra, and in 1880 they cost £4 4s. and £5 10s. respectively. Marine barometers continued to be made in decorated wooden frames for use on private yachts. All these types were replaced early in the twentieth century by the aneroid, but examples reproduced for collectors and interior decorators have been made in 1979 and 1980.

Also for use at sea, Robert Hooke devised, and described to the Royal Society in 1668, an instrument which had air instead of a vacuum in a bulb above the mercury in a syphon tube. An associated, sealed spirit thermometer measured the ambient temperature, and so an allowance could be made for the effects of temperature on the air in the bulb. The sailor chiefly wanted advance warning of storms, not absolute measure, so this instrument, which prevented the mercury from oscillating, did what was required. A much-improved version was patented in 1818 by the Edinburgh instrument maker, Alexander Adie, and he called it a *sympiesometer* [7], derived from the Greek word for compression.

The sympiesometer has a short column of mercury as an indicator, and in place of the normal vacuum, there is a bulb of gas, so that the

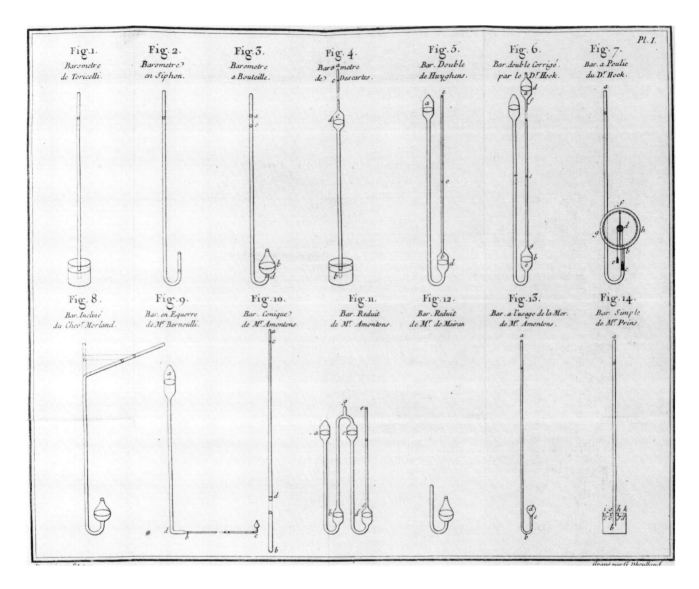

Pl. 1.

Fig. 1. *Barometre de Toricelli.*
Fig. 2. *Barometre en Siphon.*
Fig. 3. *Barometre a Bouteille.*
Fig. 4. *Barometre de Descartes.*
Fig. 5. *Bar. Double de Huyghens.*
Fig. 6. *Bar. double Corrigé par le D.r Hook.*
Fig. 7. *Bar. a Poulie du D.r Hook.*

Fig. 8. *Bar. Incliné du Chev.r Morland.*
Fig. 9. *Bar. en Equerre de M.r Bernoulli.*
Fig. 10. *Bar. Conique de M.r Amontons.*
Fig. 11. *Bar. Reduit de M.r Amontons.*
Fig. 12. *Bar. Reduit de M.r de Mairan.*
Fig. 13. *Bar. a l'usage de la Mer. de M.r Amontons.*
Fig. 14. *Bar. Simple de M.r Prins.*

Gravé par G. Dheulland.

[8] From J. A. de Luc, *Recherches sur les modifications de l'Atmosphère* (Geneva, 1772), plate 1. This plate was drawn by De Luc, and represents all the types of barometer that existed in the mid-eighteenth century, before the appearance of his own portable barometer.

pressure of the atmosphere acts against the mercury plus the resistance of the confined gas. A thermometer is used to correct the reading for changes in the volume of the gas, brought about by temperature. Adie made several thousand of these instruments in the 1820s and 1830s, and they were also produced by some London makers, though they faded out of favour by the 1880s. They are small, no longer than 2 feet (600 mm), and there are pocket versions that are much shorter. The aneroid barometer quickly superseded the mercury instrument for all travel purposes, and then more gradually for domestic use.

The *mountain barometer* is intended to measure the elevation above a known base level. It was essential that it should be portable, so its construction presented similar problems to those met in devising a sea barometer. One idea for trapping the mercury was the insertion of a tap near the open end of the tube, proposed by Jean André de Luc (1727–1817), a Swiss who published in 1772, in Geneva, his *Recherches sur les modifications de l'atmosphère* [8]. Later de Luc became tutor to the royal household at Windsor. By the turn of the century, suitably modified, syphon-tube barometers were being made, provided with a collapsable tripod stand, with a leather case into which the entire apparatus could be stowed. A mountain barometer has to have a long scale running from 32 inches (810 mm) down to 14 inches (350 mm). At the highest point of the Alps, the pressure would be 17 inches (430 mm). Balloonists also needed a barometer for use as an altimeter, in which case the scale reads down to about 5 inches (125 mm), the pressure at about 9 miles (14.5 km) above the earth's surface.

The *standard barometer* for scientific use in the nineteenth century is that devised by Jean Nicolas Fortin (1750–1831), the foremost precision instrument maker of Paris [9]. In about 1800 he made the barometer easier to transport and more accurate, by so arranging the reservoir at the bottom that it had a glass portion through which could be seen the level of mercury and an ivory pointer [10]. The tip of the pointer was exactly the zero point of the inch, or millimetre scale at the top of the instrument. Any variations in temperature could be compensated for by adjusting the level in the reservoir so that it exactly touched the ivory pointer. The adjustment was made through flexible leather holding the mercury, and it was possible to close off the bottom of the barometer tube when transporting it. The glass viewing portion at the bottom makes the Fortin-type barometer easy to identify. By using a vernier, readings on the scale can be taken to 0.002 inch, or to 0.1 mm.

Extra large standard barometers were made for observatory use, and some scientific barometers have wide-bore tubes and no scale. The

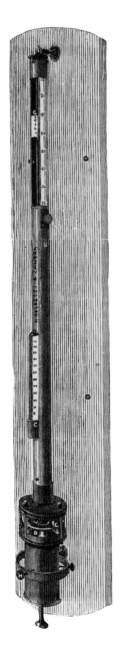

[9] Engraving of a Fortin standard barometer, named after Jean Fortin's design of 1800.
c. 1880. *Negretti & Zambra, p. 4.*

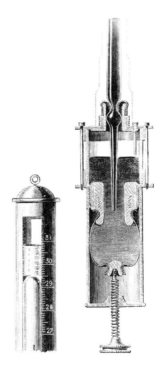

[10] The top and bottom of a Fortin barometer. The glass barometer tube, containing boiled mercury to remove air, is enclosed and protected by a brass tube, the upper part having two long openings on opposite sides. On one side is the barometric scale in English inches, on the other is usually a millimetre scale. The reservoir of the cistern is of glass closed at the bottom by a leather bag which can be squeezed by means of a thumb-screw (see cross-section). This is necessary to adjust the level of the mercury in the cistern to the tip of an ivory pointer, which is the zero mark for the barometric scale.
c. 1870. *Deschanel, p. 147.*

[11] Engraving showing, *left to right*: Board of Trade Standard, or Kew Marine, barometer with bronze frame and iron cistern; mountain barometer, Newman's type; Negretti & Zambra's mountain barometer on brass tripod stand (the instrument is a Fortin barometer); standard siphon tube mountain barometer fitted with Gay Lussac's air trap for portability. Negretti & Zambra's prices were: 4 guineas; £4.10s.; 10 guineas; 8 guineas, respectively. *c.* 1880. *Negretti & Zambra, p. 10.*

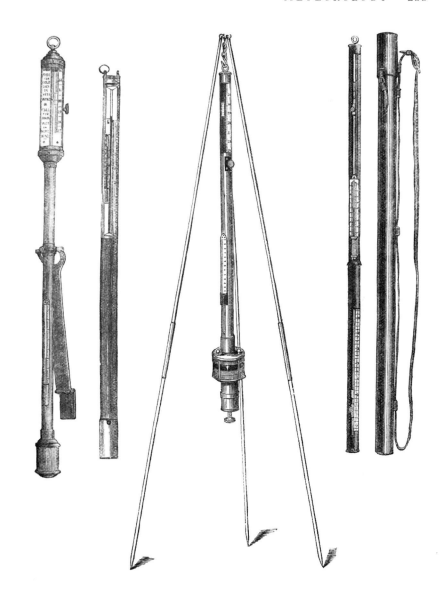

difference in levels is read using a cathetometer, which is a telescope mounted on a vertical stand and capable of being moved over a precision-cut linear scale.

In their catalogue for 1880, Negretti & Zambra published estimates for supplying instruments for the three classes of observing station recognized by the Second International Meteorological Congress at Vienna of 1873. The first class was for scientific observatories, requiring all features to be measured, including electrical phenomena. The cost would lie between £330 and £450. The second class cost merely £22 to £25, and it was 'strongly recommended to *private observers*, where complete and regular observations are taken of Barometric Pressure, Temperature, Humidity, Rain, Wind, and Electrical phenomena'. The kit comprised: a standard barometer, a maximum thermometer, a minimum thermometer, a solar radiation thermometer in vacuo and another with exposed bulb, a terrestrial radiation thermometer, a rain

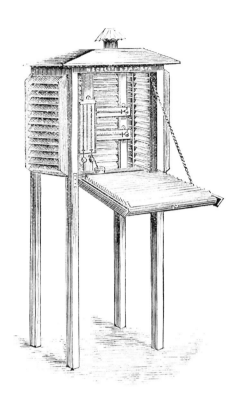

[12] Engraving of a Stevenson's thermometer screen, with louvres to allow free air circulation, but to stop radiant heat and rain. First devised by Thomas Stevenson (1818–87) in 1864, it continues in use today. *c.* 1880. *Negretti & Zambra, p.* 68.

gauge, an anemometer, a wet and dry bulb hygrometer, and a Stevenson's screen to house certain thermometers. The Stevenson screen is still seen today, a miniature house, with louvered walls, painted white, standing four feet above the ground and twenty feet from any obstruction [12]. It was invented in 1864 by the Scottish engineer and meteorologist, Thomas Stevenson (1818–87).

A very simple *weather glass* is in the form of a pear-shaped, closed glass vessel with a long spout rising from the bottom. When the vessel is half filled with water, changes in atmospheric pressure will cause the water level in the spout to rise for a storm (low pressure), or to fall for fine weather (high pressure). As water is about twelve times more sensitive than mercury to changes in pressure, the approach of a storm is very quickly seen by the level in the spout.

The origins of this weather glass are obscure, and it has been thought they were made in the seventeenth century. They were certainly made during the nineteenth, and can often be seen in Holland, where they are called 'Donderglas', or thunder glass. It is also claimed that glass blowers of Liège produced these cottage weather indicators, and the name 'Baromètre liègeois [XXII, facing p. 256] has been given to them. These are decorated with strips of crimped glass, but plain vessels were sold in London and elsewhere. An example illustrated here is signed on the back by etching into the glass: F. DAVIDSON & C⁰. 29 GRᵀ. PORTLAND Sᵀ. and it most probably dates from between 1890 and 1910. When unsigned, these vessels are impossible to date.

The Aneroid Barometer

Great inventions seem simple with hindsight, and one such is the aneroid barometer (from a Greek word meaning 'not wet'). The mechanism consists of a metal bellows, with most, but not all, of the air withdrawn, and then sealed up. This package is very sensitive to changes in pressure, and with a mechanical linkage such changes can be indicated by a rotating pointer. Although the idea of a semi-evacuated chamber came to Nicolas Conté in 1799, the invention of a complete, workable, and practical device is that of Lucien Vidie (1805–66), who patented it in his native France in 1845, and in Britain on 9 November 1850 [13]. He had had the instrument tried out in England in 1844, when it was taken to the dome of St Paul's Cathedral, and in 1848 when it was tried out on train journeys. It passed all tests, including, of course, comparisons with a mercury barometer. Nevertheless, it is not an absolute measure of atmospheric pressure, and has to be calibrated and checked against a mercury instrument. Vidie showed his new invention at the Great Exhibition of 1851, where 'this beautiful instrument' was rewarded by a Council Medal, the highest award.

Unfortunately for Vidie, he had a rival, the French engineer and inventor Eugène Bourdon (1808–84), who produced in 1849 a metallic manometer for measuring pressures on steam engines, capable of going up to 500 lb per square inch (the atmosphere exerts a pressure of 15 lb

[13] Vidie type of aneroid barometer, signed: F.W. FUNCKLER Haarlem Baromètre Anéroid 8985. The air pressure acts on a brass capsule that is partly evacuated, and its movements are transmitted to a pointer. It was purchased in 1860 for Dfl.32. Diameter 160 mm; depth 55 mm.
1860. *Teyler's Museum (755/2).*

[14] Bourdon type of aneroid barometer, signed: F.W. FUNCKLER BAROMÈTRE MÉTALLIQUE. Also inscribed: MÉDAILLE D'OR EXPOSITION 1849 PARIS EXPOSITION UNIVERSELLE LONDRES 1851 GRANDE MÉDAILLE DE 1r CLASSE. Such instruments, of French manufacture, were still produced early in the twentieth century. Based on Bourdon's pressure gauge, variations on a curved, evacuated tube cause it to flex, and so to move the pointer. It was purchased in 1860 for Dfl.54. Diameter 170 mm; depth 65 mm.
1860. *Teyler's Museum (754).*

per square inch at sea level). Vidie felt obliged to sue for patent infringement, and eventually he won his case and received damages. Bourdon also exhibited in London in 1851, and he, too, received a Council Medal. The Reports by the Juries to the Exhibition have a good description of the construction of this type of aneroid barometer [14], which is as follows:

> Bourdon's barometers consist of an elastic flattened tube of metal, exhausted completely of air, and bent very nearly in the form of a circle; they are in this state possessed of the property of expanding, a further separation of the ends being effected when the atmospheric pressure is diminished, a contrary or contracting effect taking place when the pressure increases. A lever is attached to the end of the tube by suitable mechanism, and connected to an index or hand, which traverses a divided dial-plate.
>
> The dial-plate is graduated by placing the instrument with a standard barometer within the receiver of an air-pump, and the points of coincidence determined by varying the pressure.

The Bourdon type [14] did not sell well outside France, but there it continued to be offered by instrument makers alongside the more popular Vidie type even as late as 1901.

Admiral Fitzroy thought the aneroid barometer a 'great boon' to the navigator, as it could be put anywhere and was unaffected by the ship's motion. James Glaisher took one up in a balloon on 5 September 1862, when he reached seven miles above the Earth. Altitude aneroids

have a scale of heights outside the inches of mercury scale. The zero point is fixed at the 31 inch mark, and the scale runs to 20,000 feet. Sometimes the altitude scale rotates so that the zero is set to the position of the pointer, to give a rough estimate of the height travelled, but this is not as accurate because the scales are not quite compatible throughout the length unless the zero is opposite 31 in.

An aneroid can be made five inches in diameter, or pocket sized at $2\frac{3}{4}$ inches [15], and there is an even smaller model the size of a watch similar to a hunter, and cased in gold, silver, or base metal. Travellers' sets in red morocco leather cases comprise a watch-size aneroid, a compass, and a small thermometer on an ivory base. Such sets were sold over many years up to World War II.

The Thermometer

A thermometer is a device that is used to measure the temperature of a substance. It can take very different forms and is dealt with more fully in Chapter 7. Here the thermometer used to measure the ambient air temperature will receive attention. The range covered is not great, from around 60°C (140°F) down to about −45°C (−50°F). When measuring the upper air in a balloon, lower temperatures may be recorded, around −70°C.

The liquid thermometer is a descendant of Galileo's thermoscope which was an air-filled glass bulb and a thin tube containing water – an air thermometer, in fact, had it been fitted with a scale. The two main problems encountered in making thermometers were: to find a substance that was most responsive to changes in temperature, and to

[15] Pocket aneroid altitude barometer with a thermometer and a magnetic compass, signed: C.W. DIXEY. Optician to the Queen, 3, New Bond Street, LONDON. The altitude scale is 0 to 20,000 feet, the pressure scale 15 to 31 inches, and the temperature scale 14° to 136° F. Leather-covered case, lined with purple velvet and white silk. Brass casing diameter 51 mm.
c. 1860. *Museum of the History of Science* (*75-1/9*).

[16] Group of eight thermometers for special purposes. *Left to right:* horticultural hot-bed thermometer; the same; brewer's for use in the mash tun; chemical, graduated to 300° F; chemical, graduated to 600° F; chemical, to insert into the tubulure of retorts; alongside, its protective glass case for corrosive liquids; brewer's malt kiln thermometer, in oak and brass casing. *c.* 1880. *Negretti & Zambra, p. 136.*

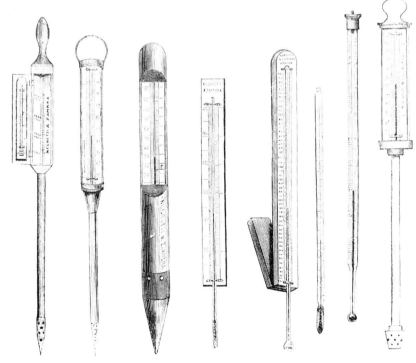

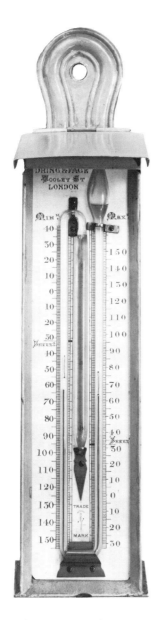

[17] Maximum and minimum thermometer to the 1780 design of James Six (1731–93). Signed: DRING & FAGE, TOOLEY ST, LONDON. The calibration runs from 160° F on the right-hand branch (maximum) to −40° F on the left-hand branch (minimum). The central tube contains alcohol as the thermometric fluid; the U-tube has mercury to act as the indicator, which pushes steel indices to show the extremes. The indices have springy tails to prevent falling; they are reset by a magnet. The frame is japanned metal. *c*. 1876. *Science Museum (1876–856).*

work out a suitable scale for measurement. Daniel Gabriel Fahrenheit (1686–1736) of Amsterdam, was the first maker to produce really accurate thermometers. He used mercury for the first time in 1717. It proved more satisfactory than alcohol, though it was more difficult to use in narrow tubes. But it does have a reasonably uniform expansion rate and a wider temperature range than alcohol. Fahrenheit also worked on producing a suitable scale. The scale he made in 1724 had three fixed points: 0° was the freezing point of a mixture of ammonium chloride and snow, 32° was the freezing point of water, and 96° the mouth temperature of the healthy human being. This Fahrenheit scale was used on the majority of English thermometers during the next two centuries.

Many other scales were devised in the middle of the eighteenth century, but only two are important, those of the French physicist René Antoine Ferchault de Réaumur (1683–1757) and Anders Celsius (1701–44), a Swedish astronomer; these are generally found on Continental-made instruments. The Réaumur scale had only one fixed point, freezing water was 0°; 80° was then assigned at the water boiling point. The Celsius scale was the first to be divided into 100 degrees between these points, but it was inverted at 0° for boiling and 100° for freezing water. A year later, in 1743, Jean Pierre Cristin (1683–1755) of Lyons inverted the Celsius scale to the centigrade that we use today, although since 1948 it has been called the Celsius scale by international agreement. Mercury is used in most scientific thermometers, although an alcohol mixture is necessary for temperatures near and below the freezing point of mercury, which is −39°C.

An early meteorological thermometer to record maximum and minimum temperatures without the presence of the observer was devised by James Six (1731–93) of Canterbury, in 1780 [17]. He employed an alcohol thermometer to push a column of mercury which, in turn, pushed steel indices into place to record the maximum and minimum positions. His book on the proper conduct of such an instrument was published by his son in 1794 and entitled: *The Construction and Use of a Thermometer, for Shewing the Extremes of Temperature in the Atmosphere, During the Observer's Absence. Together with Experiments on the Variations of Local Heat; and other Meteorological Observations.* This pattern of instrument due to Six continues with us today, frequently to be found in the greenhouse.

The book also shows how Six used his thermometers to measure diurnal variations in temperature, and discovered that during calm weather the upper air was much warmer than that close to the ground, a result that he 'was at first very much surprised to find' – yet another occasion when scientific information had to wait on the invention of an instrument.

The Hygrometer

The atmosphere always carries a certain amount of water vapour in it, and the proportion varies with the temperature. Because cold air

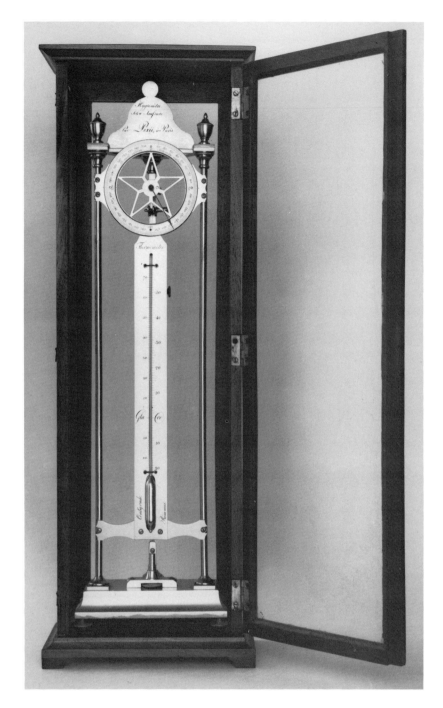

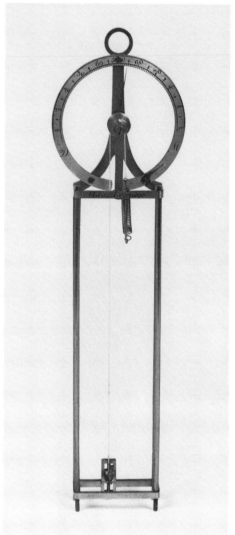

[18] Hygrometer to the De Saussure design, signed: *Hygromètre selon Saussure Par Pixii, à Paris*. The scale is divided as a complete circle into 360°, with the ends marked *Humidité extrème* and *Sécheresse extrème*. The thermometer is calibrated into degrees *Centigrade* and *Réaumur*. The hygroscopic material used by the Swiss, Horace Bénédict de Saussure (1740–99) was human hair, and he published his design in 1783. Nicholas Constant Pixii (1776–1861) succeeded the Dumotiez brothers *c.* 1815. His son, Antoine Hippolyte Pixii (1808–35) invented a magneto-electric machine in 1832. Brass frame 490 × 140 mm.
c. 1825. *Museum Boerhaave (Th 34)*.

[19] De Luc type of hygrometer, signed: *Haas, LONDON*. The dial is engraved from 0 to 100, and the extremes are marked D (dry) and W (wet). The hygroscopic material is whale-bone measuring 115 × 3 mm, and it acts against a light, brass spring, the connexion being string passing over a pulley to move the pointer. The design is that of J. A. de Luc (1727–1817), a Swiss meteorologist. Overall height 161 mm; diameter of dial 45 mm.
c. 1800. *Whipple Museum (2356)*.

[XVIII] Cabinet of coal-tar products. A silver plaque is inscribed: Products Obtained from Coal According to the PROCESS of Mr. Winsor. Prepared by F. Accum. Lecturer on CHEMISTRY in the Surry [*sic*] Institution. The cabinet contains fourteen bottles and three boxes of specimens of useful products extracted from ammoniacal liquor and tar, the by-products of the gas industry. Dating from *c*. 1815, these are the earliest forerunners of the modern coal-tar industry. Fredrick Accum (1769–1838) began his business in 1800. Albert Winsor (or Winzer, 1763–1830), promoted a gaslighting company. Chest 380 × 300 × 300 mm.
c. 1815. *Museum of the History of Science* (336).

[XIX] Kit for building molecular structure models, described as: G L Y P T I C F O R M U L A E. The coloured balls are colour-coded for elements, and are drilled with holes corresponding to valency. Connexions between the balls are made by brass rods. These represent the first such 'ball and spoke' models, which were described in 1867. 'Glyptic' means, in this context, 'figured'. Case 630 × 310 × 60 mm; diameter of balls 30 mm.
c. 1867. *Museum of the History of Science (395).*

[XX] An illustration of the spectra of various sources of light: 1 and 2 from the Sun, 3 from sodium, 4–12 various elements, 13 phosphorous, 14 hydrogen. 1872. *Deschanel, plate III.*

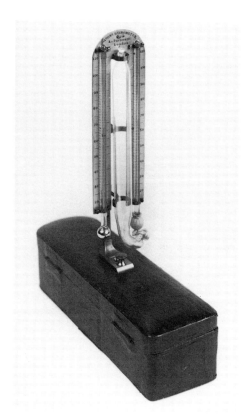

falls, the invisible water vapour condenses into moisture as it falls leaving, after a sunny day, the grass at night covered in dew. In a mist or fog, the air is completely saturated with water vapour, and this is called 100 per cent humidity. To measure the amount of humidity in the air, hygroscopic materials were used to move a pointer. Hooke used the beard of a wild oat, a tiny spiral which, as was described in the introduction to this chapter, unwinds as it becomes damp. The effect can be recorded by attaching an indicator of straw to the oat beard. Other materials used as humidity indicators were hair, whalebone, catgut and impregnated paper.

Horace Benedict de Saussure (1740–99) was Professor of Philosophy at Geneva and the author of a treatise on meteorology, published in 1783. He used human hair in his hygrometer, to rotate a pointer, using a pulley [18]. A fellow-Swiss, J. A. de Luc, used a thin strip of whalebone cut across the grain as his hygroscopic material [19]. The strip was attached to thin brass wire wound over the axis of the index arm, and then held by a weak spring. The whole device is contained in a light, brass framework. The semi-circular scale is divided from 0 to 100, whereas with the similar-looking de Saussure instrument, the scale is circular, and divided from 0 to 360. De Luc obtained his extreme point by immersing the indicator in water, while de Saussure obtained his by using saturated air, a difference in method which led to a controversy between the two men. Such instruments can be found dating from the first half of the nineteenth century.

[20] Hygrometer signed: MASONS HYGROMETER A. Pastorelli London. This instrument is also known as a psychrometer. There are two mercury thermometers, scales 10° to 112° F, one of which is wrapped round by cloth with a wick to a reservoir of water. Evaporation cools this bulb, and the humidity is found by consulting a set of tables for the difference in the readings between the thermometers. The design was published by John Abraham Mason in 1836. A. Pastorelli was at 4 Cross Street, Hatton Garden, from 1829, and was joined by a son in 1848. Maroon, leather-covered case, 180 × 52 × 50 mm, which acts as a stand for the instrument; overall height mounted 218 mm.
1836–48. *Museum of the History of Science.*

[21] German hygrometer signed: LAMBRECHT'S POLYMETER. A normal hair hygrometer with a pointer passing over a scale reading 0 to 100 per cent humidity. Above this scale is another to be read in conjunction, which is in degrees Celsius. (Note: the pointer does not read temperature.) A mercury thermometer reads the air temperature, and the numerical difference between this and the value indicated by the hygrometer needle gives the temperature at which there will be onset of dew or fog. Wilhelm Lambrecht made meteorological instruments at the end of the nineteenth and beginning of the twentieth centuries. Overall length 240 mm; diameter of dial case 76 mm.
c. 1900. *Teyler's Museum.*

[22] Popular dew-point hygrometer to the design published in 1820 by J. F. Daniell, signed: *J. NEWMAN LONDON*. Ether is poured over the muslin-covered bulb, which cools the fluid inside the tube to cause water vapour to condense on the outside of the black bulb. The temperature inside the bulb is read on a thermometer and compared with the air temperature recorded by the outside thermometer; so, from tables, it is possible to determine the relative humidity. John Newman flourished 1816–38, first in Lisle Street, then at 122 Regent Street. Overall height 140 mm; base diameter 51; mahogany box 170 × 136 × 41 mm. *c.* 1830. *Whipple Museum (659)*.

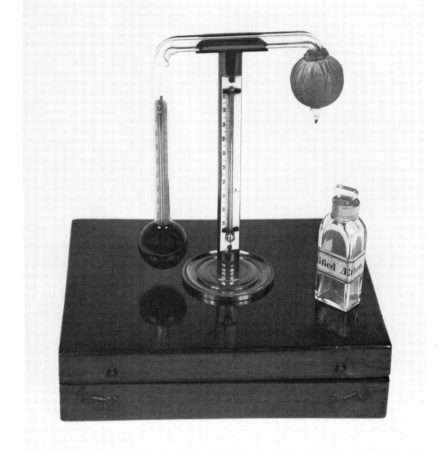

John Leslie (1766–1832), Professor of Mathematics at Edinburgh University from 1805, modified the differential air thermometer, which was based on Galileo's thermoscope. A U-shaped, thin glass tube has a bulb at each end, one covered with silk (see also Chapter 7). The tube contains coloured liquid, so that when the silk is wetted with pure water, it evaporates, and so cools the air in the bulb, causing the liquid to rise up the branch of the tube to indicate the humidity. This instrument developed into the wet and dry bulb hygrometer, using an accurate pair of thermometers, with the bulb on one kept constantly damp. The cooling by evaporation depressed the temperature, so that the difference in temperature recorded by the pair of thermometers is a measure of the humidity. The measure is obtained from a set of printed tables, the best of which were deduced empirically by James Glaisher, and published in 1847. For greater accuracy, the pair of thermometers can be held in a sort of rattle which is whirled in the air at a specified rate; this is the form of the instrument used today.

The form of hygrometer that uses evaporation is called a psychrometer (cold-meter), a word coined in 1818 by the German inventor,

[23] Variation of Lind's anemometer for measuring wind speed. Signed: LILLEY & SON *Opticians etc.*, LIMEHOUSE LONDON; also inscribed: SIR W. SNOW HARRIS F.R.S. INVENTOR. The glass tubing is bent back in the form of a 5 without the top bar, so that the Beaufort wind scale can be more easily displayed. The wind blows into the open end of the tube, and so pushes water into the bent tube. The movement of the water level measures the wind speed. This form of instrument was invented by James Lind (1736–1812) in 1775, and it continued into the twentieth century. William Snow Harris (1791–1867, FRS 1831) was well-known for his electrical researches. The Beaufort wind scale was first officially logged on HMS *Beagle* in 1831. Lilley & Son were mathematical and nautical instrument makers at 7 Jamaica Terrace, Limehouse, during the 1830s. The board holding the tube measures 186 × 139 mm. The instrument is contained in a mahogany box (240 × 190 × 54 mm), with a sliding lid.

c. 1835. Whipple Museum of the History of Science (2305).

Ernst Ferdinand August (1795–1870). In England, on the other hand, the instrument was called 'Mason's Hygrometer' [20], after John Abraham Mason, a surgeon of Pentonville, who described and so named the instrument in 1836.

The humidity of the air can be measured directly at any time by the dew point method; an apparatus for doing this was invented in 1820 by John Frederic Daniell (1790–1845), later Professor of Chemistry at King's College, London. His hygrometer [22] consisted of a bent glass tube with a bulb at each end, the lower one containing ether, the other empty and covered with muslin. The bulb that contains the ether is coloured dark blue to give contrast. To use the instrument, ether (from a glass bottle contained in the case), was poured onto the muslin-covered bulb, and the temperature at which condensation first occurred on the other bulb was read from the thermometer sealed within the glass tube. The temperature of the air was read from the thermometer on the brass stand. With this information, it was possible to determine the humidity of the air, by the use of tables.

[24] Thomas Romney Robinson invented this pattern of anemometer in 1846. Four cups rotate on an axis at a speed between $2\frac{1}{2}$ and 3 times as slow as the wind that drives them, the correct factor being found experimentally. *c.* 1870. *Deschanel, p. 503.*

Henri Victor Regnault (1810–78) devised a condenser hygrometer similar to Daniell's. He used two highly polished silver cylinders with glass upper sections, both fitted with thermometers. Ether is poured into one chamber, and then air is sucked through both. The dew point is noted, and the humidity found from tables.

The Anemometer

As might be expected, the swinging plate, like a shop sign, was a method for making a crude estimate of wind speed; this idea originates, as far as can be known, from the middle of the fifteenth century. A variation was the fixed plate, with some means to measure the resistance, such as a steelyard. Negretti & Zambra sold their 'Pendulum Anemometer' at six guineas for 'unscientific observers'.

The first satisfactory syphon wind gauge, or manometer, is that of James Lind (1736–1812) invented by him in 1775. A U-shaped glass tube was blocked at one end, except for a vent hole, the other end having an elbow joint that faces into the wind [23]. The tube is half filled with water to a central zero mark, and the air forced into one end of the tube will push the water up towards the other end. The difference from zero in both arms of the tube is added to give a measure of the force of the wind; 1 inch represents 5.21 lbs per square foot, called a 'high wind'.

A familiar wind speed indicator is the windmill type, invented by the Rev. Dr Thomas Romney Robinson (1792–1882) while he was in

[25] Air meter signed: L. CASELLA, MAKER TO THE ADMIRALTY & ORDNANCE, LONDON. Air Meter No. 104. to 1000 FEET. The idea of a windmill type of wind speed meter goes back to Robert Hooke or even earlier. This instrument is for measuring the lighter currents of air in coal mines, flues, ventilators, and so on. Made of brass, with eight aluminium alloy vanes. Diameter of guard ring over vanes 70 mm; diameter of base 59 mm.
c. 1900. *Museum of the History of Science.*

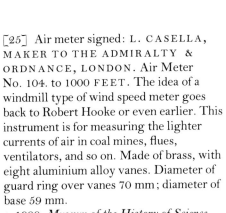

charge at Armagh Observatory, and published in 1850 [24]. Four hollow, spherical cups are fixed to cross arms that rotate at their centre point on a vertical shaft. At the bottom of this shaft is a worm gear operating a count wheel. The cups revolve with a speed of less than a third that of the wind, a factor that has to be worked out experimentally for the particular apparatus. All these pieces of equipment were developed so that recording was made automatic, by pen or electric impulse.

An instrument similar to the anemometer is the air meter [25] used for measuring the currents of air in mines, sewers, flues, hospitals and prisons. The air meter uses eight to twelve blades to form a fan as in a turbine, and this is set with its axis horizontal to the air current. Four or more dials count the revolutions of the fan, which is timed for exactly one minute. The result is in feet per minute, divided by 88 to give the velocity in miles per hour.

The Hypsometer

In the course of his research expeditions in the Swiss Alps, De Saussure established that the temperature of boiling water decreased 1° centigrade for every 978.5 feet of ascent, where the mean temperature of the atmosphere was estimated at 0° centigrade, or freezing point. The exact temperature at which water comes to the boil could therefore be used to measure the height of an ascent. An instrument was devised in the mid-nineteenth century to register the boiling point, called the hypsometer [26], or boiling-point thermometer. It was made to be portable in a case, and was both lighter and less easily damaged than a mercury barometer, advantages that caused it to be used by field geologists, and on other scientific expeditions. Its use declined after the invention of the aneroid barometer, but it was still being sold at the end of the century.

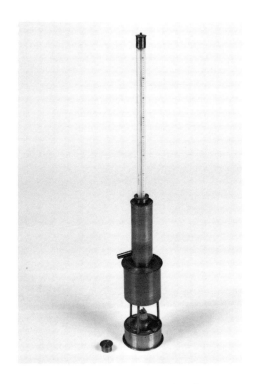

[26] Hypsometer for taking heights by measuring the temperature at which water boils. This example is not signed. In the base section is a spirit lamp and, above, a boiler. Above this is a tube with two telescoping sections that can contain a thermometer. Height when set for use about 270 mm; diameter of base 49 mm. Late 19th century. *Teyler's Museum.*

14 · Surveying & Navigation

*The true and moste lively and perfecte description,
and instruction, of the most necessarie and
commendable Science of Surveying of Landes:
drawne and devised by the industrie of
Valentyne Leighe.*

Heading to Leigh's treatise (1577)

*What can be more difficulte than to guyde a shyppe engoulfed, where only
water and heaven may be seene.*

Martin Cortes (1551),
translated by Richard Eden (1561)

The instruments used for surveying and for navigation, being so closely of the same kind, can be considered together. They are geodetic, that is, they are concerned with mapping and charting positions on the Earth's surface. Most are mathematical instruments, devised to make angular measurements, which depend on division of the circle.

Surveying and navigation are professional activities that are intensely practical. The theory involved – of mathematics and positional astronomy – was established by the early seventeenth century, and changed little until the twentieth century brought a revolution in technique with aerial photography, lasers, and computers. In the history of surveying and navigation, the actual development of the instruments was the important factor, as they came to be more accurate and efficient, and were adapted for use in differing conditions.

From the mid-eighteenth century the economic and social demand for a wide variety of surveying techniques markedly increased. In addition to the well-established requirements of landowners, military and administrative pressures led governments to undertake national surveys. The economic impetus of the Industrial Revolution in Europe and the United States produced a boom of road, canal, and railway building, while expansion of all kinds of mining developed another specialist type of surveying.

The basic problem in navigation was how to find the longitude on the open sea. Once ships began to venture into the oceans, the need to plot a position by the use of instruments and calculation became of paramount importance. In the nineteenth century the longitude was calculated either by the use of the marine chronometer, or by the lunar distance method, which involved taking astronomical sightings and using lunar tables.

Used by both surveyors and navigators are the magnetic compass and the sextant, though in different forms. The most important surveying instruments are the plane table, the level, the circumferentor and the theodolite. The nineteenth-century ship's officer used the octant, and its improved descendant, the sextant, as well as the accurate but costly reflecting circle. These instruments existed alongside the marine chronometer (see Chapter 2), which gradually found a place in most ocean-going ships in the course of the century. Also in the category of navigational instruments are those connected with hydrography, or the charting of coasts, and those for computing distance travelled at sea.

THE HISTORY OF SURVEYING

Surveying consists in plotting the position of certain landmarks on the surface of the Earth (or below it, when mines are surveyed) for the purpose of producing a graphic representation of the area, accurately reduced to scale. Surveys, therefore, depend on making linear and angular measurements.

The need to measure land developed as soon as communities became settled. Until the sixteenth century, however, surveying was a simple process carried out with direct measures of length, chiefly poles and ropes. The trained eye played an important part, and simple calculations were, of course, involved. The earliest extant book on surveying was the work of a Greek engineer, who is known to us as Hero (or Heron) of Alexandria, in which town he was known to be living around AD 100. He not only described the basic principles of surveying, but also some instruments to help the surveyor in the field. It was during the sixteenth century that the profession of surveyor became definitely established in Europe, in the wake of the expansion of trade and wealth brought about by the Italian Renaissance. In England, the dissolution of the monasteries by King Henry VIII in 1539 was followed by the creation of new estates, and an urgent need for surveyors. The new angular measuring techniques and the skills of the engraver – needed both in map-making and for dividing the scales on surveying instruments – came to England from Italy, via the Low Countries.

Textbooks on surveying published during the seventeenth and early eighteenth centuries are concerned to strike a balance between the practical needs of field work and the often complex instruments devised by some mathematicians. William Leybourn (1626–1700), who published *The Compleat Surveyor* in 1653, chose three instruments as being 'in most esteem among Surveyors', namely, the theodolite, the circumferentor, and the plane table. These continued in use throughout the next two centuries, but with important additions and improvements.

A crucial impetus to the development of surveying from the mid-seventeenth century onwards was provided by the geat national surveys, the first of which was undertaken in France from 1666 onwards, due to the enlightened encouragement of Louis XIV. Things moved more slowly in England, because of Parliament's reluctance to provide the necessary funds. An exception, however, was the remarkable Down Survey of Ireland, under the direction of Sir William Petty (1623–87). Petty was a notable scholar, mathematician, and medical man who, under the Commonwealth, was appointed Physician-General to the army in Ireland. Being a follower of Francis Bacon, he believed that the social and economic development of a country could best be furthered by carrying out a detailed geographical study of it. He persuaded Parliament to accept his proposal for a survey in 1654, and organized the 1000 men who carried out the work with such efficiency that the project was completed in three years.

Apart from this, it tended to be in response to immediate military pressure that extensive survey work was initiated in Great Britain. Scotland was mapped first, following the 1745 Jacobite rebellion, and it took the threat of a French invasion in 1791 to bring about the official foundation of a national survey of England under the control of the Board of Ordnance. The map of Scotland was the work of William Roy (1726–90), who was appointed in 1765 Surveyor-General of Coasts and Engineer for Making Military Surveys in Great Britain. In 1763 he had first proposed 'a general survey of the whole island at public cost', but the scheme was deferred by the American War of Independence. It was the French, nearing the end of their national survey, who provided the next stimulus. A triangulation of south-eastern England was proposed, to link up with that in Northern France, connecting the Greenwich and Paris observatories. The Royal Society – much incensed by a French suggestion that the latitude of Greenwich had been incorrectly calculated – undertook direction of the proposed survey. On 16 April 1784 a base was measured on Hounslow Heath by General Roy. He died in 1790, but the next year work on a full national survey was begun. A decision to re-map Ireland was made in 1824, the work being carried out by English military surveyors.

Different practical problems were presented by the task of surveying largely unsettled and uncultivated countries. Survey work in India began as early as 1767, under the control of the East India Company, the instruments used being the chain, the quadrant and the waywiser. Surveying was, from the first arrival of the settlers, a major preoccupation in the American Colonies. Throughout the eighteenth century, it was, together with navigation, the most popular mathematical subject taught in schools and colleges. There was a keen demand for basic surveying instruments, first used simply for establishing local boundaries, in the hands of farmers and tradesmen. But the surveying of provincial and inter-colonial boundaries required greater skill, and a knowledge of astronomy.

To begin with, the skill came from England. The famous Mason-

Dixon Line was plotted in the 1760s by two Englishmen, invited for the purpose: Charles Mason, an astronomer, and Jeremiah Dixon, a mathematician. Later surveyors were native Americans, one of the most notable being Andrew Ellicott, who carried out many surveys in virgin territory at the turn of the nineteenth century. He made his own instruments, including an astronomical clock, sectors, a quadrant, and a transit and equal altitude instrument. In unexplored areas, particularly when heavily forested, the surveyor was in much the same situation as the navigator, needing instruments for astronomical sightings, and the magnetic compass. The latter – which becomes the circumferentor for surveying use – was, together with the chain, the basic instrument of the American surveyor. When, in 1803, Meriwether Lewis and William Clark undertook their expedition from the mouth of the Missouri River to its source and thence to the Pacific, they took with them a surveying compass, an artificial horizon, two sextants, and an Arnold chronometer.

The absence of existing landmarks created special problems and needs in mine surveying. This specialized branch of the profession had, according to the author of a textbook on the subject published in 1888, 'not kept pace with the advances in other branches of surveying; for it is to be regretted that, in many cases, mine-surveys are still made with instruments which have long been set aside as too inaccurate for surveys aboveground'. However, with the dramatic growth in all kinds of mineral extraction in the second half of the nineteenth century (the annual value of mineral raised in the United Kingdom in the 1880s was £136m), specialist mining survey instruments were developed.

SURVEYING INSTRUMENTS

The Theodolite

The *simple theodolite* was so called in the nineteenth century to distinguish the instrument without a vertical arc from the altazimuth type. It still found a place in the range of surveying instruments offered by W. F. Stanley & Co. Ltd., at the end of the century. In his book *Surveying and Levelling Instruments Theoretically and Practically Described* (1890), William Stanley (1829–1909) wrote that it may 'be made into a simple angle measurer for laying out or plotting small parcels of ground, small estates in building ground, local sewage, gas and water works, and many other cases of small surveys for which purpose it will be found sufficient, with a saving of about half the cost of a perfect theodolite' (i.e. the altazimuth type).

The altazimuth theodolite consists of a horizontal divided circle, whose diameter gives the size of the instrument (5-inch) with verniers and possibly also with lenses to read them; a compass; a semi-circular divided arc (the curve of the arc can be upward or downward-facing), surmounted by a telescope with a bubble tube attached. This was called the *'plain' theodolite* [1] and its function was described by Stanley as follows:

[1] Plain theodolite, signed: *Adie & Son Edinburgh*. Brass, horizontal circle divided 0°–360° to 30′, with a vernier reading to 1′. Vertical circle divided 60°–0°–60° to 30′, vernier to 1′. Adie & Son traded in Edinburgh from 1835 to 1880. Length of telescope 264 mm; diameter of horizontal circle 122 mm.
c. 1840. *Whipple Museum (2556).*

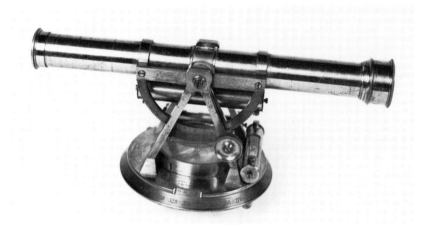

The Theodolite is the most perfect instrument for measuring both horizontal and vertical angles by the aid of a telescope and graduated circles. For the purpose of surveying, the theodolite is mostly employed to take a system of triangles upon the horizontal plane of the surface of the land, and of objects at any position in which they may be placed. When altitude angles are taken separately, these are generally applied to give corrections to chain or other actual measurements upon the surface, by calculation of the difference of hypotenuse and base.

Telescopic sights had been added to the instrument in 1725 by the London instrument maker, Jonathan Sisson, whose improvement was closely followed by a similar instrument from Thomas Heath. Towards the end of the century, Jesse Ramsden (1735–1800) brought his great

[2] 8-inch Everest theodolite, signed: *Troughton & Simms LONDON.* Horizontal circle divided on silver 0°–360° to 10′, vernier and microscope read to 10″. The vertical arcs are divided on silver 0°–40°–0° to 10′, with vernier to 10″. Also divided 24–0–24 and marked: *Diff of Hypo & Base.* This type was devised by George Everest for work in India. Length of telescope 130 mm; diameter of horizontal circle 215 mm.
c. 1880. *Whipple Museum (1877).*

[3] Theodolite, signed: C. BECKER
ARNHEM. On the horizontal circle the
silver scale is divided 0°–360°, to 30′, the
vernier reads to 1′. The vertical arc is
divided 55°–0°–55° to 30′. Christopher
Becker (1806–90) was working in Arnhem
from *c.* 1850, and later founded Becker &
Sons in Brooklyn, New York. Length of
telescope 225 mm; diameter of circle
180 mm.
c. 1850. *Private collection.*

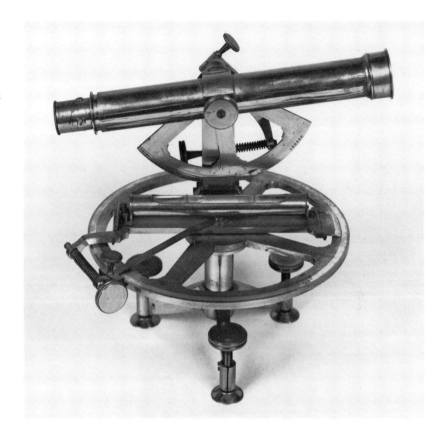

skill in degree-scale division to the instrument. It was he who was asked
to provide a theodolite for the work on the Hounslow Heath base. His
'Great Theodolite', made between 1784 and 1787, had an accuracy of
two seconds of arc over 70 miles.

A distinctive type of plain theodolite was that devised by Sir George
Everest (1790–1866), Surveyor-General of India, and consequently
given his name [2]. Its distinguishing features were three vernier arms
to read the horizontal circle, in place of the more usual vernier plate,
and two vertical arcs at each end of the telescope. Stanley said of it:
'In service in India, it has proved an excellent instrument', but commented also that it lacked the convenience of the transit principle, and
that the working parts were open to dust and dirt.

In the 1840s came what proved to be a revolutionary improvement
in the instrument. It was given a 360° vertical circle (instead of an
arc), so that the telescope was able to pivot through 180 degrees, this
movement giving the name *'transit' theodolite* [4]. The arrangement
made much quicker, easier, and more accurate the taking of a back and
fore sight. The plain theodolite still had the advantages of being both
lighter to carry and cheaper to buy, and therefore continued to be made
and sold, alongside the superior instrument.

By the end of the century transit theodolites were being produced
in a wide range of sizes, from 3-inch to 12-inch. Stanley commented:

A 5-inch or 6-inch theodolite is the largest size that may be carried

[4] 6-inch transit theodolite, signed:
Baker 244 High Holborn London.
Horizontal circle divided on silver 0°–360°
to 20′, with vernier and microscope
reading to 20″. 'A' frame supporting
vertical circle divided 0°–90°–0° twice to
20′, vernier to 20″. Also divided for
inclines and marked: *Diff of Hyp & Base.*
Length of telescope 281 mm; diameter of
horizontal circle 170 mm.
c. 1890. Whipple Museum (2470).

[5] American transit instrument, signed:
E. Brown & Son New York. This type was
commonly used by American surveyors
and engineers. Horizontal circle divided on
silver 0°–180°–0° to 30′, and to 1′ by
vernier. The vertical arc is missing. Length
of telescope 292 mm; horizontal circle
diameter 196 mm.
c. 1850. Whipple Museum (2805).

comfortably in a single case; and no great advantage is gained by
having an instrument beyond this size if the work is that of the ordinary surveyor on town or country surveys. The verniers of 4- and
5-inch instruments read sharply to single minutes of arc, which is
as nearly as can be plotted with any degree of certainty with an ordinary protractor reading by vernier also to minutes only; 6-inch instruments read to 30, but generally to 20 seconds.

The large, 12-inch theodolites, equipped with micrometer microscopes,
were capable of an accuracy of one second.

Further developments in the design of the theodolite consisted in
providing accessories that could be added, usually to the larger instruments, and in re-designing the frame. Accessories included illumination
for the transit axis; a specially sensitive spirit level; and a solar attachment, adapted from an American invention, the solar compass, to determine a true meridian by observation of the sun only. Attempts were
also made to incorporate photographic apparatus into the structure of
the theodolite, but this combination remained highly specialized
because of expense and bulky extra equipment, until the twentieth century. The most significant improvement to the structure was Stanley's

[6] Builder's level, signed: JOHN RABONE & SONS MAKERS BIRMINGHAM WARRANTED CORRECT. A bubble level is set into the top of a wooden bar which is mounted in brass. Sights run through the bar. It is supported on a tripod with iron tips. Length 290 mm; width 28 mm; overall height 240 mm.
c. 1850. *Private collection*.

U-frame model, introduced in the 1890s. This restructuring of the theodolite, so that the number of separate parts was reduced, both increased stability and decreased weight, as well as simplifying the cleaning of the instrument.

The Level

Surveyors need the instrument known as the level to provide an accurate record of a plane truly tangential to the surface of the Earth. The simple level, or bubble tube, is a part of nearly all surveying instruments. It consists of a glass tube marked with a scale, supported in metal or wood, and containing a liquid, water or later a spirit, with a bubble to act as marker. The surveyor's level is a composite instrument consisting of a telescope set parallel to and above a level, mounted on a tripod, and incorporating a compass. Credit for devising the combination of telescope and level should probably be shared by Jonathan Sisson and Thomas Heath, both of whom worked on variations of the instrument in the second quarter of the eighteenth century. But it was

[7] Y level, signed: *Troughton & Simms LONDON*. Named from the Y-shaped brackets that support the telescope. Length of telescope 709 mm; objective diameter 38 mm.
c. 1860. *Whipple Museum (2450)*.

[8] Dumpy level, signed: *Adies Improved level No. 40 Manchester & Leeds Railway Comp^y J. CASARTELLI MANCHESTER ADIE LONDON*. The dumpy level, developed by William Gravatt in the 1830s, had improved optics, i.e. larger objective and shorter focus. There were also mechanical improvements. No compass is fitted in this example. Joseph Casartelli moved to Manchester in 1851. Patrick Adie set up a business in London in 1852 which continued until 1942. Length of telescope 310 mm; objective diameter 34 mm.
c. 1855. *Whipple Museum (2555).*

Sisson's version, known as the Y-level because the telescope had Y-shaped supports, that became standard [7].

The railway boom of the first half of the nineteenth century created an urgent demand for a level that was easy and quick to use. The first major improvement was by Edward Troughton (1753–1835) who gave the instrument great stability, but William Gravatt's level, known as the 'dumpy' [8], developed in the 1830s, was the model that proved most popular in England. Gravatt, says Stanley, 'was of the opinion that firm construction, compact form, and plenty of light in the telescope were more important than easy facilities of adjustment'.

Troughton, too, made a level 'in which there was no adjustment to the supports of the telescope after it left the hands of the maker' [9]. Apart from reducing the length of the telescope to 12 inches (305 mm) – a modification also applied to the Y-level – Gravatt also added a transverse bubble, with a hinged mirror above, so that it could be read from the telescope eyepiece. The final form of the surveyor's level in the nineteenth century was, therefore, compact and sturdy, needing minimal adjustment and thus thoroughly practical for field work.

[9] Level, signed: *Troughton & Simms London*. This was regarded as an improvement on the Y level, as it was more compact and the adjustments were less easy to derange. Length of telescope 357 mm; objective diameter 32 mm.
c. 1845. *Whipple Museum (2449).*

[10] Miner's dial, or circumferentor, signed: *Cary London*. The instrument can be used with slit and wire sights or with a vertical semi-circle. The latter is divided 90°–0°–90° to 30′, and also 6–0–6 *Perpendicular* and 6–0–6 *Base*. Overall length 290 mm; radius of semi-circle 130 mm.
c. 1820. *Whipple Museum (88).*

[11] Lean's miner's dial, signed: *Henry Barrow & Co 26 Oxendon St., LONDON*. The detachable vertical semi-circle is divided 90°–0°–90° to 1′, or to 3′ with the vernier. Also a scale for *Diff of Hypo & Base*. Joel Lean, a Cornish mine manager, introduced this design in the 1790s. Length of telescope 215 mm; radius of semi-circle 100 mm.
c. 1870. *Whipple Museum (2802).*

[12] Hedley's miner's dial, signed: *Davis & Son, Derby*, No. 216. John Hedley, an Inspector of Mines, commissioned in 1850 the Derby firm of Davis & Son to make a dial to his own design. The vertical arc of Lean's dial obstructed the view of the compass, so a rocking circle was provided with a small vertical circle at one side, to leave the compass clear. This circle is missing. Diameter of compass box 140 mm.
c. 1880. *Private collection.*

The Circumferentor

This is the name given to the surveyor's compass: a magnetic compass surrounded by a divided circle, and equipped with fixed sights. It has sometimes been confused with Digges' theodolite, and thence with the simple or altazimuth theodolite. The latter is, however, a different instrument, in that the reading in the simple theodolite was marked by an alidade, instead of the magnetic needle used in the circumferentor. The essential part of the circumferentor was the compass, of primary importance both in surveying new territory and in mine surveying. Stanley described it as 'being best adapted to underground surveying', so that its most important adaptation in the nineteenth century was into the *miner's dial*.

The simple miner's dial [10] was a circumferentor mounted upon

[13] Trade label of John Davis & Son, Derby, in the lid of the box for the miner's dial shown above. The Hoffmann patent referred to is dated 1878.

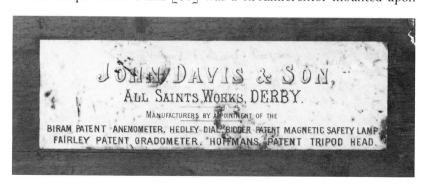

[XXI] Example of the common Fitzroy barometer, engraved: Admiral Fitzroy's Barometer. It is named after the man rather than invented by him. Fitzroy had been responsible for organizing the Meteorological Office and for writing on the subject. The example shown is unusual in having a retailer's plaque: E.G. WOOD. 74 CHEAPSIDE, LONDON. A popular and inexpensive instrument suitable as an indicator, not an accurate instrument, it was sold between the last quarter of the nineteenth and the first quarter of the twentieth centuries. Besides the barometer, there is a thermometer and a 'storm glass', which is a curiosity and no prognosticator of weather. Height 945 mm; width of base 267 mm. Late 19th century. *Private collection*.

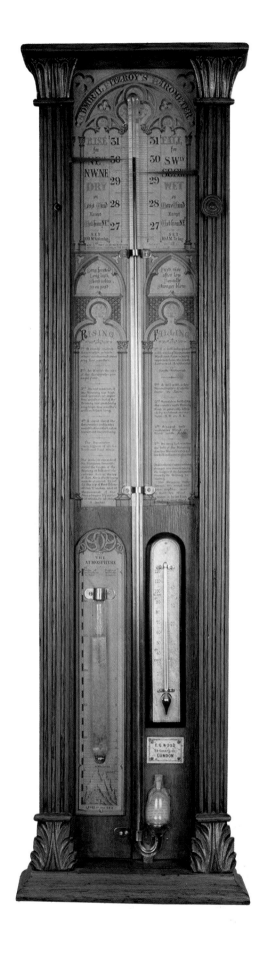

[XXII] Baromètre liègeois, signed by etching in the glass at the back: F. DAVIDSON & CO. 29 GRT. PORTLAND ST. [London]. This glass vessel, part filled with coloured water, is called a 'weather glass', 'donderglas' in the Netherlands, or 'baromètre liègeois', because it was produced at Liège from the seventeenth century. Height 255 mm; width 115 mm. Late 19th century. *Private collection*.

[XXIII] Prismatic compass, signed:
SCHMALCALDER'S PATENT, 399
STRAND, LONDON. Charles
Schmalcalder registered his patent in 1812.
It allows the sighting and the compass
reading to be taken simultaneously.
Diameter 98 mm.
c. 1825. Private collection.

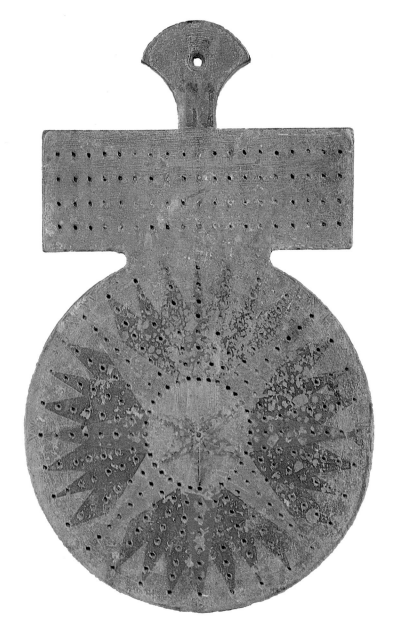

[XXIV] English traverse board. Above is
a rectangle (width 197 mm) with a series
of holes: this is the log speed record.
Below is a disk (diameter 225 mm) with
the 32 points of the compass, and a series
of holes: this records the direction sailed.
Very few traverse boards survive as, unlike
the sextant, they were not the property of
an officer.
19th century. *Museum of the History of
Science (79–51).*

[14] Surveyor's compass, signed: *Charles Chevalier Ing^r Palais Royal 158 à Paris*. A telescope and a sighting tube are pivoted to one side. Charles Chevalier died in 1859. Compass diameter 140 mm.
c. 1850. *Private collection.*

[15] De Lisle's reflecting clinometer. This simple device was invented by General A. de Lisle, (1823–99). The half mirror in the diamond frame reflects the observer's eye when the instrument is suspended from the thumb and held at arm's length. A sighting on a distant object through the clear glass will be on the same level as the observer's eye and its mirror image. In this model the mirror can be tilted by the weighted arm running over the scale on the arc. This will give a measure of the inclination of the distant object. Overall length 160 mm.
c. 1900. *Whipple Museum (2216).*

a stand. A later eighteenth-century adaptation which continued to be popular was made by Joel Lean, a Cornish mine manager. *Lean's dial* [11] had a semicircular vertical arc, with telescope and level mounted above, that fitted over the compass. Plain sights could be fitted as a quickly interchangeable alternative to the telescope, for use underground.

A later adaptation of the miner's dial was that made by an H.M. Inspector of Mines, John Hedley, in 1850. The feature of this dial [12] was that the sights moved on a framework centred on a horizontal axis, so that they could rock to take horizontal angles without obstructing the compass. A telescope could be added to the Hedley's dial instead of plain sights.

The Graphometer

This was invented by Philippe Danfrie (d. 1606) in Paris in about 1597. It is described by Stanley as a semi-circumferentor, 'a cheap instrument for taking angles approximately'. It is a semi-circle divided into degrees, with two alidades, or sighting rules, one fixed to the semi-circle and the other movable over the scale. It usually also includes a compass, and is mounted on a tripod. This instrument enjoyed its greatest popularity on the continent of Europe.

The Prismatic Compass

This instrument was invented and patented in 1812 by Charles Schmalcalder, a mathematical instrument maker in the Strand, London [xxiii, facing p. 257]. It brought much greater accuracy to an essential item of surveying equipment. The prism was attached to the back-sight positioned over the rim of the compass card, so that the degrees could be read while sighting the point of observation. The card was divided into 360°, inscribed on the South point, because the eye and prism looked due North. The figures on the card were printed in reverse, because they were seen in reflexion. The prismatic compass was capable of reading to an accuracy of one-third of a degree.

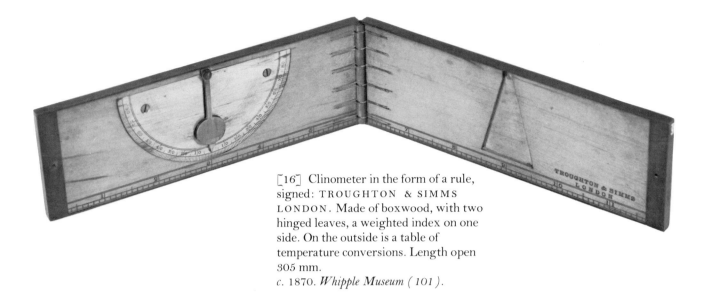

[16] Clinometer in the form of a rule, signed: TROUGHTON & SIMMS LONDON. Made of boxwood, with two hinged leaves, a weighted index on one side. On the outside is a table of temperature conversions. Length open 305 mm.
c. 1870. *Whipple Museum (101).*

The Clinometer

Often associated with the prismatic compass for surveying was a clinometer [15 & 16], which measures vertical angles with a weighted wheel that keeps its position while the sights are turned to the point of observation. The angle is then read through a prism attached to the back-sight. The purpose is to measure degrees of slope, and the clinometer scale gives the rise or fall. One of the most popular pocket clinometers was the Abney level (or clinometer) [17], devised by Captain William Abney (1843–1920) of the School of Military Engineering, Chatham, England. It consists of a small telescope in a rectangular tube with a semi-circle attached which is divided into degrees, and a clinometer scale. At the centre of the arc is a pivot with a bubble tube visible through a hole in the telescope, via a mirror, so that the point sighted and the level bubble can be seen together. The angle through which the pivot has been turned is read off the scale.

[17] Abney reflecting level and clinometer, with telescopic sight and arc divided to read 10′ by the vernier, and to a scale of gradients. Engraving, *c.* 1890, from J. H. Steward catalogue.

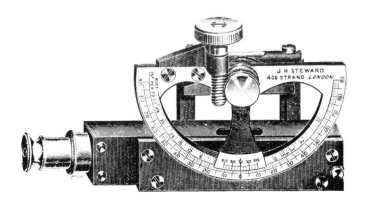

[18] Engraving of a simple plane table, as advertised by W. F. Stanley *c.* 1900. On the top is an alidade, or rule, with sights at the ends; a trough compass, which is a magnetic needle used merely to point North, and so covers an arch of some 20° only; and a bubble level.
c. 1900. *Stanley (1901), p 473.*

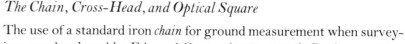

The Plane Table

This piece of equipment (the spelling before 1830 was plain table) is the simplest and longest lived of all the surveyor's instruments. It enables bearings to be marked directly on paper in the field, and a simple sketch-map to be drawn. It was, therefore, useful for the unskilled and the surveyor in training. As Stanley points out, its usefulness is greatly increased by a dependable climate. It consisted of a flat, square board, mounted in a universal joint, with a surround bearing a graduated scale, which fits on to the table's edge and holds a sheet of paper in place. A separate straight rule, or alidade [19], engraved with scales and with sights attached, rests on the paper. Likely additions would be a magnetic compass, a level and a telescope. The plane table, already in use by surveyors in the sixteenth century, is still being made and sold today.

[19] Plane table alidade, signed: *Fahlmer à Strasbourg*. Also engraved: *Dépot de la Dir^{on} de la Rochelle*. It is fitted with open and telescopic sights, quadrant, and plumb-bob. Length 437 mm; length of telescope 374 mm.
Early 19th century. *Whipple Museum (928).*

The Chain, Cross-Head, and Optical Square

The use of a standard iron *chain* for ground measurement when surveying was developed by Edmund Gunter (1581–1626), Professor of Astronomy at Gresham College, London, in 1620. His chain was divided

[20] Gunter chain, signed:
CHESTERMAN SHEFFIELD ENG.
Made of steel, with brass handles, swivels,
and tellers. 22 yards in 100 links.
Late 19th century. *Whipple Museum
(2722)*.

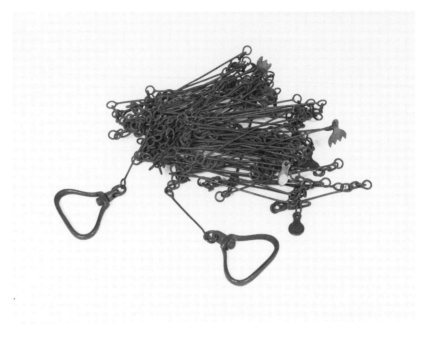

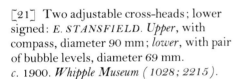

[21] Two adjustable cross-heads; lower
signed: *E. STANSFIELD. Upper*, with
compass, diameter 90 mm; *lower*, with pair
of bubble levels, diameter 69 mm.
c. 1900. *Whipple Museum (1028; 2215)*.

[22] Surveyor's sextant, signed:
Troughton & Simms, LONDON. Also
inscribed: I. K. B. No. 9. Made of brass,
with a silver scale divided –5° to 130°, to
30′, vernier reading to 30″, with
magnifying lens. This sextant belonged to
Isambard Kingdom Brunel (1806–59), the
civil engineer and railway pioneer. Brunel
also possessed a box sextant by
Troughton. Radius 90 mm.
c. 1840. *Museum of the History of Science
(33–8)*.

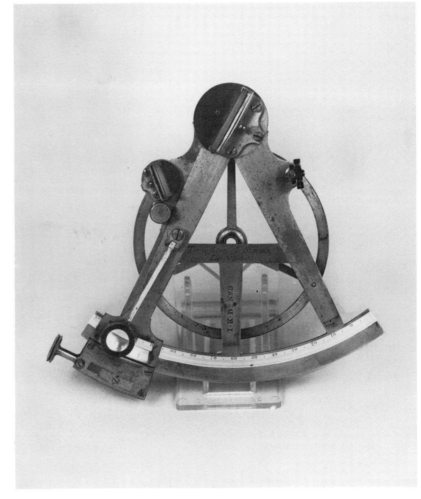

into 100 links, and measured 22 yards [20]. This distance, squared, equals one-tenth of an acre, and ten chains equal one furlong, or one-eighth of a mile. Each tenth link was marked with a notched piece of brass. This was the standard chain throughout the eighteenth century, but by the nineteenth there were other chains in use – for example, 50-foot, 100-foot and 20-metre with centimetre links. Jesse Ramsden made a 100-foot steel rule for calculation of the Hounslow Heath base in 1784, and others for subsequent national survey work.

As essential accompaniment to the chain was the *cross-head* [21], sometimes called a cross-staff, or simply a cross. This was a cross-sight, of brass or boxwood, set at the top of a pole, the sightlines being at 90° to one another. This was used for measuring off-sets, that is, features to each side of the direct line of the chain. A more sophisticated version housed a compass, set over a tubular cross, rotating on a graduated base. Stanley, at the end of the nineteenth century, described as the 'modern instrument' the French form, made of an eight-sided brass tube, but he criticized the small diameter of the tube, which caused the sighting slits to be too close together.

A nineteenth-century improvement on the cross-head was the *optical square*, consisting of two mirrors set at 45° to each other in a small, drum-shaped box. These enabled the surveyor to see the end of the chain line and the features at right angles, superimposed in the mirror. The instrument was also made in a double form with two pairs of cross sights.

The Pocket or Box Sextant

This tiny instrument, only about 3 inches in diameter, was devised by Edward Troughton in about 1800. It worked like the nautical sextant, but with the mirrors enclosed in a cylindrical case and only the index arm and divided arc exposed. This was regarded as making the instrument very practical for field work. Since it could take any angle in the vertical or horizontal, it was 'deservedly popular with British surveyors as a land-surveying instrument and is equally so as a military one' (Stanley).

The Waywiser or Perambulator

This is a very ancient instrument for measuring distance upon the ground, dating from pre-Roman times. It consisted of a wheel of known circumference, with a dial to record the distance covered [23]. The common version is pushed by hand, but another type was made to be attached to a carriage. The wheel is made of wood, care being taken to avoid warping, and is then shod with iron or brass. The circumference of the wheel is usually half a pole in English-made waywisers, and records the distances in poles, furlongs and miles. Stanley also described a 'light form of perambulator', like a bicycle wheel, with a circumference of two yards, which was portable, with a detachable handle, so that the instrument could be packed away into a case. This instrument is also sometimes called a hodometer.

[23] Waywiser, hodometer, or perambulator, signed: *CARY LONDON.* Iron, 12-spoked wheel (diameter 580 mm) with its circumference measuring six feet, or two yards.
Late 19th century. *Whipple Museum (503).*

THE DEVELOPMENT OF NAVIGATION

The sea is studied in three distinct branches of scientific activity: navigation, hydrography, and oceanography. Navigation deals with the practical problems of steering a ship from its point of departure to its destination. Hydrography is the charting of the seas and oceans, and their coasts, to provide the information needed by the navigator. Finally, oceanography is concerned with the physical nature of the sea: the composition, temperature and behaviour (i.e. tides and currents) of the water; the substance of the sea bed; and the study of marine life.

As far as instruments are concerned, oceanographers used either specialist laboratory equipment, or instruments dealt with in the chapters on hydrostatics, heat and meteorology such as thermometers. The hydrographer used a combination of surveying and navigation instruments. It is, however, arbitrary to make rigid distinctions between the branches of marine science, for in practice there was much overlap. The oceanographer and the hydrographer used ships for transport, and therefore needed to navigate. Hydrographers were encouraged to collect all sorts of scientific information, in addition to the physical measurements needed for charting. The great oceanographic voyages of the nineteenth century often combined the two activities. The second voyage of HMS *Beagle* (1831–36) is famous because of the presence on board of Charles Darwin (1809–82), but its hydrographic achievement – under Robert Fitzroy – in charting the coasts of South America was also monumental. By the time HMS *Challenger* set out in 1873 on the voyage that laid the foundations of modern oceanography, twenty-five years of intensive activity in hydrography had produced such results that the charting function was less important.

Hydrography was crucially important during the nineteenth century, when increasing trade gave an impetus to maritime activity, and hence to the need for detailed and accurate charts. One of the key figures in the expansion of hydrography was Francis Beaufort (1774–1857) who, in 1829, became Hydrographer to the British Admiralty. The Hydrography Office had by then been in existence for thirty-five years, but had received little official support, so that it had not been able to initiate much maritime surveying on its own account. The situation when Beaufort took office was summed up by his biographer thus: 'There was scarcely what could be termed a correct chart of any portion of the globe in existence, even of the shores of the United Kingdom itself, excepting only the Channel'.

Beaufort, energetic and dedicated, changed the entire picture. In the next twenty-five years his department published 1446 new charts, the majority based on surveys carried out directly under his control. Even the French, nearest rivals to the British in hydrography, admitted the pre-eminence of Beaufort. An article in the *Revue des Deux Mondes* in the 1850s described the Hydrography Office as 'the first great emporium of hydrography in the whole world'.

In the United States pressure from Thomas Jefferson and the American Philosophical Society, among others, led to an Act of Congress in 1807, authorizing a systematic survey of the American coasts, under the control of the Treasury. For the next twenty-five years, however, many setbacks, mostly bureaucratic, delayed the project, though surveys were carried out by individuals, notably by Edmund Blunt, and his son of the same name. Through all its vicissitudes the US Coast Survey was under the direction of a Swiss, Ferdinand Rudolph Hassler (1770–1843), and Edmund Blunt Jr was appointed Hassler's First Assistant when the Survey was reconstituted in 1832. In his book *Thinkers and Tinkers* (1975), Silvio Bedini thus assessed the achievement of the Survey:

> Despite the problems and frustrations, the Survey made progress, and many Army and Navy officers, as well as scientists from the private sector, were enrolled in what gradually became an impressive corps of geographers, hydrographers and surveyors. Its efforts in the field were being supported by and combined with work being independently carried on in astronomical observatories in colleges and universities, and this first major Government support of science promised great achievement for the future.

There are obvious and important similarities between surveying unexplored territory on land and the work of the hydrographer and navigator. In both cases the position of the planets and stars played an essential part, as well as sightings of natural features – hills, headlands, woods, and so on. Coastal navigation is simple surveying, with the additional factor of the effects of currents, tidal flow, and wind on the progress of the ship; navigation in the open sea presents additional problems. The latitude can be measured by taking the elevation above the horizon of the Pole Star, or the altitude of the Sun at noon when it crosses the meridian. Longitude is more difficult to ascertain. It can be discovered by means of a clock because the difference between the time at the port of departure and the local time (noon by the Sun) gives the longitude, one hour equalling 15° of longitude. The stumbling block with this method was that, for centuries, no clock mechanism could be devised that would withstand a ship's motion. The importance to both commerce and discovery of the invention of the marine chronometer can hardly be over-estimated. John Harrison produced his first chronometer in 1735, and gradually refined it to the size of a large watch by 1759. At about the same time a new method of finding the longitude, by means of taking the distance of certain stars from the Moon, was devised. Based on accurate astronomical sightings and lunar tables, this so-called lunar distance method was made effective by the German astronomer, Tobias Mayer (1723–62). Chronometers gradually found their way first on board the ships of the merchant companies, then onto naval ships. The lunar distance method continued to be used as well throughout the nineteenth century. The marine chronometer, being a time-telling device, is discussed in Chapter 2.

NAVIGATION INSTRUMENTS

A variety of angular measuring instruments have been devised for the purpose of taking astronomical sightings on board ship. The earliest were the altitude quadrant and the sea astrolabe, both in use in the sixteenth century. The cross-staff, also adapted for navigational use from an astronomical instrument, was an improvement for measuring the altitude of the Pole Star, but it had the drawback that, when used for measuring the Sun's altitude, the observer had to face the Sun. To remedy this deficiency, the back-staff was invented by Captain John Davis (1550–1605), and it had a life of nearly two hundred years, being also known as the Davis, or English, quadrant. Back-staves of the eighteenth century exist, but by the nineteenth century the Davis instrument had been replaced by the octant, or Hadley quadrant.

The Octant

This instrument, invented by John Hadley (1684–1744) and described by him to the Royal Society in 1731, measures angles by reflexion. It was an improvement on the back-staff because of its more accurate construction, and also because it made possible the sighting and measurement of the angle between two objects, by bringing the reflexion of one into coincidence with the sighted image of the other in one mirror.

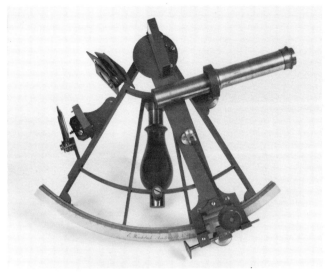

[24] Sextant, signed: *King's Patent,
GILBERT, WRIGHT & HOOKE, London*. The
brass frame has three cross-bars in A form,
and a triangular subframe. Scale divided on
brass, –5° to 139°, to 20′, vernier to 30″.
A silvered reflecting plate can be attached
by the vernier to give it light. In 1794, the
three-man group was at 148 Leadenhall
Street, Navigation Warehouse, London.
c. 1800. *Museum of the History of Science
(27–24)*.

[25] Sextant, signed: *E. Wenckebach,
Amsterdam, No. 46*. Brass frame with
radial and circumferential bars. Scale
divided on silver, 0°–140°, to 10′, vernier
to 10″. Eduard Wenckebach (1813–74)
had a considerable business in laboratory
apparatus as well as astronomical
instruments.
c. 1860. *Teyler's Museum (329)*.

Thus, the novelty of the octant was the use of a mirror mounted over
the pivot of a radial arm which moved over a graduated arc. The arc
actually occupies only one-eighth of a circle, hence the name of the
instrument, though it can measure 90° by means of the mirror. The
octant was superseded in the 1770s by the more accurate, and therefore
more costly, sextant, but it was not replaced completely until about
1900 because of its cheapness. In the first half of the nineteenth century
all-brass octants gradually replaced those made of ebony; after 1850
all-metal instruments took over the market. On cheap models boxwood
scales were sometimes used, but generally the scale was engraved on
ivory or brass.

The Sextant

In direct response to the need for increased accuracy of altitude measurement, the sextant [24 & 25] was devised in about 1758. It resulted

[26] Position-finder (type of station-
pointer), inscribed: *McCombies Patent*.
Made by Henry Hughes & Son. This
combines the functions of a station-pointer
and a double sextant in a single
instrument. Circle diameter 136 mm; arm
length 385 mm.
c. 1900. *Whipple Museum (2753)*.

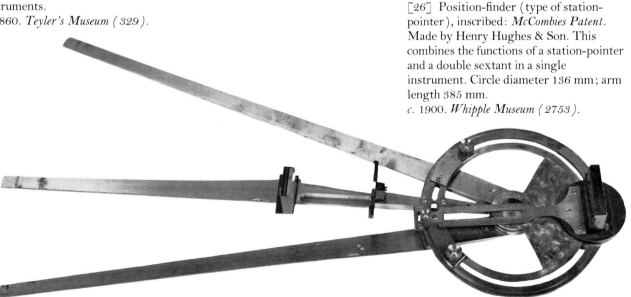

[27] Borda circle, or reflecting circle, signed: *J.M. Kleman & Zoon, Kon. Inst-makers, Amst.* The circle is divided on silver, and the degrees are indicated from 140°–0°–140°, the remainder of the divisions being unnumbered. The reading is taken through microscopes from three verniers (to 20″) to eliminate errors. J. M. Kleman was an exceptionally fine craftsman, with the highest reputation, from 1800 to 1840. Diameter 250 mm. *c.* 1820. *Museum Boerhaave (C 12).*

[28] Trade card advertising the Massey frictionless log. Edward Massey patented his mechanical log in 1802. He had many patents to his credit, the last in 1857. His firm was continued after his death by his nephew, Thomas Walker. *c.* 1870. *Science Museum (1879–34).*

Description of Drawing.

AA—The Log Tube and cones in one length, and contains the register.

BB—The vanes or wing, soldered and secured by brass stays, obliquely on the Log tube; from the action of the water against which the tube and register are caused to revolve.

C—The dial plate, with its indices, which show the distance run.

D—The milled-edge to the cover, by turning which the indices are exposed or protected.

E—The gun-metal convex cup or protector, attached to the shaft on which the Log revolves, and which prevents anything fouling between the shaft and the cone's point.

F—The thimble to which the towing rope is fastened.

NOTICE.—These machines should be occasionally rubbed with sweet oil or neat's foot oil, especially when not in use, and when in use some should be poured inside; if these simple directions were followed, and the machine treated with the respect its importance merits, it would last for years.

Attention is particularly called to the improved Conical Fishtail end of this Log, by which greater accuracy is obtained, all suction being removed from the end, the liability of jumping from the water in quick sailing is prevented, a smoother and more constant action is the result.

The improved Patent Log consists in a compound register and rotator; the conical ended tube with its vanes or driving planes, revolves freely on a fixed axis, which passes through the cone-point, the revolutions are communicated by means of this stationary shaft or axis to the endless screw, and so on to the wheels which move the indices on the dial plate.

Some of the advantages of this improved mode of construction are increased accuracy, greater durability, and lightness in towing.

The faults existing hitherto in Ship's Logs have been principally owing to their being constructed in two parts, one of which remains stationary. This is particularly illustrated in one of the new Logs now selling, in which though the rope connecting the register has been done away with, THE LOG IS STILL CONSTRUCTED IN TWO PARTS; yet in fact owing to the peculiar manner in which this has been effected (doing away with the rope), the previous faults have been more than doubled, and the Log rendered almost worse than useless. But in constructing the new Frictionless Propeller Log, the inventor has taken advantage of past experience, and introduced such improvements as, it is confidently asserted, will, with ordinary care, render errors in the result given by this Log impossible. The Log is used in the same manner as the usual ones, but care must be taken that the towing-rope is of sufficient length to allow the Log to fall sufficiently astern of the ship to clear the eddy of the wake.

ESTABLISHED 1802.

EDWARD MASSEY

ORIGINAL

BY SPECIAL APPOINTMENT

NEW

INVENTOR,

MAKER TO THE ROYAL NAVY.

PATENT

Frictionless Propeller Conical-End Log.

CAUTION.—The inventor and Patentee begs respectfully to put Merchants, Captains, the Shipping Interest, and the Public in general on their guard against spurious imitations of MASSEY'S LOGS, as some persons have dishonourably circulated Machines bearing his name, but which are not his make. It is essential that intending purchasers will be careful to notice that the Log obtained is marked with the following Registered Trade Mark :

L

EDWD. MASSEY L L PATENTEE,
LONDON.

The three L's stand for the seaman's motto, "Log, Lead, and Look out."

No Logs but those thus marked are genuine.

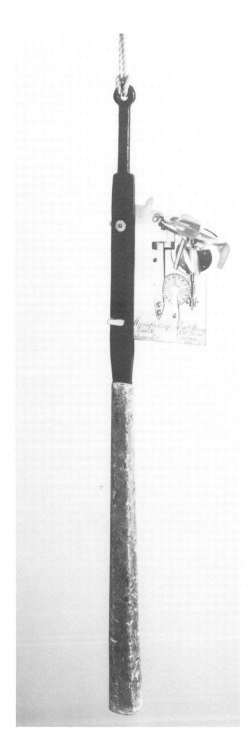

[29] Massey's sounding lead, for finding the depth of the sea from a ship, signed: *Edwd Massey EMP Patentee LONDON* 10323 *Manufactury 33, Tysoe St Clerkenwell.*
c. 1876. *Science Museum (1876–837).*

from experiments made at sea by Admiral John Campbell to test the new lunar distance method of finding the longitude. Its arc is one-sixth of a circle, but, again because of the use of a mirror, it is calibrated from 0° to 120°. Sextants were normally constructed of brass, their scales being divided with great accuracy by leading London instrument makers. By the end of the nineteenth century Stanley described nautical sextants as being made of cast gun-metal (an alloy similar to bronze) with struts carefully designed to give rigidity with minimum weight; two telescopes were generally incorporated in the instrument.

For use in hydrographic surveys a version of the sextant was made called the *sounding sextant*. This was an adaptation for measuring horizontal angles, having a wider field of view and lacking the usual light filters (called shades). It was employed to fix the position of the ship when a sounding or current measurement was made, by measuring the two angles between three landmarks on shore. A variant of this instrument, to speed up the measuring process, was the double sounding sextant, with two movable sights and two degree scales.

The Station-Pointer

For hydrographic surveys the station-pointer is essential. It is a kind of double-arm protractor, where two angles relative to a base may be laid off at the same time. For taking coastal soundings the angles between three points on land are measured with a sextant, the two movable arms are set relative to the fixed arm and the instrument is placed over the chart. When the arms match the features on the shore, the ship's position is fixed exactly, and the point at the centre is pricked onto the chart. This instrument was the invention of the Admiralty Surveyor, Murdoch Mackenzie, who published its details in 1774 in his book, *Treatise on Maritime Surveying*.

The Reflecting Circle

This instrument was devised in the 1750s by the German astronomer, Tobias Mayer, in order to achieve the ultimate in accuracy through the use of a circle of 360°, instead of the arc of 120° as in the sextant. A number of improvements were made to the circle, notably in 1787 by the Chevalier de Borda (1733–99), as a result of which it was given the alternative name of Borda circle [27]; and by Edward Troughton, whose instrument had three index arms with verniers, so that three readings could be taken at different points of the circle. This instrument was more popular with the French navy than with British seamen.

The Log

The purpose of a log is to discover the speed of a ship passing through the water. The non-mechanical log is a piece of wooden board, attached to a length of line knotted at intervals. The line was run out behind the ship for a specified period of time. Though the principle of a mechanical log was described to the Royal Society by Robert Hooke in 1688, the first effective model to be commercially produced was patented by

Edward Massey in 1802 [28]. Earlier types, some of them patented, proved unreliable in use. Massey's log was a towed rotator with a recording device.

The Mechanical Depth Sounder

Edward Massey was also responsible for patenting in 1802 a mechanical sounder based on the same principle as his log. Successive improvements were patented by him in later years, and his nephew and successor in his business, Thomas Walker, took out a further patent in 1866. J. Ericsson of the United States patented a sounding device in 1836 which depended upon water being forced into a glass tube, creating increasing air pressure with increasing depth. This was exhibited, together with other nautical instruments by Ericsson at the Great Exhibition in 1851, and was awarded a Prize Medal. Another of Ericsson's

[30] Dip circle, signed: *Brunner f res à Paris*. Such a circle is used for measuring the vertical component of the Earth's magnetic field.
1884. *Science Museum (1889–62)*.

winning instruments was a device to measure the distance of moving objects at sea, 'by means of a single observation, taken at sight'.

The Traverse Board

The helmsman's traverse board is first mentioned as part of a navigator's stock of instruments in a book published in 1528, and it was used by seamen in northern waters. The round, wooden board is marked out with lines corresponding to those on a compass rose, each line having a series of holes at regular intervals; the helmsman pegs the direction steered. A rectangular part of the board serves to peg the speed, as found by the log line. This simple nautical tally continued to be used throughout the nineteenth century on small boats [xxiv, facing p. 257].

The Dip Circle, or Dipping Needle

The magnetic needle in this instrument [30] moves in a vertical plane, in contrast to the compass (see below), where the needle moves in a horizontal plane. Its purpose is to measure the vertical component of the Earth's magnetic field, discovered in about 1576 by the Elizabethan navigator and instrument maker, Robert Norman (fl. 1570–90), who invented the dip circle. The angle of dip was at first thought to provide the means of finding the latitude, but this proved not to be true. But the dip circle continued to be made as equipment for the scientific explorer, who needed to study the Earth's magnetic field. In this rôle, it was taken on scientific expeditions throughout the nineteenth century.

The Compass and Binnacle

By the sixteenth century, mariners were using the magnetic compass, with an iron needle which had to be re-magnetized at intervals with a natural magnetic stone, or lodestone. In 1745 Dr Gowin Knight developed a method of improving the magnetic strength of the compass needle artificially, by a system of magnetized bars; he also introduced the use of a steel, instead of a soft iron needle. Knight took out a patent for his compass in 1766. The nineteenth-century mariner's compass was of this type, usually encased in brass. Some were made with a double-faced card, or rose, so that the compass could be read when hanging above the Master's bunk. The altazimuth compass [31] was designed for taking bearings of both terrestrial and celestial objects and particularly to determine the deviation of the compass from true North, having plotted the meridian passage of the Sun. In addition to the compass rose, this instrument was equipped with a sighting device, and other aids to the taking of bearings.

William Thomson (1824–1907), Professor of Natural Philosophy at the University of Glasgow at the age of 22, reformed the mariner's compass by making lighter the moving parts to prevent protracted oscillations, and shortening the needles, to help correct the quadrantal and other errors that arise from the magnetism of the hull of an iron ship. The Kelvin compass [33] (Thomson became Baron Kelvin of

[31] Altazimuth compass, signed: MADE BY SPENCER BROWNING & RUST, LONDON. Made of brass, and hanging in gimbals, the mahogany box acts as a support. The base of the compass housing is glazed, so that the compass may be read from another face when the seaman is in a bunk. Box 178 × 165 mm; compass card diameter 95 mm.
c. 1810. *Museum of the History of Science (63–34).*

[32] Stadiometer, signed: *Invented by G. H. Blakey, Master, R. N. Sole Maker, W. Heath, Optician, Devonport.* Also bears the serial number 165. It is made of nickelled brass and black leather, with a table of distances fixed to the outer barrel (diameter 46 mm). There are no lenses: at the front is a graticule and the tubes are adjusted so that a ship's mast fits the graticule marks. The number on the draw-tube gives the range from the table. Length closed 210 mm.
c. 1855. *Museum of the History of Science (78–37).*

Largs in 1892, and the name Kelvin is now usually associated with his inventions) was first patented in 1877. It used eight or more thin, light magnetic needles held by a 'cat's cradle' of cords to the compass card [34]. At either side of the binnacle, in which the compass was mounted, there were two soft iron spheres, and underneath were correcting magnets to neutralize the iron of the ship.

Wireless telegraphy was to transform both navigation and surveying in little-explored parts of the world. The possibilities that resulted from the discovery in 1887 of radio waves by Heinrich Hertz were developed by Oliver Lodge, with his spark-gap coherer of 1889, and by Guglielmo Marconi, who sent a message from Cornwall to Newfoundland in 1901. From about 1910 portable receiving sets were available for use on sea and land, representing a great advance in the determination of an exact figure for the longitude.

[33] Ship's compass and binnacle to Lord Kelvin's design, and presented to
the Science Museum by him in 1876. There are soft iron globes to correct
the quadrantal error, and adjustable magnets to correct fore and aft, athwart
ships, and heeling errors.
1876. *Science Museum (1876–739).*

[34] The Kelvin floating compass card from a ship's binnacle, signed: LORD KELVIN'S PATENT No. 5044 JAMES WHITE GLASGOW. The compass invented by William Thomson (1824–1907), from 1892 Baron Kelvin of Largs, owes its superiority to a system of very light needles grouped parallel to one another and attached to a light card. Diameter 250 mm.

c. 1895. *Museum of the History of Science.*

15 · Drawing & Calculating

If the first calculation is wrong, we make a second better.

Jane Austen, *Mansfield Park* (1812)

There are some basic tools that all scientists and technicians make use of, whether they be surveyors, astronomers, navigators, architects or engineers. They all need to make accurate drawings, frequently to scale, and they need to calculate. The simpler forms of calculation – addition, subtraction, multiplication, division, trigonometrical functions – are tedious and time-consuming, so for centuries ingenious attempts have been made to speed up the calculating processes by mechanical means.

DRAWING INSTRUMENTS

Technical drawing involves ruling straight lines, parallel lines, and lines at a given angle to others, as well as measuring parts of lines. Circles also have to be drawn and divided. Because of requirements of accuracy and the need to draw to scale, drawing instruments have to be divided, and the scales clearly marked. These needs have remained constant through the centuries, and the basic composition of a set of drawing instruments has changed little. A typical set would include: ruler and scale; parallel rulers; circular and/or semi-circular protractor;

[1] Architect's triangular plotting scale, signed: *D & S BANGOR, Me.* U.S. Stnd. Made of silver-plated brass, the six sides are divided into scales based on the inch. Darling and Schwartz worked at Bangor, Maine, until Darling moved in 1866. He was one of the finest makers of rules and gauges of his time. The case bears the date 1866. Length 310 mm.
c. 1866. *Private collection.*

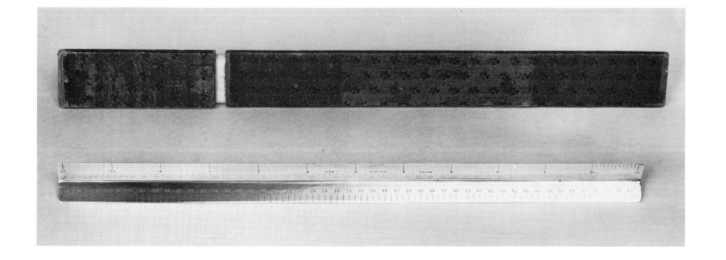

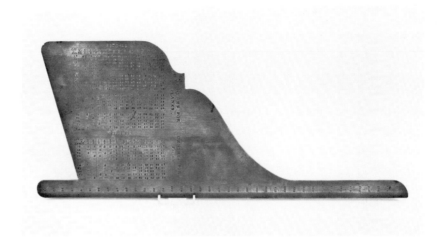

[2] Odontograph, invented and named in 1838 by Robert Willis (1800–75) for the use of engineers. It served to determine the layout of involute, as opposed to epicycloidal, gear teeth, and could be applied to gear-cutters. Widely used in factories, they were sold by Brown & Sharpe in the United States of America during mid-century. Maximum length 509 mm; maximum width 205 mm. *c.* 1840. *Museum of the History of Science (61–13).*

plotting scales and rectangular protractor combined; a pair of compasses; spring bows for small circles; a pair of dividers for pricking off lengths; pens, pencils and other attachments for the legs of the compasses [xxv, facing p. 288]. Additional instruments could be included for special needs, or bought separately.

These basic instruments for drawing are very ancient in origin. Compasses and dividers can be traced back to Babylonian times, and Leonardo da Vinci (1452–1519) sketched drawing pens and proportional compasses. There are superb examples in museums of sets of drawing instruments made by Italian and French craftsmen of the sixteenth and seventeenth centuries as courtly gifts. The instruments are elaborately decorated, made from gilded copper or brass, and fitted into tooled leather cases. Eighteenth-century sets were commonly contained in cases covered in black fish-skin, with flip-top lids, though there are some examples in ornate, hinged boxes. By the nineteenth century there is a distinction between sets of drawing instruments produced for professional use, and the cheaper, less extensive sets for students in technical schools. Cases of drawing instruments for surveyors or engineers were made from mahogany or rosewood, with brass-bound corners, and a number of lift-out trays, the whole thing lined in velvet, usually dyed blue. In contrast, there was also a demand for flat, leather-covered cases, with rounded corners and a bolt fastening, that were slim enough to be carried in a pocket. These were first imported from France, and later copied in Britain.

The traditional materials for drawing instruments are brass, with steel points for compasses and dividers, and boxwood, brass, or ivory for rulers and scales [3]. By the middle of the nineteenth century the British trade was suffering strong competition from the Continent. The Swiss were introducing instruments of light construction, while the French were using pearwood for set-squares and curves, which gave a better drawing edge than those of English manufacture. This stimulated William Stanley (1829–1909) to set up his drawing equipment business in 1853. In 1861 he applied for a patent to use aluminium

[3] Rolling ruler of ivory, ebony, and brass, signed: W & S JONES 30 HOLBORN LONDON. Length 235 mm, width 46 mm.
c. 1830. *Whipple Museum of the History of Science (453).*

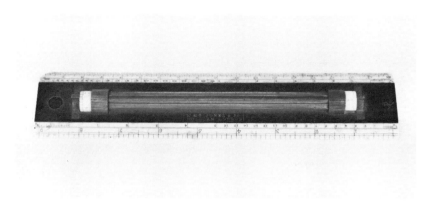

in the manufacture of drawing instruments, and by the late 1860s, his firm was one of the leaders in the field. Another metal that became popular for drawing instruments was German silver, a copper, zinc, and nickel alloy used in sets supplied in the 1880s by the firm of Negretti & Zambra. Its merit was that it resisted corrosion better than brass, and was therefore best suited for use in warm, damp climates.

The nineteenth-century drawing office was a product of the Industrial Revolution. The fields of activity for the surveyor, engineer, architect, and navigator were widening all over the world. Vast areas, such as the continent of India, were being surveyed, and great tracts of ocean charted; railway networks were being built, as were locomotives, and steam-ships to replace sail; the gas industry was born; a rapidly increasing population needed homes, schools, offices, shops, and public buildings. The scale of production, and the range and complexity of products, required technical drawing to become ever more exact and more specialized. The *drawing board* can be regarded as the fundamental drawing instrument. A good drawing board should have a surface that is perfectly level, and which will stay so under changes of temperature; its edges must be straight and square; it should be light in weight. Well-seasoned pine is normally used, the boards about 20 mm thick, tongued and glued together. The underside is strengthened by cross-pieces, so arranged and fixed that expansion and contraction can occur without straining the boards or the joints.

The mid-century board took some rough treatment. The paper was damped on the underside and then the edges of the paper were carefully glued to the board. Allowed to dry, probably near a fire, the paper would be taut and suitable for the work in hand. When completed, the plan would be cut away from the board at the glued edge. Damping, drying, glueing and cutting would spoil drawing boards, and so, after they were replaced they would be destroyed. Consequently, one can expect few survivors.

The *T-square* is used in conjunction with the drawing board edge for marking horizontal lines. The blade is the same length as the board, and it fits into the top of the T, called the stock. T-squares are made of hardwood, pear-wood being about the best, although mahogany with ebony is very suitable.

[4] Circular, brass protractor, signed: *Thomas Jones Charing Cross.* The degree scales are divided into six groups of 60°, the degrees divided to 20'. The inner scale can be rotated inside the outer by the gearing. The scales are read by the magnifying lens. Diameter 223 mm. *c.* 1820. *Museum of the History of Science (31–6).*

[5] Trade card of Thomas Jones (1775–1852). He was at 120 Mount Street in 1806, at 21 Oxendon Street from 1811, and at 62 Charing Cross from 1816 to 1850. One of the most eminent of instrument makers, he was elected a Fellow of the Royal Society in 1835. 1811–16. *Museum of the History of Science.*

The Protractor

This is the general name for the instruments used to divide the circle. As with most other drawing instruments in the nineteenth century, a number of different variations on the basic design were produced for particular needs. Protractors may be circular [4], semi-circular, or rectangular; for accurate work, they were often fitted with a vernier, and they could also have other attachments, such as folding arms, or reflectors, or a plumb-line (on the Sandhurst military protractor). The *station pointer* (see Chapter 14, plate 26) is a kind of double arm protractor which was used particularly for hydrographic surveys (see p. 267).

The Elliptical Trammel; Ellipsograph

An ellipse is one of the curves of some importance to the draughtsman, for example in connexion with the design of bridges. The common, crude method employs two pins at the focii holding down a string, then a pencil always pressed into the string will draw the ellipse. There are two types of instrument, however, that will draw accurate ellipses, even though they are rather cumbersome in use. The smaller device will draw large ellipses and the larger instrument small ellipses.

The simpler in construction is the *elliptical trammel* (compas à ellipse) [6], which consists of a cross-shaped base of brass that pins to

[6] Elliptical trammel, of brass, with steel pins, contained in a fish-skin case. Used for drawing larger ellipses. Overall length of bar 185 mm; diameter of circle 45 mm. *c.* 1800. *Museum of the History of Science.*

the drawing board, and a bar with a pen at one end, that runs through two sliding heads. The heads run in tracks cut into the cross, and so constrain the pen on its bar that an ellipse is drawn. Because the curve is outside the cross, the smallest ellipse that can be drawn with a trammel has a minor axis of about five inches. The instrument was in use from early in the eighteenth century, and was employed by joiners, among others.

The ellipsograph [7 & 8] was invented in 1813 by the English civil engineer, John Farey (1791–1851). It has a large framework so that the cross is above the pen, by which construction very small ellipses can be drawn. Later developments were by James Finney and by Edward Burstow, and both versions were made and sold by the firm of Stanley during the latter part of the nineteenth century.

Map-measuring Instruments

First attempts to make an instrument that would measure directly an area bounded by an irregular curve – notably an area on a map – were made in the early years of the nineteenth century, in Germany and in Italy. But all inventions proved to be inaccurate until, in about 1854, Jakob Amsler, professor of mathematics at the University of Schaffenhausen in Switzerland, constructed his *polar planimeter* [9]. This ingenious instrument consists of two arms, one with a pin to fix to the board, and the other with a tracing point. At the junction of the arms is a small wheel that rotates as the tracing movement is performed, and the area is read off a dial. Since it was both cheap and effective, over 12,000 examples of Amsler's instrument were produced in the next thirty years. Also for use on map work are devices for measuring the length of roads, rivers, walls, etc. The *opisometer* consists of a milled wheel on a screw thread with a handle. The wheel traces the line on the map, and is then wound backwards on the scale at the edge of the

[7] Ellipsograph made of brass and steel, signed: W. & S. JONES 30 *Holborn London*. This instrument, for drawing smaller ellipses, was invented in 1813 by John Farey. W. & S. Jones were in business throughout the first half of the 19th century. Dimensions 150 × 120 mm. *c.* 1815. *Museum of the History of Science.*

[8] Ellipsograph made of brass and steel, signed: *Holtzapffel & Deyerlein Fecirunt LONDON Joseph Clement Invenit.* Holtzapffel & Deyerlein were at 64 Charing Cross from 1826; the name changed to Holtzapffel & Co. in 1851, after the death of Charles Holtzapffel (1806–47). The firm was known for woodworking tools, lathes and scales. Clement published his invention in 1819. Base frame 380 × 228 mm; outer diameter lower circle 306 mm; top circle 300 mm. *c.* 1830. *Museum of the History of Science (26–66).*

[9] Polar planimeter, signed: J. Amsler facsimile signature. Also inscribed: 61033. The fitted case (not shown) has the retailer's label: T. MASON OPTICIAN 5, DAME STREET DUBLIN. The instrument is made of brass and steel, with ivorine count wheels. This design was the invention of Jakob Amsler, a Swiss professor, in about 1854, and is used for computing areas. Length of base bar 170 mm.
Late 19th century. *Museum of the History of Science (73–24)*.

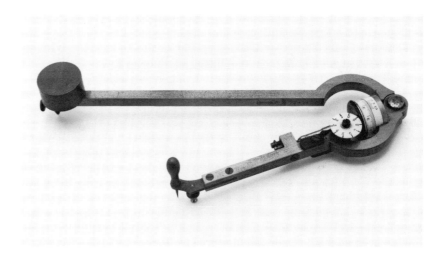

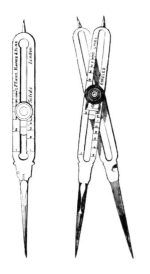

[10] Engraving of proportional compasses, for enlarging or reducing plans, or for making calculations. This type of instrument has not altered from the 18th century to the present day. Usill, *Practical Surveying*, 13th edn (1926), p. 265.

map. The *chartometer* is a refinement which has a dial and pointer to give the measure immediately, without winding back on the scale.

Copying Instruments

Copies of drawings and plans are frequently required, either the same size, or on another scale. For copying to the same size, the *three-legged*, or triangular, *compasses* are used. Starting with any three points on the original, successive points are taken off one at a time, a pair of points already copied being necessary to preserve the orientation.

The *proportional compass* [10] is used to enlarge or reduce a drawing. It has two arms, each with a slot, and in the slots runs a moveable pivot which is tightened by a thumb screw. Points are fitted at each end of the arms, and if the pivot is set at the position on the Scale of Lines marked 3, then the ends of the compass will be spaced in the ratio 1:3. The Scale of Circles provides the setting for inscribing a regular polygon in a circle, usually with the number of sides from 6 to 20. The pivot is tightened at the number of sides required, and the lower points set to the radius of the circle, when the top points will give the length of the side of the polygon that can be inscribed inside the circle. The Scale of Plans (or Area) is used to reduce or enlarge areas in a given proportion, and the Scale of Solids serves likewise for volume.

The proportional compass derives from the 'whole and half' compass, which has a fixed pivot to give the one ratio of 1:2. (A specimen was found in the ruins of the Roman town of Pompeii.) The proportional compass was the invention of the Swiss instrument maker, Jost Bürgi (1552–1632), at the beginning of the seventeenth century. At about the same time, Galileo was working on his sector, which he called a compass, and this has given rise to a linguistic confusion between the English and Continental usage. The proportional compass is known in Italian as 'compasso di riduzione' and in French as 'compas de réduction'. The English sector, on the other hand, is 'compasso di proporzione' in Italian, and 'compas de proportion' in French.

[11] Pantograph, made of brass, with ivory wheels. The positions of the tracing point and the pencil are adjustable for different degrees of reduction or enlargement of the figure to be copied. A lead weight is over the pencil. The mahogany case is not illustrated. Overall length 250 mm.
c. 1830. *Museum of the History of Science.*

[12] Example of the eidograph, signed: *Eidograph No. 2 Invented by W. Wallace Prof.r of Math University of Edinburgh Constructed by R. B. Bate Poultry London.* This device was invented in 1801 by William Wallace as an improvement on the pantograph. Bar length 700 mm; width 50 mm; diameter wheels 155 mm.
c. 1824. *Whipple Museum (1898).*

A number of other instruments were invented to speed up and make easier the task of changing scale. The *pantograph* [11] was first devised between 1603 and 1605 by the German astronomer, Christoph Scheiner, and improved a century and a half later by the Parisian instrument maker, Claude Langlois (fl. 1730–50). It consists of four brass bars, jointed in pairs, one pair being twice the length of the other. Under the joints are small castors, and one long bar has a tracing point, while a short arm has a pen held by a sliding head, that is set to the required ratio. On the other long bar is a pivot point in the form of a heavy brass disk. The *eidograph* [12] was an improvement on the pantograph invented in 1801 by William Wallace (1768–1843), later professor of Mathematics at Edinburgh University. It enabled any ratio to be taken between the limits of one to three.

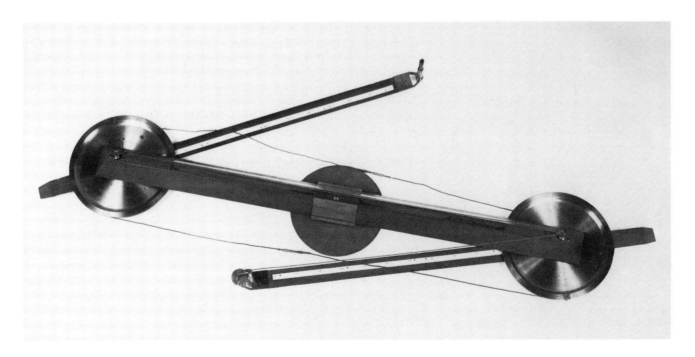

The *cymograph* was invented by Robert Willis (1800–75) of Cambridge University in 1841. Its chief usefulness was to take outlines of solid objects, such as mouldings and carvings, or taking off outlines from drawings to material for pattern-making or carving. It consists of two free-jointed parallelograms of metal. The one with the shorter sides is fixed to a small drawing board, and the other carries a rod with a small knob that 'feels' the moulding that is being traced.

CALCULATING INSTRUMENTS

The *abacus* [13], which is familiar to us today as a frame containing beads mounted on wires, means in Greek a disk or table; the Greek, and later the Roman abacus was a convenient flat surface on which pebbles could be placed. So the first aids to numerical calculation were groups of small objects, usually pebbles, in Latin 'calculi'. The Latin

[13] Two abaci. *Above:* Chinese, rosewood frame (148 × 103 mm) and beads, bamboo runners; purchased in a Chinese shop in San Francisco in October 1877. *Below:* Japanese, cherry-wood frame (193 × 68 mm), oak and ivory, with bamboo beads and runners. Bought at a sale in 1929, but this is a traditional form that continues in production today. Below the bar, the beads count 1 unit, above the bar, 5 units. The Chinese employ two beads above, but the Japanese only one. The number set, as photographed, is 1982. *Museum of the History of Science* (*LE 2385; nn*).

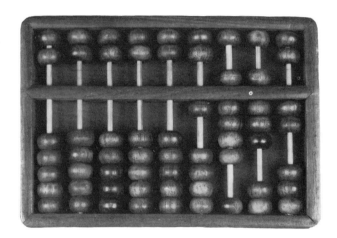

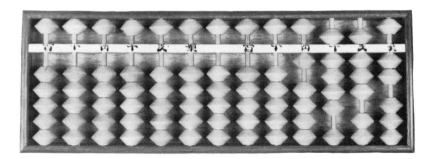

phrase for reckoning up accounts was 'ponere calculos', which means to place the pebbles, and from this word derive our words 'calculate' and 'calculus', a branch of mathematics. As well as the calculating board, the Romans also used small bead calculators. These are small enough to hold in one hand, and consist of beads that are moved in vertical slots. Both of these simple calculating devices continued in use for centuries. Calculating boards, with counters, were used in commerce, and by government officials, throughout Europe from medieval times until the eighteenth century. The counters, known as jettons (from the

French, 'jeter', to throw) were latterly made of brass, and are stamped on one side with the head of the reigning monarch, and on the other with the maker's name; from the sixteenth century, these tokens were made in Nuremberg. The bead-frame abacus is still in use today in China, Japan, Russia, Poland, and some other eastern countries.

Before geometrical surveying techniques could be imported from the Continent during the middle of the sixteenth century, it was necessary for practitioners to have a knowledge of arithmetic, and for arabic numerals to replace roman. (The notation included the zero, so giving positional significance to the cyphers.) In the Exchequer Records, arabic numerals were first used at the end of the sixteenth century, but roman did not entirely disappear in this stronghold of tradition, until the mid-seventeenth century. Accounts were done on ruled boards with casting-counters, hence the phrase 'to cast accounts'. Pen-reckoning was very necessary for any technical subject; and the highly influential work of Robert Recorde (*c.* 1510–58), *The Ground of Artes Teaching the Worke and Practise of Arithmetike*, published in 1543, and the standard work until 1700, was the first of several books written by Recorde, in English rather than Latin, that contributed to British excellence in applied science. John Napier of Merchiston (1530–1617) devised logarithmic tables, and published his work in 1614. The tables reduced the tedious and error-prone multiplication of large numbers to simple addition and subtraction. Not content with this important step, he produced in 1617 his set of rectangular rods inscribed with numbers, which became known as Napier's Bones. These were the forerunner of several of the later calculating machines. The first step was to speed up calculation with the rods by substituting rotatable cylinders bearing the numbers, and fixing them in a box.

The first geared arithmetical machines were devised in the early seventeenth century, the two leading pioneers being the Frenchman, Blaise Pascal (1623–62), and Sir Samuel Morland (1625–95) who became Master of Mechanicks to King Charles II. Pascal, after many attempts, produced his definitive model of an addition machine in 1645.

[14] Arithmometer, signed: THOMAS, de Colmar A PARIS INVENTEUR No. 696. This type, the first multiplication machine to be made commercially, was invented in about 1820 by Chevalier Charles Xavier Thomas (1785–1870). *c.* 1860. *Science Museum (1868–1).*

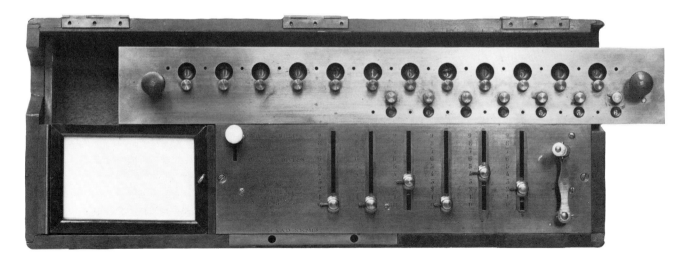

[15] Brunsviga calculating machine, signed: BRUNSVIGA No. 262. G. N. & C. c. a. A. Patented by W. T. Odhner in Germany in 1891, who sold it to Grimme, Natalis & Co. of Brunswick. The Odhner wheels give a compact design, and multiplication and division require no gear change, merely reversal of the sense of the handle. 1892. *Science Museum (1893–17)*.

Morland invented a machine for the same purpose in 1666, and in his book describing the operation of the addition machine, also described another, adapted for multiplication and division. Three years earlier, he had devised a trigonometrical machine and, in 1664, it was constructed by Henry Sutton and Samuel Knibb, two leading London instrument makers. The next advance was made by Gottfried Leibnitz (1646–1716), who conceived, in 1671, the idea of a multiplying machine that worked by repeated addition. This was finally made in 1694, and an important feature of the machine was the stepped reckoner. During the eighteenth century, a number of different mathematicians and instrument makers attempted to devise an arithmetical machine that could be made commercially, but failed to achieve the necessary degree of accuracy. It was not until the early nineteenth century that the first successful calculating machine was invented.

It was in 1820 that Chevalier Charles Xavier Thomas, of Colmar in Alsace, produced his *arithmometer* [14], which proved to be the first multiplication machine capable of successful commerical production. This was known as the Thomas de Colmar Arithmometer. Improvements in details of its construction were made over the years by various makers but the main features of the design remained unaltered. The mechanism is devided into three parts, concerned with setting, counting, and recording, arranged in order from front to back of the machine. Any number up to 999,999 may be set by moving the pointers in one or more of the six slots in the fixed cover plate, which has the numbers 0 to 9 engraved to the left of each slot. The movement of any of these pointers slides a small pinion with ten teeth along a square axle, underneath and to the left of which is a Leibnitz stepped cylinder. A lever at the top left-hand corner of the fixed plate can be set for

'Addition and Multiplication' or 'Subtraction and Division', and sets in motion bevel wheels that rotate either clock-wise or anti-clockwise.

The next stage in the development of the calculating machine was the replacement of the Leibnitz stepped cylinder by a wheel having a variable number of projecting teeth. This was first patented by F. S. Baldwin in 1875, but the more important patent was that of W. T. Odhner in 1891, that resulted in the production, from 1892, of the so-called '*Brunsviga*' calculating machine [15]. Its operation is similar to that of the Thomas de Colmar machine, in that it performs multiplication by repeated addition, but the use of the Odhner wheel makes it much more compact in design. The Odhner wheels, of variable number, fit very closely together on the axle at the back; the amount of gearing is reduced, and the machine somewhat resembles the old-fashioned type of cash register.

Another variant of the calculating machine, developed chiefly in the United States, used figure keys instead of slot markers. Some of these were key-driven, that is, the mechanism was actually operated by the depression of the keys; in others, the keys were simply set in position and the mechanism operated by a handle. The key-driven machine became fully effective in the form of the *comptometer*, patented by Dorr E. Felt in 1887. Printing was incorporated into an adding machine for the first time in 1872 by E. D. Barbour. From 1892 well into the twentieth century, the leading developers and producers of this type of adding machine were the Burroughs company.

Direct method multiplication by machine was invented by the young

[16] Adding and listing machine, signed: BURROUGHS' ADDING & REGISTERING MACHINE COMPANY LIMITED. PATENTED SEPT. 1893 NOTTINGHAM ENGLAND. The keyboard design of adding machine, with a paper roll, introduced by William S. Burroughs *c.* 1880, was intended to type a column of figures and then, almost automatically, to type the sum total. The machine illustrated was used at Barclay's Bank Head Office between 1897 and 1913. 1897. *Science Museum (1913–534).*

son of a French bell-founder, Léon Bollée, in 1887, but the full development of this more complex instrument had to wait till this century, in the form of the Mercedes-Euklid machine produced in Germany. Another early-twentieth-century development was the incorporation of electric motors into calculating machines.

The rapid increase in the scale of commerce during the nineteenth century gave a strong impetus to the invention of instruments that could perform numerical calculations quickly and accurately. These were used not only for dealing with masses of figures in banks and insurance offices, but also in retail shops. A German mathematical encyclopaedia published in 1901 recorded that its author, Professor R. Mehmke, was able to list over 80 distinct calculating machines. Alongside the commercial demand, however, there was the interest of mathematicians and scientists in these machines, which were also of use in research. Scientists invented machines with far more complex powers than the arithmometers used in business and commerce, that were known as difference or analytical machines.

The requirement also continued, however, for readily portable instruments that could aid the professional man in the particular type of calculations he had to make most frequently. This need was filled by the sector, and more particularly in the nineteenth century, by the slide rule.

The Sector

The sector and the slide rule [18 & 19] were both devised around 1600, but the former, after a life of about 300 years, was falling out of use by the mid-nineteenth century; William Stanley in 1866 described it as 'a kind of established ornament' often found in cases of drawing instruments. The sector was in use in Britain by the 1590s for surveying, and was later made with scales specially suitable to navigators, surveyors, and draughtsmen. Galileo worked on the sector in about 1600, but he called it a compass, so that, on the Continent, the sector became known as the proportional compass. Since this latter name is given in Britain to an entirely different instrument, it is important to be aware of this linguistic problem (see above).

The sector has been called a universal scale; it is used with a pair of dividers or compasses. In appearance like a jointed rule, it is found

[18] Four six-inch sectors. *Top:* ivory, signed: THOMAS JONES 64 CHARING CROSS; *c.* 1850; *left:* ivory, signed: ELLIOTT BRO.ˢ STRAND, LONDON; *c.* 1860; *right:* silver, signed: *Dollond London; c.* 1820; *bottom:* brass, signed: *J. Long London; c.* 1825. Radius of each 153 mm. *Private collection.*

in 6-inch, 9-inch and 12-inch sizes which, when opened right out, form rules of double the length. Sectors are to be found made of boxwood, brass, ivory, or sometimes of silver. The sides are engraved with a number of mathematical scales, the English instrument differing from the French, which was intended for gunnery. The English instrument is essentially a draughtsman's aid, and it normally bears the following scales, with its symbol in brackets: line of equal parts (L); line of chords (C) used to protract an angle; line of sines (S); line of tangents (T); line of polygons (P or POL), for inscribing a regular polygon inside a circle of a given radius; line of numbers (N) used for multiplication as with a slide rule. Sometimes further scales are marked for the construction of sundials.

The Slide Rule

The slide rule [19] is based on logarithms, and owes its origin to the scale devised by Edmund Gunter in 1607, and published in 1623. The Gunter scale, or 'line of numbers', consists of two scales of logarithms placed end to end and used with dividers to multiply and divide. William Oughtred placed the two scales side by side to make the first slide rule in 1630; the two scales could move past each other, thus doing away with the need for dividers. Also devised in the early seventeenth century was the circular slide rule, first published under the name Mathematical Ring by Richard Delamain in 1630, and two years later as the Circles of Proportion by Oughtred himself. This type was made only in comparatively small numbers. The runner or cursor, found on all modern slide rules, was designed by the original inventor of the circular slide rule, but, despite being used in some prototypes, was not

[19] Five slide rules. *Top:* musician's slide rule, boxwood (314 × 38 mm); late 19th century; *upper middle:* carpenter's, boxwood (305 × 40 mm), signed: F. B. COX MAKER LATE THO.ˢ & CO; *c.* 1860; *middle:* Excise Officer's, boxwood (305 × 27 × 20 mm), with four slides, one in each side, signed: DOLLOND LONDON; *c.* 1830; *lower middle:* boxwood (305 × 48 mm), signed: HOARE'S IMPROVED DOUBLE SLIDE RULE 12 BILLITER SQUARE LONDON; *c.* 1867, the date of publication of Charles Hoare, *The Slide Rule and How to Use It; bottom:* ivory (187 × 35 mm), signed: DICAS PATENTEE LIVERPOOL; *c.* 1810. John Dicas patented in 1780 his excise hydrometer, with a slide rule for correcting for temperature; his business was continued by Ann Dicas to *c.* 1822. *Museum of the History of Science* (33–35; 52–60; L.E.; 68–401; nn).

[20] French accountant's slide rule, signed: J. LELUBOIS INVENIT TABLE D'INTERETS. Made of silver on a mahogany base (455 × 88 × 20 mm), the slider is reversible. Columns marked: 4% MILLIÈMES; NOMBRES DE JOURS; MOIS. Mid-19th century. *Museum of the History of Science.*

found on the straight slide rule until the mid-nineteenth century. The effectiveness of the slide rule as a means of rapid calculation, where results to only two or three significant figures were needed, was appreciated from the second half of the seventeenth century. Special versions were devised for use by particular trades. Among the most widely used types of slide rule in the eighteenth and nineteenth centuries were the *Coggeshall* and the *Everard*. In 1677 Henry Coggeshall published a book that ran to many editions, in which he described a two-foot folding slide rule adapted to timber measure. The *Coggeshall* rule, usually made of boxwood, has a brass hinge and end-caps, with a brass slider in one arm. The slider bears a Gunter-type logarithm scale. On one side is a conventional double 1–10 scale, while on the other is a broken Gunter scale from 4 to 40, which is called the girt line, for measuring the volume of timber. On the back edge is marked the 24-inch rule, and on the back of the brass slider is a 12-inch rule, so that the whole thing can measure a yard (915 mm). Also marked on one arm is a table which gives the sterling price of various units of timber. Along the edge of the rule is a scale dividing the foot into 100 parts.

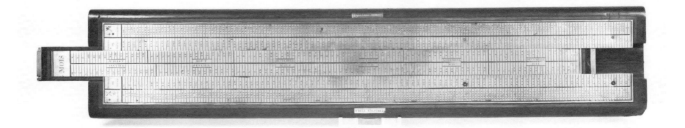

In 1683 Thomas Everard described a slide rule for use by excise officers, in assessing duty on wines and spirits. The *Everard* slide rule was nearly square in section with sliders on all four sides. It is a foot long and an inch square, with Gunter's scales, and is marked with standard points important for Excise use, including: WG – wine gallon; AG – ale gallon; MB – malt bushel.

More general purpose was the *Coulson* slide rule, which was flat, about 10 inches (250 mm) long and 2 inches (50 mm) wide. It has two sliders of the same thickness as the rule, graduated on both faces. So there are in effect four sliders, each with a pair of scales above and below. Gauge points act as constants to be used in calculating the contents, weights etc. of timber, iron bars, casks, cattle, and so on.

In addition to the long-established carpenter's and excise officer's slide rules, the first half of the nineteenth century provided some innovations. There was Mark Roget's invention in 1814 of the log-log scale (logarithm of the logarithm of x) which allowed powers to be read off quite simply. It was used for compound interest and making estimates of future population increases.

Silvanus Bevan produced an engineer's slide rule, one of many in this class, which all carry the main mathematical scales and a few for particular industrial calculations. Woollgar's Pocket Calculator had two slides, and scales of sines, tangents, areas of polygons, circular

[21] Circular slide rule, signed: PALMER'S COMPUTING SCALE IMPROVED BY FULLER [Registered] *in the year 1843, by Aaron Palmer . . . and by J. E. Fuller 1847.* This device was invented and produced in Boston Massachusetts. For the reverse side, see Chapter 2, plate 18. Dimensions 285 × 285 mm. 1847. *Whipple Museum (1475).*

[XXV] Large set of drawing instruments, signed on the case: L. CASELLA LONDON. Signed on the circular protractor (diameter 162 mm): *L. Casella Maker to the Admiralty & Ordnance London*. The 6-inch ivory sector is signed: HOLTZAPFFEL & CO 64 CHARING CROSS LONDON. Among the equipment are a nickel-plated 20° set square, eleven French curves, a three-legged compass, and a beam compass. Louis P. Casella was trading separately from 1848 at 23 Hatton Garden, London, and the firm continued into the twentieth century. Case 405 × 200 × 118 mm.
c. 1880. *Museum of the History of Science (78–48).*

[XXVI] Small orrery, made of printed paper on oak, and contained in a marbled-paper-covered wooden box. This instrument demonstrates the motions of the Earth and Moon relative to each other and to the Sun. W. & S. Jones of London sold a very similar model. Diameter 195 mm. *c.* 1810. *Museum of the History of Science (CHE).*

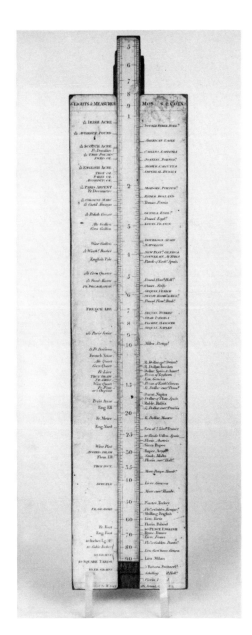

segments, interests, and annuities. Ewart's Cattle Gauge, made by Cary and others, was marked with weight in stones and girth in feet and inches. The nautical slide rule was introduced to help in the tedious calculations of latitude from observations of lunar distances with the sextant. The most prominent makers in the first half of the century were R. B. Bate, J. A. Rooker, and W. Cary; followed in the later years by Dring & Fage (especially for excise), W. F. Stanley, and L. Casella.

Specialist slide rules were also made in such variety that only a few can be mentioned here. Wollaston's scale of chemical equivalents was in the form of printed paper on a mahogany board and was made by W. Cary in 1814. (See Chapter 12.) In 1815 W. Cary produced a similar-looking slide rule for currency and bullion calculations [22]. Among other rules are those for cargo weights, rents, proof spirit, photographic exposure, barometric height, and computing run-off to sewers. Florian Cajori, writing on the history of the slide rule in 1909, made a list of slide rules designed and used since 1800. He recorded 256 different types, of which 90 were produced during the first nine years of the twentieth century.

Cylindrical slide rules [23] have the advantage that they can be equivalent to many times the length of the normal slide rule. The cylindrical rule became popular at the end of the nineteenth century. A very large cylindrical slide rule was patented in 1881 by Edwin Thacher and made in New York. But by far the most popular rule of this type was the

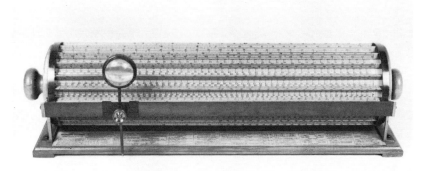

[22] Slide rule for calculating rates of exchange, signed: *Published by W. Cary, 182, Strand, Apr.! 1,1815 . . . Apr.! 24, 1815.* The scales are printed on paper from engraved plates, the base being mahogany (307 × 73 × 11 mm). Scales are labelled: exchanges, bullion, weights and measures, monies and coins, etc.
c. 1815. Museum of the History of Science (35–RO).

[23] Cylindrical slide rule, inscribed: *Patented by Edwin Thatcher* [sic] *C. E. Nov. 1st 1881. Divided by W. F. Stanley, London, 1882.* Also inscribed: THACHER'S CALCULATING INSTRUMENT. The instrument was made by Keuffel & Esser Co., New York; the plate for printing the scales was divided by Stanley in London. The scales are 40 times as great as on an ordinary slide rule of similar length, thus giving accurate readings to four figures. The invention was patented by Edwin Thacher of Pittsburg. Base board 545 × 140 mm; cylinder diameter 125 mm; length of scales 457 mm; height 150 mm.
c. 1885. Whipple Museum (228).

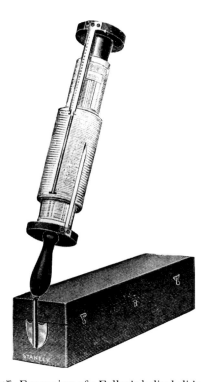

[24] Engraving of a Fuller's helical slide
rule, which was patented in 1878 by
Professor George E. Fuller. The cylinder
is made of papier-maché, 162 mm in length
and 81 mm in diameter. There is another
cylinder inside the first, and a third inside
that, each with an index arm.
c. 1900. *Stanley (1901), p. 593.*

invention of Professor George Fuller in 1878. The *Fuller* slide rule
[24] was equivalent to eight times the length of a rectangular rule,
and gave the possibility of reading to three or four places of decimals.
It was sold in a box, and was fixed by its handle to a bracket at one
end of the box when in use.

In 1851, Amedée Mannheim (1831–1906), who later became a col-
onel in the French artillery, published his pattern of a slide rule, and
it became the one used by that branch of the French army. It was made
by the prestigious Parisian firm of Tavernier-Gravet. The *Mannheim*
rule employed a cursor, also called a runner, and gained acceptance
on the Continent before crossing to England in about 1880, and to
North America in the 1890s. After this, it became the standard slide
rule in all parts of the technical world. Another Continental development of the slide rule occurred in 1886, when the firm of Dennert and
Pape in Germany began dividing the scales for slide rules onto strips
of a white synthetic material. Ivorine was the trade name of this material, which allowed more accurate scales to be engraved, since, unlike
wood or ivory, it had no grain.

The long life of the simple slide rule, along with its junior, though
more complex relative, the mechanical calculator, ended with the dramatic development of the electronic calculator in the late 1960s and
the early 1970s. The last small, mechanical calculator, used by many
scientists in the 1940s and 1950s, was the Curta, made by Contina AG
in Vaduz, Principality of Lichtenstein. Two models were made, both
easily held in the hand, that could show results to 11 or 15 figures
respectively. This was replaced by the first of the electronic calculators
which made immense calculating power available inexpensively, on the
desk or in the pocket.

16 · Recreational Science

By 'Recreative Science', we understand the cultivation of the various branches of physical and mathematical inquiry in a way to afford amusement as well as instruction.

Editorial in *Recreative Science*, volume 1, no. 1, p. 1 (1860)

In the eighteenth century science became for the first time a subject of interest and study for the layman. Those who were sufficiently wealthy formed their own collections of items of natural history and scientific instruments and apparatus. Similar collections were formed by learned societies and institutions, and gradually this interest extended into many homes all over western Europe, and in the United States, where relatively common recreational items were the microscope, the air-pump, and the telescope. These collections served the purpose of providing education and recreation. The nucleus of the very large collection of King George III, much of which survives in the Science Museum, London, was the apparatus owned by his tutor, Stephen Demainbray (1710–82), who had a considerable reputation as a lecturer. The lecture-demonstration proved equally popular in aristocratic circles – the Abbé Nollet (1700–70) achieved fame through his lectures to the French court – and in towns, where the itinerant lecturer would arrive with his apparatus loaded into a cart. Educational content there certainly was, but a large part of the popularity of these lectures lay in the spectacular demonstrations of physical effects, notably those associated with frictional electrical machines and air pumps.

Education and amusement are so closely akin that it is not surprising how many of the pieces of demonstration apparatus used in these eighteenth-century lectures were the direct forerunners of toys and amusements made for family entertainment in the Victorian period. A child's spinning top is almost as old as play itself, but the demonstration of a gyroscope provides an explanation of the dynamics behind the top's motion, and also that of the Earth. The facts of dynamic motion may be absorbed by a child through watching a gyroscope, or he may simply be fascinated to watch it, and try to make it spin evenly. The fact that yesterday's science so often becomes today's recreation does not make it any the less scientific. Indeed, much scientific knowledge is absorbed, consciously or unconsciously, through play.

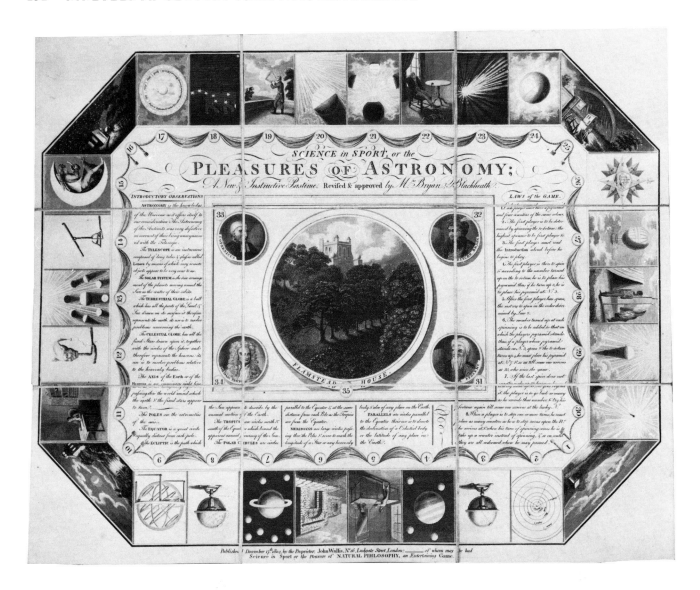

[1] Board game, inscribed: *Published December 17th, 1804, by the Proprietor,* JOHN WALLIS, *No. 16 Ludgate Street, London.* A similar game was called 'the Pleasures of Natural Philosophy', and both were also sold as dissected puzzles. Dimensions 565 × 442 mm. 1804. *Private collection.*

Throughout the nineteenth century popular interest in science was stimulated by an apparently endless series of books. These reproduced for the ordinary reader the well-established subject-matter of eighteenth-century Dutch, English and French writers on experimental philosophy. The idea of science as recreation, however, had its origins in the seventeenth century. In 1803 a four-volume work entitled: *Recreations in Mathematics and Natural Philosophy: containing Amusing Dissertations and Enquiries concerning a Variety of Subjects the most remarkable and Proper to excite Curiousity and Attention to the Whole Range of the Mathematical and Philosophical Sciences* was published by Charles Hutton (1737–1823), who was a self-taught mathematics teacher, appointed in 1773 as professor in that subject at the Royal Military Academy at Woolwich. This book was a translation from the French of Jean Étienne Montucla (1725–99), and he in turn had made a revision and extension of *Recréations mathématiques et physiques . . .* by

Jacques Ozanam (1640–1717), a private tutor of mathematics in Paris. His book, first appearing in 1694, went through eight editions during the eighteenth century, and was also translated. He, too, relied heavily on earlier writers, one of whom, Henry van Etten (a pseudonym) wrote in French a work that was published in London in 1633, under the title, *Mathematicall Recreations. Or a Collection of sundrie Problemes, extracted out of the Ancient and Moderne Philosophers*. This book included tricks with coins, dice and cards, mathematical puzzles, and experimental 'wonders' in optics, hydrostatics, and mechanics. The pattern set here can still be discerned 250 years later in *Letters on Natural Magic*, by Sir David Brewster (1781–1868), first published in 1868, and, three generations on, in *Scientific Magic* by Sam Rosenfeld, published in New York in 1959. This series of books perpetuates the common theme of science providing a simple, reasonable explanation for apparently magical or miraculous effects: science, in fact, as the casting-out of superstition and fear.

The nineteenth century had an insatiable appetite for self-made entertainment to be enjoyed by all ages. Scientific demonstrations could provide this, supplying in addition the element of instruction which made amusement respectable. So Hutton had many imitators, including the attractively named *Philosophical Recreations, or Winter Amusements: A Collection of Entertaining and Surprising Experiments* (*c.* 1840). Other books were aimed directly at the young, the pill of learning being sugared by the use of such words as 'magic', 'fairyland', and 'playbook'. Examples of this genre are *Philosophy in Sport made Science in Earnest*, published in 1827 by John Ayrton Paris, the eighth edition of which appeared in 1857, and *The Fairyland Tales of Science* (1889), by the

[2] Gentle instruction in discovering the depth of a well by timing the fall of a stone. An illustration in the book published by John Ayrton Paris, anonymously, as *Philosophy in Sport made Science in Earnest* (Vol. 1, p. 56, 1827).

[3] Toys showing the principle of inertia. Two yo-yos, one in wood, *c.* 1900 (diameter 72 mm), one in turned ivory, *c.* 1850 (diameter 70 mm), and two boxwood tops, *c.* 1890 (diameter 100 and 60 mm). The tops have square openings to a resonating chamber so that they 'sing' as in a siren. *Private collection.*

Rev. J. Gordon M'Pherson, with chapters on 'Formation of Dew', 'The Rainbow', 'Lightning', and 'Micro-organisms in Water'.

It was with this sort of encouragement that science as instruction and amusement found its way into the home, and so into the consciousness of many people, from an early age. Scientific toys can conveniently be considered within the categories chosen by the demonstration-lecturers of the preceding century, that included mechanics, hydrostatics, optics, electricity, magnetism, and pneumatics.

Some of the travelling lecturers specialized in astronomy, using geared models of the solar system. Such a model was usually given the name 'orrery' [xxvi & xxvii, facing pps. 289 & 304], and though some orreries of the eighteenth century are both expensive and elaborate, using clockwork, simple wooden versions were also made, incorporating a crank handle to rotate the wire arms holding balls to represent the planets. Chemistry was usually taught separately from the other topics which are now grouped together as 'physics', and the apparatus and materials used for chemical experiments were provided by specialist suppliers. By the 1840s chemistry sets for children were being advertised, and they continued to be popular well into the present century, with little change in the ingredients. The popularity of natural history specimens, minerals, fossils, seeds, shells, spread from adults to the young, and small chests containing sea-shells and other such items were made for the delight and instruction of children.

Mechanical Toys

Two of the most ancient of toys are the whip-top and the hoop. To these can be added the yo-yo [3], a flat reel on which a length of fine

[4] Gravity toy. The puppets descend the steps because the side bars contain mercury, the displacement of which alters the centre of gravity.
c. 1880. *Tissandier, p. 30.*

string is wound, with a loop at the loose end that fits over the player's middle finger. The reel is then thrown lightly from the hand towards the ground and will return as the string recoils itself. The winding-up process acts against the force of gravity through the continuing rotational momentum from the downward motion. The name 'yo-yo' derives from the 1932 craze for this toy, but under a variety of names it dates back at least to the classical Greek period. All these three traditional playthings can be categorized as mechanical, in that they display the principle of inertia, their stability depending on conservation of momentum. Tops can be made of wood, bone, or ivory; there are yo-yos from the Regency period made of ivory, elaborately carved on a lathe, but most nineteenth-century examples are made of wood. By 1820 another inertial toy had become sufficiently popular to be described in a book of games: the diablo, or 'devil on two sticks'. This consisted of a double cone rotated by a string held between two sticks. The diablo only retains its stability in the air when thrown up if it is first made to rotate rapidly by rolling on the cord between the sticks – an effect similar to that of the gyroscope. This instrument found its way into the playroom after its dynamics had been the subject of mathematical treatises.

Anthropomorphic toys, or life-like human figures, often made use of physical forces to produce their special effects. One of the oldest balance toys is the tumbler, usually the figure of a clown, heavily weighted at the base, so that it always rights itself when pushed over, showing a gravitational effect. The figure of an acrobat could be balanced on a point because he carried a curved bar with counterweights at each end, so that the centre of gravity of the combination was brought below the point of support. A mobile centre of gravity, provided by a quantity of mercury placed in the hollow, flexible body of an acrobat, enabled the figure to somersault down a flight of steps [4]. Another version placed the mercury in hollow bars held by two acrobats, who somersaulted over each other. Toy acrobats could also be attached to a rod which then rolled down gently-inclined parallel bars in a frame, causing the figures to rotate. Yet another gravitational effect was demonstrated by the toy figure with pivoted legs and leaded feet which, when placed on a slope, performed a shuffling walk.

The operation of the lever found its way into the playroom in the form of lazy tongs, either with a joker's head at the end, or a parade of wooden soldiers at the joints. Wooden birds perched on a flat board are given animation, moving to peck in turn as a pendulum weight swings below the board. Centrifugal force is used in the toy consisting of a circular wire track with a handle, on the inner side of which a ball can be made to roll at speed, and stay in position, by a small circular motion of the track.

Water Toys

During the seventeenth and eighteenth centuries, the behaviour of water was seriously studied, and the knowledge put to use for many practical and ornamental purposes. The great houses and public gardens of the period were replete with fountains, and models of those made to the pattern of Hero of Alexandria were used by demonstration-lecturers. Two other of their pieces of apparatus became playthings. One was designed to show the effect of buoyancy and specific gravity, and consisted of tiny figures, usually imps [5], so blown from glass to have a specific gravity close to that of water. If these were placed in a jar of water with a membrane over the top, varying pressure on the membrane would make the figures rise and sink. The other device was known as the Tantalus beaker, the figure of a man being placed in a glass goblet, into which water is gradually poured. When the water reached the level of his mouth, the water slowly syphoned out by means of a tube secreted in the figure. During the nineteenth century, with the improvement of domestic plumbing, the large, fixed bath was to be found in an increasing number of homes, and the first bath toys appeared. Model boats were powered by camphor pellets, the drive produced by the surface tension of the water-camphor solution.

Optical Toys

Sight is man's chief sense, and optics, therefore, the chief provider of illusions that were often thought to be magical. The simplest optical toys are those which make use of mirrors. Anamorphic drawings, or distorted pictures [6] have been popular since the sixteenth century,

[5] 'Bottle Imps', or Cartesian divers, an illustration from Ayrton Paris, *Philosophy in Sport*, (1853), p. 197. The enamelled glass figures have nearly the specific gravity of water. When a bladder across the top of the jar, which is completely filled with water, is pressed, air in the imps is compressed and they sink. Versions of this toy have been produced from the seventeenth century to the present day.

[6] Anamorphic drawings. The distorted pictures are 'rectified' by the cylindrical mirror. Overall height of mirror 105 mm; diameter of base 40 mm; cards 200 × 167 mm.
c. 1830. Museum of the History of Science (C. 981).

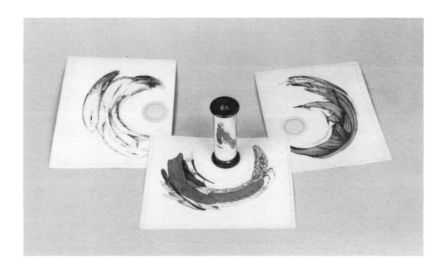

the trick being that the distortion is rectified by a conical or cylindrical mirror of glass or metal. In the early nineteenth century, a toy of enormous popularity was invented by David Brewster (1781–1868). This was the *Kaleidoscope* (beautiful-form viewer) [7], patented in 1817, and made under licence by several instrument makers. Over 200,000 were sold in London and Paris within a few months of its production. It was an improvement on the Debusscope, and consists of a tube about a foot long with two glass mirrors running along the whole length separated from each other at an angle of 60°. At the eye end is a small hole near the junction of the mirrors, and at the other end is the object box. This is formed of two disks of glass between which are fragments of coloured glass. As the tube is rotated the fragments alter their positions and different symmetrical patterns are seen. Modifications are made for use with opaque objects, and in one version the object box was replaced with a short-focus lens so that patterns are seen when the tube is directed towards any object. The *Debusscope* was a late-eighteenth-century device in which two mirrors set at an angle of 45° reproduce symmetrically any design on which they are placed. In those cases where the mirrors are adjustable, the toy was called a Polyscope. The

[7] Kaleidoscope, the invention (patented in 1817) of David Brewster. Length 315 mm; diameter of wide end 100 mm.
c. 1825. Museum of the History of Science.

[8] Engraving of a camera obscura, employing a mirror and lens at the top of the tent to focus the view onto a table. Such a device in a portable tent was popular for sketching landscapes. *c.* 1870. *Deschanel, p. 941.*

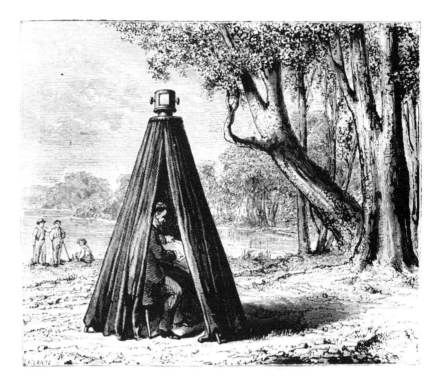

[9] Portable camera obscura for sketching. The head is inserted through the curtains. The whole device packs into the flat, mahogany case for transport. Case 590 × 428 × 88 mm. *c.* 1840. *Museum of the History of Science (C.704).*

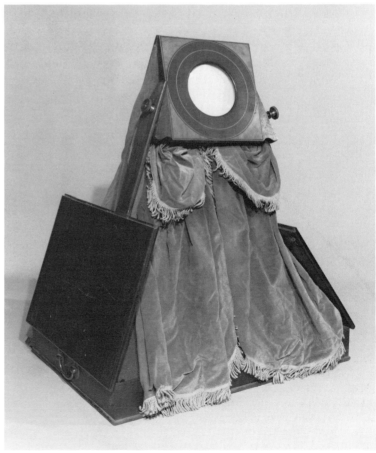

Designograph was a type of Kaleidoscope for viewing opaque objects. The objects are placed on a wooden disk which may be rotated by turning a knob on the top of the base. On looking through a small hole down the pillar, the object can be seen with its reflexions in two sheets of glass backed with black paint. The mirrors are set at an angle of 45°.

One of the oldest of all optical tricks was that employed in the so-called *camera obscura* (dark room) [8 & 9], from which our modern word camera is derived. A room was darkened by shutters with a pin-hole through which an inverted image of the outside scene was thrown on to the opposite wall. Later, a lens in the hole and a mirror rectified the image, recreating the outside scene in life-like manner. The camera obscura, complete with pin-hole, ground glass screen and lens, was produced, from the eighteenth century onwards, in box form, as a recreational device. The early nineteenth-century interest in sketching also extended to those with little natural skill, who were able to use optical aids, such as Wollaston's *camera lucida* [10] and Varley's *graphic telescope* [11]. To create the illusion of seeing pictured scenes with the vivid, three-dimensional effect of actual vision, mirrors and lenses were used in a number of ways.

The *Zograscope* or 'optical diagonal machine', was made for viewing prints of landscapes, thereby endeavouring to create an illusion of seeing the landscape directly. The origins of this device are obscure, but it is thought to have first appeared in Paris early in the eighteenth century. To counter the reversal of the image brought about by the mirror, the prints had to be made reversed. Such reversed prints were certainly on sale in 1753, and the device continued to be popular into the nineteenth century. The *Stereoscope* (solid-view) is an instrument intended to produce a single mental image, giving the impression of solidity as in ordinary vision, from two pictures of the same scene. The original form, the reflecting stereoscope [12], was invented by Charles Wheatstone in the 1830s; the user looks at two mirrors set in a 'V',

[10] Camera lucida, signed: ALEX^R. ALEXANDER OPTICIAN TO THE KING EXETER 1283. The G clamp fits to the edge of a table, the arm adjusted to suit, and a sketch is made by viewing through the prismatic end. Here, mirrors bring to the eye a superimposed image of the landscape and the sketch pad on the table. The camera lucida was invented by W. Hyde Wollaston and patented in 1806. Alexander Alexander worked in Exeter from 1812 to 1820. Overall length, as photographed, 380 mm.
c. 1815. *Museum of the History of Science.*

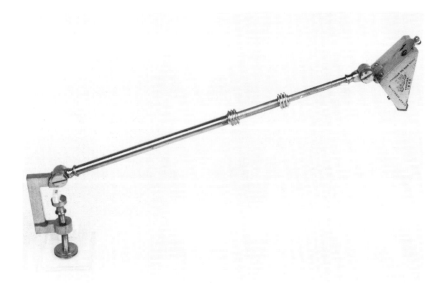

[11] Graphic telescope, signed: Cornelius Varley's Patent Graphic Telescope. The patent was registered on 5 April 1811. Light is received by a plane mirror at 45° to the axis of the tube. A lens and mirror system at the eye end superimposes the distant and sketchpad images. Length of body 230 mm; overall height 142 mm. *c.* 1820. *Museum of the History of Science* (*C.963*).

[12] Wheatstone stereo viewer. This type works by reflecting the image of a pair of drawings to the eyes by two mirrors set at 90° to each other, the joint edge towards the person viewing. With appropriate drawings, or photographs, a distinct impression of three dimensions is conveyed. Charles Wheatstone had made a stereoscope by 1832 but did not publish it until 1838. *c.* 1870. *Science Museum* (*1884–6*).

which reflect pictures placed at the sides. The refracting or lenticular form of the device was invented by David Brewster and consists of two tubes containing lenses through which the two pictures are seen, one by each eye [XXVIII, facing p. 304]. Brewster first announced his invention in 1849, but could find no British optician willing to manufacture it, so he went to the Parisian firm of Duboscq, who made and exhibited the first stereoscope at the Great Exhibition in 1851. Queen Victoria saw it there and was amused by the optical illusion, giving the instrument a drawing-room vogue which produced sales comparable to those of the kaleidoscope.

[13] The first illustration of a
Thaumatrope, invented by John Ayrton
Paris and described in his book, *Philosophy
in Sport* (1827), Vol 3, p. 1. Paris, a
doctor, realized that the retina of the eye
retains an image for about $\frac{1}{30}$th of a second.
In the book it is called: 'A new optical toy
invented by the author, and termed a
thaumatrope', which he translated as
'wonder-turner'.

Cheap and simple devices intended to create a three-dimensional effect were the *peepshow*, in the form of a paper concertina, and the peep-
egg. The peepshow has the plates so arranged that they can be pulled
out into an extended tube, giving an effective 'distance' view of scenes
where length is particularly significant, for example, the Thames Tun-
nel, opened in 1843, and the nave of Westminster Abbey on the occasion of Queen Victoria's wedding. The *peep-egg* was made of alabas-
ter, a translucent material, with a lens in the top, through which up
to three different scenes could be viewed by rotating a knob. These
objects were sold as souvenirs at holiday towns.

A whole range of optical illusion devices which became popular during the nineteenth century are based for their effect on the phenomenon
of persistence of vision, that is, the ability of the eye to retain the
impression of an object for a fraction of a second after its disappearance.
These devices, which for some reason attracted elaborate Greek names,
were the direct forerunners of the modern cinema, and the first was
actually invented by a leading medical man to illustrate his research
into persistence of vision. He was Dr John Ayrton Paris (1785–1856),
who became president of the Royal College of Physicians in 1844 and
first demonstrated his invention in 1825. The *Thaumatrope* (wonder-
turner) [13 & 14] consists of a card disk with two different figures

[14] *Left and right*: both sides of two
thaumatropes, which, when spun, will
show the lady riding on the horse and the
dog confronting the cat. The images of the
two sides appear as one through the
persistence of vision effect. Cards measure
115 × 78 mm.
Mid-19th century. *Museum of the History of
Science* (77–17).

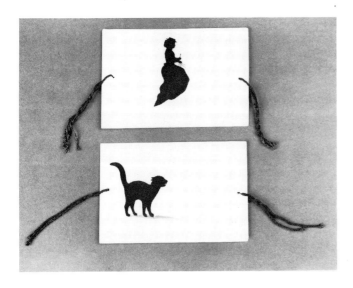

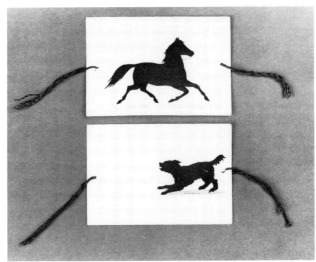

drawn on the two sides, which are apparently combined into one when the disk is rotated rapidly. An impression made on the retina of the eye lasts between $\frac{1}{50}$ and $\frac{1}{30}$ of a second after the object that produced it is withdrawn.

The *Phenakistoscope* was invented in 1832 by Professor J. A. F. Plateau of Brussels, and almost simultaneously by Professor S. Stampfer of Vienna, who called his instrument the *Stroboscope*. A disk with figures arranged radially representing a moving object in successive positions is spun on an axle. Reflexions of the figures in a mirror are viewed by looking through radial slits cut in the disk. Persistence of vision produces the impression of actual motion. This invention was the first of all the later and more complicated forms of motion picture. The *Zoetrope*, or Wheel of Life, a development of the Phenakistoscope, was invented by W. G. Horner of Bristol in 1834, but it was not marketed until 1867. The device consists of a slot-pierced drum which revolves horizontally on a pivot. Inside the drum below the slots is a paper band on which are drawn figures in various stages of movement. When the drum is set in motion and the figures are viewed through the slots an impression of action is given. The French *Praxinoscope* [15, xxix & xxx, facing p. 305], an improvement on the Zoetrope, was invented and patented in 1877 by Professor Émile Reynaud. Instead of slots to peer through there are rectangular mirrors set round an inner drum which reflect the image drawn on the paper strip fixed to the inside of the outer drum. When set in motion the impression of movement is smoother and less fatiguing to the eyes than is the case with earlier devices.

The magic lantern, which, in its simplest form, cast the image of a picture painted on glass onto a screen by means of a candle set behind the glass, enjoyed great popularity in the home throughout the nineteenth century, gradually developing into the cinematograph projector.

[15] Engraving to show how the Praxinoscope theatre was used. *c*. 1880. *Tissandier, p 127.*

[16] Magic lantern show in a drawing room. 1867. *Marion, p. 167.*

The desire to animate the image projected by the 'magic lanthorn' [16 & 17] led to the production of mechanical slides. The scene is painted on two glass disks or plates which can be moved relative to each other. One plate may be pushed across another to give the impression of a procession, a side lever may rock a ship or cause a part of the scene to be alternatively obscured and exposed, and one disk may be rotated by a crank to show the daily motion of the earth or the movements of the planets. The *Chromatrope* gave the effect of rapidly expanding and contracting patterns of coloured lines, and the earlier *Eidotrope* consisted of two pierced metal disks which contra-rotate to give moving shadow patterns. This moiré pattern effect is used today in the electron microscopical investigation of thin metal foils.

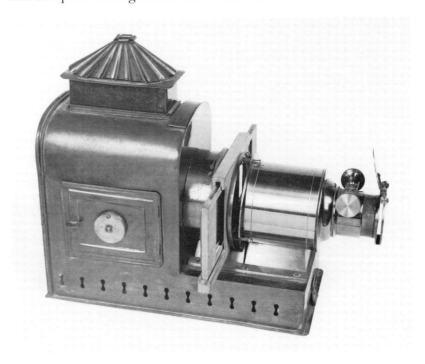

[17] Magic lantern, made of tin-plate (known as Russian iron) and brass, with wooden slide carrier. The lens holder is engraved: L.C.C. This stands for London County Council, which first came into existence in 1888.
c. 1890. *Museum of the History of Science.*

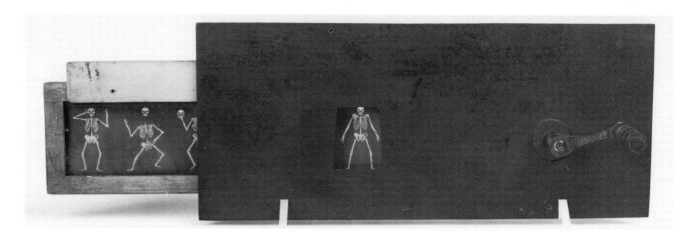

[18] Example of Beale's Choreutoscope, which is an attempt to animate a slide for a magic lantern. It was invented in 1866 by Lionel S. Beale. The six views of a skeleton are successively brought into view by turning the handle. Brass frame 272 × 113 mm.
c. 1866. Museum of the History of Science.

The *Choreutoscope* [18] was one of the first attempts to project a moving figure onto a screen. This device was invented in 1866 by Lionel S. Beale (1828–1906), physician and microscopist, and assistant to Sir Henry Acland at Oxford in 1847. Intermittent movement and the shutter action are achieved by means of a circular disk carrying a pin attached to a handle. As the disk revolves the pin engages with a notch on the slide, moving it on by the space of one picture and at the same time raising the shutter. This arrangement is a forerunner of the maltese cross device used in cinematography. Another device for use with a projector was the Wheel of Life. Patented in 1871 it was basically a Phenakistoscope disk, but now of glass, with a contra-rotating sector disk in front of it. Eadweard Muybridge (1830–1904) used this technique in 1880 to project photographs of the successive movements of animals. He called his instrument the Zoopraxiscope.

The *Kinora* was a form of peepshow devised by an American, Herman Casler in the 1890s, a smaller version of his Mutoscope. By the turn of the century Mutoscope Parlours had been set up all over the United States, and the machines were also installed on seaside piers in England.

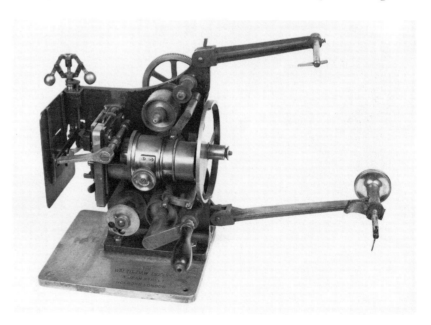

[19] 35-mm cinematograph projector, signed: THE WALTURDAW BIOSCOPE 3, DEAN STREET HOLBORN LONDON. The Lumière brothers patented a projector in 1895.
c. 1903. Museum of the History of Science.

[XXVII] Astronomical screen, described on a printed sheet stuck to the back: ELTON'S MINIATURE TRANSPARENT ORRERY. It is dated: *Princes-Street, Cavendish-Square, February, 1817*. The screen is a roller blind pierced with illustrations of the constellations and heavenly bodies. The case is mahogany, with gilt-brass feet. Overall height 260 mm; width 190 mm.
1817. *Museum of the History of Science (2920).*

[XXVIII] Brewster stereo viewer. This type employs a pair of lenses angled to view a card with a pair of specially prepared photographs mounted on it. David Brewster first announced it in 1849. After Queen Victoria saw it in 1851 it sold in vast quantities, second only to the kaleidoscope. Box 200 × 105 × (height) 105 mm; glass screen in viewer 140 × 90 mm.
c. 1865. *Whipple Museum (780).*

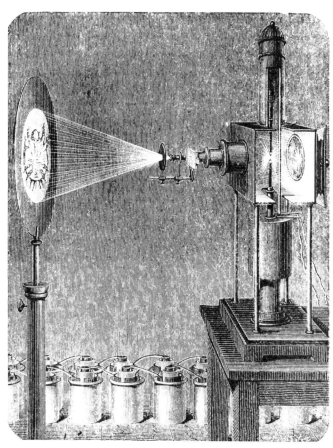

[20] Educational compound microscope of French manufacture. The microscope was the most popular of scientific recreations in the second half of the nineteenth century.
1867. *Marion, p. 130.*

[21] Projection microscope, with the light source a carbon arc, the electricity generated by a battery of voltaic cells.
1867. *Marion, p. 134.*

OPPOSITE:

[XXIX] 'Praxinoscope Théatre', patented in 1877 by Émile Reynard in Paris. This was an improvement on earlier moving picture machines, because instead of looking through slits, the successive images were reflected in a rotating drum of twelve mirrors. Mahogany box
250 × 267 × (height closed) 125 mm; diameter of outer drum 220 mm.
c. 1889. *Private collection.*

[XXX] Part of an animated strip from the Praxinoscope. Total length of each strip 658 mm; width 55 mm.

The effect was produced by mounting small photographs of an animated scene on to strips of paper which are then mounted radially on an axle boss. When the boss is rotated each photograph is held momentarily in front of the lens before being replaced by the following photograph. Persistence of vision gives the impression of continuous movement.

A cheap, manually-operated version of the Kinora was popular around the turn of the century, in the form of flip, or flicker, books. These incorporated sets of prints which, when the pages were flipped by the thumb, gave the impression of a sequence of natural movement. Many people contributed to the development of instruments to photograph and project film strips between the years 1885 and 1895. Among these must be mentioned Louis Aimé Augustin Le Prince (1842–90), William Friese-Greene (1855–1921), who patented celluloid ribbon film in 1889, and the Lumière brothers. Louis Jean (1864–1948) and Auguste Marie Louis Nicolas Lumière (1862–1954) patented a camera and projector contained in a single apparatus on 13 February 1895. It incorporated the important invention of an eccentrically driven claw drive for moving the film strip. Their first film was shown in Paris on 22 March 1895. The device was called Kinétroscope de projection, but soon altered to Cinématographe.

Of the two most important optical scientific instruments, the microscope [20 & 21] and the telescope [22 & 23], it was the former, because

[22] Divided telescope, a device for producing an optical illusion dependent on mirrors. Brass tubing, on a mahogany base. Baseboard 221 × 112 mm; overall height 202 mm; diameter of tube 45 mm. *c.* 1870. *Whipple Museum (1356)*.

of its convenient size, which became most popular with the layman. Through it, all manner of common, but minute objects could be examined: insects, hairs, seeds, minerals, plant organs. Its use encouraged the systematic collection of material from ponds, rivers and hedgerows, and fitted in excellently with the nineteenth-century vogue for the study of natural history. By the 1860s there were microscopes to suit every taste and pocket, from the simple bead of Canada balsam in a piece of card, costing a penny, to elaborate and expensive boxed microscope kits in mahogany boxes. Many books were produced for the amateur microscopist, from the age of ten upwards. An example of their continuing popularity was a small volume entitled *Common Objects of the Microscope*, first published by the Rev. J. G. Wood in 1861, which was still in print in 1949.

[23] Engraving showing a divided telescope in use, apparently seeing through a stone. *c.* 1880. *Tissandier, p. 135.*

[24] Game for teaching French grammar, employing a secret magnetic needle, and strips of iron embedded in three question disks. The magnetic needle points to the correct answer. Inscribed: LA GRAMMAIRE JEU MAGNÉTIQUE — INSTRUIRE EN AMUSANT. Box 295 × 230 × 35 mm. *c.* 1900. *Private collection.*

Electrical Toys

The recreational use of electricity goes back far beyond the modern battery-powered cars and train-sets. Natural philosophers of the eighteenth century investigated the production of static electricity from friction, using vast machines of brass and plate glass. These machines, when scaled down for use in the home, could create amusing and startling effects; therefore, from about 1800, kits were sold, that included, as well as the manually-cranked machine, pith puppets that could be made to dance, a model head with long hair that would stand on end, and electrically operated chimes (see also Chapter 11). Another electrical toy was the thunder house, which demonstrated the effect of lightning, the walls being made to collapse in response to an electric shock. Other pieces of apparatus which later appeared as playthings were the Geissler tube and the Volta electric pistol. In the latter part of the century, miniature versions of the Wimshurst electrical machine, and the telephone, were sold as toys. In the 1830s the electric generator was developed by Michael Faraday, and later toy dynamos were made to be driven by model steam-engines, the small current generated causing an electric lamp to light up. The origin of many moving toys of the nineteenth and twentieth centuries may be traced to models made for serious design and demonstration purposes; examples are engines, carriages, and ships.

Magnetic Toys

The magnetic compass was known in the twelfth century, but the first scientific study of magnetic attraction was published by William Gilbert in 1600. The loadstone had a practical use for making magnetic needles for compasses, but it was also a curiosity because of its power to exert a mysterious force over distance. In the nineteenth century horseshoe magnets were popular toys, and another game consisted of a peg on which circular magnets with a hole in the middle could be positioned, either fitting together in one polar orientation, or holding mysteriously apart in the other. The use of secreted magnets is found in a number of games of the period. In one of these, there is a picture of an artist painting at an easel, and a group of scenes is provided, each containing a magnet in a different position. When one of the scenes is positioned, a miniature of it appears on the artist's easel, brought into place by the attraction of another small magnet in a rotating disk which carries the sequence of scenes in miniature. Magnetic attraction is used in another game to teach grammar by question and answer [24]. As a particular question is positioned, the magnetic pointer moves to indicate the correct answer.

Air and Heat Toys

All manner of heat and air power was investigated and put to serious use during the eighteenth and nineteenth centuries, which saw the invention of the air-pump, and, in 1712, the building of the first effective steam-engine by Thomas Newcomen. Windmills, kites and air balloons naturally found their way into the playroom. The power of an up-draught of hot air, used to turn a jack in large kitchens, gave rise to a toy which incorporated a paddle wheel, turned by hot air from a gas jet, and a cranked axle that activated little figures. Popular toys which demonstrated air pressure were a ball balanced on a jet of air blown through a tube by the mouth, and the long bladder or paper tube which uncoils when inflated. Steam power was used as the motive power for toy trains, but it was hazardous, particularly for moving models, and clockwork gradually took over for most moving toys.

In the progress of science one can distinguish a high road, with markers such as Galileo, Newton, Lavoisier, Faraday, and a low road, through Ozanam, Montucla, Guyot, Hutton, Pepper, Houdin. One group worked and taught at the frontiers of science, the other followed, to instruct through amusement. Their skill is to show that the strange and fearful can be readily explained, and so they appealed to impressionable adults in the eighteenth century, youngsters in the nineteenth, and school children in the twentieth. There are several demonstration pieces popular in 1700 still available today in toyshops; and many, like the yo-yo, among the oldest of playthings, will never lose their popularity.

Instrument makers
exhibiting at the Great Exhibition of 1851

Note: Only producers of scientific instruments are included; those listed solely as inventors are omitted. Names and addresses are reproduced as printed, keeping the anglicizations and political boundaries.

Abraham Abraham & Co, 20 Lord Street, Liverpool, UK

C. E. & F. Arnoldi, Elgersburg, Gotha, Prussia

H. Ausfeld, Gotha, Prussia

Henry Baker, 90 Hatton Garden, London, UK

Robert M. Barrett, 4 Jamaica Terrace, Limehouse, London, UK

Wenzel Batka, Prague, Austria

C. Becker, Arnhem, The Netherlands

John Bennett, 65 Cheapside, London, UK

Joseph Béranger & Co, 97 Rue Centrale, Lyons, France

Desiré F. Bernard, 30 Rue des Mamourzets, Paris, France

William Bond & Son, Boston, Massachusetts, USA

Bonnet, 5 Chemin de Ronde de la Barriere, Ménilmontant, France

Eugene Bourdon, 74 Faubourg du Temple, Paris, France

John Braham, 17 St Augustine's Parade, Bristol, UK

F. W. Breithaupt & Son, Cassel, Hesse, Prussia

Breton Brothers, 23 Rue Dauphine, Paris, France

Buron, 8 Rue des Trois Pavillons, Paris, France

E. Busch, Rathenow, Prussia

W. Callaghan, 45 Great Russell Street, Bloomsbury, London, UK

Carpenter & Westley, 24 Regent Street, London, UK

Chadburn Brothers, Sheffield and Liverpool, UK

Charles Chevalier, 158 Palais National, Paris, France

J. Coffey & J. Smith, 4 Providence Row, Finsbury, London, UK

Collot Brothers, 41 Rue de l'Ecole de Médicine, Paris, France

John Crichton, 112 Leadenhall Street, London, UK

De Graeve, Short & Fanner, 59 St Martin's-le-Grand, London, UK

L. J. Deleuil, 8 Rue du Pont-de-Lodi, Paris, France; and 7 Althorpe Street, Gray's Inn Lane, London, UK

Edward John Dent, 61 Strand; and 33 Cockspur Street; and 34 Royal Exchange, London, UK

Detouche & Houdin, 228, 230, Rue St Martin, Paris, France

C. W. Dixey, 3 New Bond Street, London, UK

George Dollond, St Paul's Churchyard, London, UK

John Dover, 14 Little New Street, London, UK

Duboscq-Soleil, 35 Rue de l'Odéon, Paris, France

Electric Telegraph Co; no address given (manufacturers of Cooke and Wheatstone telegraphic apparatus in London, UK)

Elliott & Sons, 56 Strand, London, UK

J. Ericsson, New York, USA

Traugott Ertel & Sons, Reichenbach, Bavaria

Richard Facy, Wapping Wall, London, UK

Robert Field & Son, 113 New Street, Birmingham, UK

Gustave Froment, 5 Rue Ménilmontant, Paris, France

Adrien Gavard, 9 Quai de l'Horloge, Paris, France

Tito Gonnella, Florence, Tuscany

Samuel Green, 7 Helmet Row, Old Street, London, UK

John J. Griffin & Co, 53 Baker Street, London, UK

Henry Grimoldi, 31 Brooke Street, Holborn, London, UK

F. Gisi, Aarau, Switzerland

William Harris & Son, 50 High Holborn, London, UK

J. N. Hearder, 34 George Street, Plymouth, UK

William Thomas Henley, 46 St John's Street, Clerkenwell, London, UK

Soren Hjorth, Copenhagen, Denmark

Hoffmann & Eberhardt, Berlin, Prussia

Horne, Thornthwaite & Wood, 123 Newgate Street, London, UK

Imperial Polytechnic Institute, Vienna, Austria

Imperial Ijorsk Works, near St Petersburg, Russia

Franz Jerak, Prague, Austria

Johnson & Matthey, 79 Hatton Garden, London, UK

Jürgensens Sons, Copenhagen, Denmark

James Kern, Aarau, Switzerland

Thomas D. King, Bristol, UK

T. Kinzelbach, Stuttgart, Wurtemburg

George Knight & Sons, Foster Lane, London, UK

W. Ladd, 29 Penton Place, Walworth, London, UK

Jean Antoine Laur, 4 Rue St Claude au Marais, Paris, France

Alexandre Lebrun, 3 Rue Chapon, Paris, France; agent Salomon, 22 Red Lion Square, London, UK

E. Littman, Stockholm, Sweden

Willem Martinus Logeman, Haarlem, The Netherlands

J. F. Luhme & Co, Berlin, Prussia

C. Lüttig, Berlin, Prussia

J. S. Marratt, 63 King William Street, London Bridge, London, UK

Louis Masset, Yverdon, Switzerland

George Merz & Sons, Munich, Bavaria

Molteni & Siégler, 62 Rue Neuve St Nicolas, Paris, France

Nachet, 16 Rue Serpente, Paris, France

Negretti & Zambra, 11 Hatton Garden, London, UK

J. Newman, 122 Regent Street, London, UK

Wm Newton & Son, 66 Chancery Lane; and 3 Fleet Street, London, UK

Julius Nissen, Copenhagen, Denmark

F. A. Nobert, Barth, Pomerania, Prussia

August Oertling, Berlin, Prussia

Ludwig Oertling, 13 Store Street, Bedford Square, London, UK

James Parkes & Son, 5 St Mary's Row, Birmingham, UK

James Pick, Warsaw, Russia

Morrice Pillischer, 398 Oxford Street, London, UK

Francis Augustus Pizzala, 19 Hatton Garden, London, UK

Andrew Pritchard, 162 Fleet Street, London, UK

Clement Riefler, Nesselwang, Bavaria

L. Reimann, Berlin, Prussia

Paolo Rocchetti, Padua, Austria

Andrew Ross, 2 Featherstone Buildings, Holborn, London, UK

William John Salmon, 254 Whitechapel Road, London, UK

John Sang, Kirkaldy, Scotland, UK

Emil Schrödter, Dusseldorf, Prussia

Siemens & Halske, Berlin, Prussia

William Simms, 138 Fleet Street, London, UK

James Smith & Richard Beck, 6 Coleman Street, London, UK

Joseph Solomon, 22 Red Lion Square, London, UK

Somalvico & Co, Hatton Garden, London, UK

W. Suess, Marburg, Hesse, Prussia

Charles Xavier Thomas, Colmar; and 13 Rue du Helder, Paris, France; agent M. de Fontaine Moreau, 4 South Street, Finsbury Square, London, UK

James Treet & Co, 22 Charlotte Street, Blackfriars Road, London, UK

Varley & Son, 1 Charles Street, Clarendon Square, London, UK

Felix Vedy, 52 Rue de Bondy, Paris, France

A. P. Viberg, Falun, Sweden

Watkins & Hill, 5 Charing Cross, London, UK

Weiss & Son, 62 Strand, London, UK

William Wilton, St Day, Truro, UK

William Wray, 43 Havering Street, Commercial Road East, London, UK

George Yeates, 2 Grafton Street, Dublin, UK

Bibliography

No general bibliography on scientific instruments exists, though there are a few dealing with restricted topics, such as optical instruments (published in Turner, *Essays on the History of the Microscope*, see below). An important source book, first published in 1983, is Corsi & Weindling, *Information Sources in the History of Science and Medicine* (see below), which includes a chapter on scientific instruments by the present author. In its twenty-three chapters, this book contains much to assist the student in a wide range of subjects, and each chapter is provided with an extensive bibliography. Another useful guide is Ferguson, *Bibliography of the History of Technology* (see below), which includes, in addition to books, technical journals, directories, and some museums.

The bibliography printed here is necessarily selective; it is not appropriate to cite papers published in learned journals. Many trade catalogues were produced in the latter part of the nineteenth century, but these are rarely preserved in libraries, and are only likely to be found in technical museums. A few of the most comprehensive of these are included, together with some nineteenth-century textbooks, and twentieth-century studies in the history of science and technology.

Accum, Fredrick, *Catalogue of Chemical Preparations, Apparatus and Instruments for Philosophical Chemistry* (London, 1805).

Adams, George, Jr, *Lectures on Natural and Experimental Philosophy*, 5 vols (London, 1794).

Anderson, R. G. W., *The Playfair Collection and the Teaching of Chemistry at the University of Edinburgh 1713–1858* (Edinburgh: Royal Scottish Museum, 1978).

Archinard, Margarida, *Collection de Saussure* (Geneva, 1979).

Archinard, Margarida, *L'apport genevois à l'hygrométrie* (Geneva: Musée d'Histoire des Sciences, 1980).

Banfield, Edwin, *Antique Barometers, an Illustrated Survey* (Hereford: Wayland Publications, 1976).

Barclay, A., *Pure Chemistry: Part I, Historical Review*, and *Part II, Descriptive Catalogue* (London: Science Museum Handbooks, 1937).

Baxandall, D., *Calculating Machines and Instruments* (London: Science Museum Catalogue, 1926; revised edition by Jane Pugh, 1975).

Bedini, S. A., *Early American Scientific Instruments and their Makers* (Washington, D.C., 1964).

Bedini, S. A., *Thinkers and Tinkers: Early American Men of Science* (New York, 1975).

Bennett, J. A., and Olivia Brown, *The Compleat Surveyor* (published to accompany a special exhibition at the Whipple Museum of the History of Science) (Cambridge, 1982).

Bolle, Bert, *Barometers* (Watford, Hertfordshire: Argus Books, 1982). Also published in Dutch and German.

Bowers, Brian, *Sir Charles Wheatstone FRS, 1802–1875* (London, 1975).

Bracegirdle, Brian, *A History of Microtechnique: The Evolution of the Microtome and the Development of Tissue Preparation* (London, 1978).

Brachner, Alto, and M. Seeberger, *Joseph von Fraunhofer 1787–1826: Ausstellung zum 150. Todestag* (Munich, 1976).

Brewster, David, *The Kaleidoscope, its History, Theory, and Construction, with its Application to the Fine and Useful Arts*, 2nd edn (London, 1858). First edn (Edinburgh, 1819).

Brewster, David, *Letters on Natural Magic, addressed to Sir Walter Scott, Bart.* (London, 1832; new edn 1883).

Brewster, David, *The Stereoscope, its History, Theory, and Construction, with its Application to the fine and Useful Arts and to Education* (London, 1856).

Brieux, Alain, editor, *Maison Nachet: Catalogues de fonds de 1854 à 1910*, Introduction by G. L'E. Turner (Paris: Editions Alain Brieux, 1979).

Brieux, Alain, editor, *L'Industrie française des instruments de précision: Catalogue 1901–1902* (Paris: Editions Alain Brieux, 1980).

Brough, Bennett H., *A Treatise on Mine-Surveying* (London, 1888; 14th edn 1916).

Brown, Olivia, *The Whipple Museum of the History of Science: Catalogue 1, Surveying* (Cambridge, 1982).

Brown, Olivia, *The Whipple Museum of the History of Science: Catalogue 2, Balances & Weights* (Cambridge, 1982).

Bryden, David J., *Scottish Scientific Instrument-Makers 1600–1900* (Edinburgh: Royal Scottish Museum, 1972).

Burstall, Aubrey F., *A History of Mechanical Engineering* (London, 1963).

Cajori, Florian, *A History of the Logarithmic Slide Rule* (New York, 1909).

Calvert, H. R., *Scientific Trade Cards in the Science Museum Collection* (London, 1971).

Cardwell, D. S. L., editor, *John Dalton & the Progress of Science* (Manchester, 1968).

Cardwell, D. S. L., *From Watt to Clausius* (London, 1971).

Cardwell, D. S. L., *Technology, Science and History* (London, 1972).

Chaldecott, J. A., *Heat and Cold: Part II, Descriptive Catalogue* (London: Science Museum Handbook, 1954).

Chaldecott, J. A., *Temperature Measurement and Control: Part II, Descriptive Catalogue* (London: Science Museum Handbook, 1955).

Colvin, Christina, editor, *Maria Edgworth in France and Switzerland* (Oxford, 1979).

Corsi, Pietro, and Paul Weindling, editors, *Information Sources in the History of Science and Medicine* (London, 1983).

Crawforth, Michael A., *Weighing Coins: English Folding Gold Balances of the 18th and 19th Centuries* (London, 1979).

Deacon, Margaret, *Scientists and the Sea 1650–1900: A Study of Marine Science* (London, 1971).

De Luc, Jean A., *Recherches sur les Modifications de l'Atmosphère*, 2 vols (Geneva, 1772).

Deschanel, Augustin Privat, *Traité élémentaire de Physique* (Paris, 1868).

Deschanel, Augustin Privat, *Elementary Treatise on Natural Philosophy*, translated by J. D. Everett (London, 1872; 6th edn 1882).

Dictionary of British Scientific Instruments issued by the British Optical Instrument Manufacturers' Association (London, 1921).

Dunsheath, Percy, *A History of Electrical Engineering* (London, 1962).

Exhibition of the Works of Industry of all Nations 1851. Reports by the Juries on the Subjects in the Thirty Classes into which the Exhibition was Divided (London, 1852).

Ferguson, Eugene S., *Bibliography of the History of Technology* (Cambridge, Massachusetts, 1968).

Fownes, George, *A Manual of Elementary Chemistry, Theoretical and Practical* (London, 1847).

Fox, Robert, *The Caloric Theory of Gases from Lavoisier to Regnault* (Oxford, 1971).

Friendly, Alfred, *Beaufort of the Admiralty: The Life of Sir Francis Beaufort 1774–1857* (New York, 1977).

Ganot, Adolphe, *Traité élémentaire de Physique expérimentale et appliquée* (Paris, 1851; 19th edn 1884).

Ganot, Adolphe, *Elementary Treatise on Physics, Experimental and Applied*, translated by E. Atkinson (London, 1861; 18th edn 1910).

Ganot, Adolphe, *Cours de Physique purement expérimentale, à l'usage des Personnes étrangères aux connaissances mathématiques* (Paris, 1859; 9th edn 1887).

Ganot, Adolphe, *Natural Philosophy for General Readers and Young People*, translated by E. Atkinson (London, 1872; 9th edn 1900).

Gillispie, C. C., editor, *Dictionary of Scientific Biography*, 16 vols (New York, 1970–80).

Goodison, Nicholas, *English Barometers 1680–1860: A History of Domestic Barometers and their Makers and Retailers*, 2nd edn (Woodbridge: Antique Collectors' Club, 1977).

Greenaway, Frank, *John Dalton and the Atom* (London, 1966).

Greenhill, Basil, editor, *The National Maritime Museum* (London, 1982).

Griffin, John J., *Chemical Recreations: A Series of Amusing and Instructive Experiments which may be performed Easily, Safely, and at little Expense*, 4th edn (Glasgow, 1825).

Griffin, John Joseph, *Chemical Handicraft: A Classified and Descriptive Catalogue of Chemical Apparatus suitable for the Performance of Class Experiments, for Every Process of Chemical Research and for Chemical Testing in the Arts* (London, 1877).

Griffin, John J., & Sons Ltd, *Scientific Handicraft: An Illustrated and Descriptive Catalogue of Scientific Apparatus manufactured and sold by John J. Griffin & Sons, Ltd*, 14th edn (London, nd [1910]).

Guillemin, Amédée, *Les Applications de la Physique aux Sciences, à l'Industrie et aux Arts* (Paris, 1874).

Guillemin, Amédée, *The Applications of Physical Forces*, translated by Mrs Norman Lockyer (London, 1877).

Guillemin, Amédée, *Le Magnétisme et l'électricité*, 2 vols (Paris, 1890).

Guillemin, Amédée, *Electricity and Magnetism*, English translation edited by Silvanus P. Thompson (London, 1891).

Hackmann, Willem D., editor, *Alexander Bain's Short History of the Electric Clock (1852)* (London: Turner & Devereux, 1973).

Hackmann, Willem D., *Electricity from Glass: The History of the Frictional Electrical Machine 1600–1850* (Alphen aan den Rijn: Sijthoff & Noordhoff, 1978).

Harman, Peter M., *Energy, Force, and Matter: The Conceptual Development of Nineteenth-Century Physics* (Cambridge, 1982).

Heather, J. F., *Drawing and Measuring Instruments*, enlarged edn (London, 1877).

Hill, C. R., *Chemical Apparatus: Catalogue 1 Museum of the History of Science* (Oxford, 1971).

Hogg, Jabez, *Elements of Experimental and Natural Philosophy . . .* (London, 1853; 2nd edn 1861).

Howse, Derek, *Greenwich Time and the Discovery of the Longitude* (Oxford, 1980).

Hughes, Thomas P., *Thomas Edison Professional Inventor* (London: Science Museum Booklet, 1976).

Hutton, Charles, *Recreations in Mathematics and Natural Philosophy*, 4 vols (London, 1803).

Jamin, Jules, *Cours de Physique de l'École polytechnique*, 3 vols (Paris, 1858–66; 3rd edn 1878–81).

King, Henry C., and J. R. Millburn, *Geared to the Stars: The Evolution of Planetariums, Orreries and Astronomical Clocks* (Toronto and Bristol, 1979).

Knight, David, *Sources for the History of Science 1660–1914* (London, 1975).

Koenig, Rudolph, *Catalogue des Appareils d'Acoustique* (Paris, 1882; revised edn 1889).

Koning, D. A. W., and G. M. M. Houben, *2000 Jaar gewichten in de Nederlanden: Stelsels, ijkwegen, vormen, makers, merken, gebruik* (Lochem, 1980).

Lardner, Dionysius, *A Treatise on Hydrostatics and Pneumatics* (London, 1831).

McConnell, Anita, *Geomagnetic Instruments Before 1900* (London: Harriet Wynter Ltd, 1980).

McConnell, Anita, *No Sea Too Deep: The History of Oceanographic Instruments* (Bristol: Adam Hilger, 1982).

M'Pherson, J. Gordon, *The Fairyland Tales of Science* (London and Glasgow, 1889).

Marion, Fulgence, *L'Optique* (Paris, 1867).

Marion, Fulgence, *The Wonders of Optics*, translated by Charles W. Quin (London, 1868).

Middleton, W. E. K., *Invention of the Meteorological Instruments* (Baltimore, Maryland, 1969).

Middleton, W. E. K., *Catalog of Meteorological Instruments in the Museum of History and Technology* (Washington, D.C., 1969).

Negretti and Zambra, *A Treatise on Meteorological Instruments, Expanding of their Scientific Principles, Method of Construction, and Practical Utility* (London, 1864).

Negretti and Zambra, *Negretti & Zambra's Encyclopaedic Illustrated and Descriptive Catalogue of Optical, Mathematical, Philosophical, Photographic, and Standard Meteorological Instruments* (London, nd [1880]).

Paris, John Ayrton, [published anonymously] *Philosophy in Sport made Science in Earnest*, 3 vols (London, 1827; 8th edn 1857).

Pepper, John Henry, *The Boy's Playbook of Science* (London, 1860).

Pepper, John H., *Cyclopaedic Science Simplified* (London, 1869; 4th edn 1877).

Pike, Benjamin, *Pike's Illustrated Descriptive Catalogue of Optical, Mathematical, and Philosphical Instruments, Manufactured, Imported, and Sold by the Author*, 2 vols (New York, 1848).

Pullan, J. M., *The History of the Abacus* (London, 1968).

Recreative Science: A Record and Remembrancer of Intellectual Observation, vol. 1 (London, 1860).

Rees, Abraham, *The New Cyclopaedia; or Universal Dictionary of Arts and Sciences . . .* 44 vols (London, 1802–20).

Richeson, A. W., *English Land Measuring to 1800: Instruments and Practice* (Cambridge, Massachusetts, 1966).

Roscoe, Henry E., *Spectrum Analysis: Six Lectures, delivered in 1868, before the Society of Apothecaries of London* (London, 1869).

Roscoe, H. E., editor, *Science Lectures for the People Delivered in Manchester 1866–67 and 1870–71* (Manchester, 1871).

Salleron, J., *Notice sur les Instruments de Précision construits par J. Salleron*, in 4 parts (Paris, 1861–64).

Scott, Dunbar D., *The Evolution of Mine-Surveying Instruments* (New York, 1902).

Six, James, *The Construction of a Thermometer*, facsimile reprint of the 1794 edition (London: Nimbus Books, 1980).

Spottiswoode, William, *Polarisation of Light*, 3rd edn (London, 1879).

Stanley, William Ford, *A Descriptive Treatise on Mathematical Drawing Instruments . . .* (London, 1866; 6th edn 1888).

Stanley, William Ford, *Surveying and Levelling Instruments Theoretically and Practically Described . . .* (London, 1890; 3rd edn 1901).

Stock, John T., *Development of the Chemical Balance: A Science Museum Survey* (London, 1969).

Stock, John T., and Denys Vaughan, *The Development of Instruments to Measure Electric Current* (London: Science Museum, 1983).

Szabadvary, F., *A History of Analytical Chemistry* (Oxford, 1966).

Taylor, E. G. R., *The Mathematical Practitioners of Hanoverian England 1741–1840* (Cambridge, 1966).

Thomas, D. B., *The Science Museum Photography Collection* (London, 1969).

Thompson, Silvanus P., *Lord Kelvin* (published by the International Electrotechnical Commission) (London, 1912).

Tissandier, Gaston, *Les Récréations scientifiques ou l'Enseignement par les Jeux* (Paris, 1881, 7th edn 1894).

Tissandier, Gaston, *Popular Scientific Recreations in Natural Philosophy, Astronomy, Geology, Chemistry*, English translation (London, 1882).

Treneer, Anne, *The Mercurial Chemist: A Life of Sir Humphry Davy* (London, 1963).

Turner, G. L'E., and T. H. Levere, *Van Marum's Scientific Instruments in Teyler's Museum*, vol. 4 of *Martinus van Marum: Life and Work*, edited by R. J. Forbes *et al* (Haarlem: Hollandsche Maatschappij der Wetenschappen, 1973).

Turner, G. L'E., *Antique Scientific Instruments* (Poole: Blandford Press, 1980). Also published in Dutch.

Turner, G. L'E., *Essays on the History of the Microscope* (Oxford: Senecio Publishing Co., 1980).

Turner, G. L'E., *Collecting Microscopes* (London, 1981). Also published in Dutch, German, and Italian.

Usill, George W., *Practical Surveying* (London, 1888; 13th edn 1926).

Ward, F. A. B., *Time Measurement: Part I, Historical Review*, and *Part II, Descriptive Catalogue* (London: Science Museum Handbooks, 1947 and 1950).

Welford, Walter D., and Henry Sturmey, editors, *The 'Indispensable Handbook' to the Optical Lantern . . .* (London, 1888).

Williams, L. Pearce, *Michael Faraday: A Biography* (London and New York, 1965).

Woodcroft, Bennet, editor and translator, *The Pneumatics of Hero of Alexandria from the Original Greek* (London, 1851; facsimile reprint London and New York, 1971).

Wright, C. R. Alder, *The Threshold of Science*, 2nd edn (London, 1892).

Index